Parks

and

Protected

Areas in

Canada

—

**Planning
and
Management**

Dedication

This volume is dedicated to the memory of Dr Bob Graham, who passed away early in 1993. Bob was a major figure in the study of parks and protected areas in Canada and enriched us all through his infectious enthusiasm and knowledge.

Parks

and

Protected

Areas in

Canada

—

Planning
and
Management

Edited by

PHILIP DEARDEN
and **RICK ROLLINS**

Toronto
OXFORD UNIVERSITY PRESS
1993

Oxford University Press, 70 Wynford Drive, Don Mills, Ontario M3C 1J9

Toronto   Oxford   New York
Delhi   Bombay   Calcutta   Madras   Karachi   Kuala Lumpur
Singapore   Hong Kong   Tokyo   Nairobi   Dar es Salaam
Cape Town   Melbourne   Auckland   Madrid

and associated companies in
Berlin   Ibadan

This book is printed on permanent (acid-free) paper ∞.

Henderson Book Series #22

Published in association with the Canadian Parks and Wilderness Society. The Henderson Book Series honours the kind and generous support of Mrs. Arthur T. Henderson, who made the series possible.

Canadian Cataloguing in Publication Data

Main entry under title:

Parks and protected areas in Canada.

Includes bibliographical references and index.

ISBN 0-19-540908-6

1. National parks and reserves—Canada.
2. Natural areas – Canada.   3. Wilderness areas –
Canada.   I. Dearden, Philip.   II. Rollins, Rick.

QH77.C2P3 1993   333.78'2'0971   C93-094580-8

Design by Heather Delfino

1 2 3 4 — 96 95 94 93

Printed in Canada

Contents

List of Figures

List of Tables

List of Appendices

Acknowledgements

The authors would like to acknowledge the time and effort spent by Ole Heggen of the Cartographic Section of the Geography Department at the University of Victoria in preparing the diagrams for this volume and Mrs Judy Simpson in typing the manuscript.

List of Contributors

LAWRENCE BERG, University of Waikato, New Zealand

JAMES R. BUTLER, Department of Forest Science, University of Alberta, Edmonton, Alta.

PHILIP DEARDEN, Department of Geography, University of Victoria, Victoria, B.C.

DAVID A. DUFFUS, Department of Geography, University of Victoria, Victoria, B.C.

PAUL F.J. EAGLES, Department of Recreation and Leisure Studies, University of Waterloo, Waterloo, Ont.

HAL EIDSVIK, past Senior Policy Advisor, Canadian Parks Service; former Chairperson, Commission of National Parks and Protected Areas, World Conservation Union (IUCN).

TERRY FENGE, Canadian Arctic Resources Committee, Ottawa, Ont.

R. GRAHAM, Department of Recreation and Leisure Studies, University of Waterloo, Waterloo, Ont.

KEVIN McNAMEE, Canadian Nature Federation, Ottawa, Ont.

J.G. NELSON, Department of Geography, University of Waterloo, Waterloo, Ont.

R.J. PAYNE, School of Outdoor Recreation, Parks, and Tourism, Lakehead University, Thunder Bay, Ont.

GEORGE PRIDDLE, Environmental and Resource Studies, University of Waterloo, Waterloo, Ont.

RICK ROLLINS, Malaspina College, Nanaimo, B.C.

GUY S. SWINNERTON, Department of Recreation and Leisure Studies, University of Alberta, Edmonton, Alta.

JOHN B. THEBERGE, Faculty of Environmental Studies, University of Waterloo, Waterloo, Ont.

Foreword

This is a good time for a book on the planning and management of parks and protected areas in Canada. Canadians have been reared on the myth of having limitless wilderness to exploit. The truth is that we do not. A consensus of scientific opinion holds that whatever wilderness is unprotected by the year 2000 will cease to be wilderness. Furthermore, if we continue to allow development to flourish in national parks, we are not protecting even the areas we say we are protecting.

In addition to being the last stand for wilderness, national parks and protected areas are critical to the survival of our planet's economy and ecosphere. This was made clear by the United Nations World Commission on Environment and Development in the report *Our Common Future*. Known as the Brundtland Report, *Our Common Future* identifies the role and importance of national parks. It says:

> Conservation of living natural resources—plants, animals, and microorganisms and the non-living elements of the environment on which they depend—is crucial for development. Today the conservation of wild living resources is on the agenda of governments; nearly 4 per cent of the Earth's land area is managed explicitly to conserve species and their ecosystems, and all but a small handful of countries have national parks. The challenge facing nations today is no longer deciding whether conservation is a good idea, but rather how it can be implemented in the national interest and within the means available in each country (World Commission on Environment and Development, 1987, 147).

The challenge facing Canada today lies not in deciding whether national parks and protected areas are a good idea, but rather in how we can get on with the job of protecting this country's natural diversity before the opportunity is lost forever. Another no less significant question is what we should allow to happen in national parks and protected areas once they have been established.

As the Brundtland Report warns: 'There is still time to save species and their ecosystems. It is an indispensable prerequisite for sustainable development. Our failure to do so will not be forgiven by future generations' (World Commission on Environment and Development 1987 166). If we in the present generation of Canadians cannot curb our appetite for devouring wilderness and cannot learn to leave national parks and protected areas alone, we will not be forgiven by future generations. If, on the other hand, we are serious about protecting wilderness in national parks and protected areas and if we leave that wilderness alone once it is protected, we will have achieved something worthwhile.

Harvey Locke, President
Canadian Parks and Wilderness Society
Calgary, July 1991

REFERENCES

World Commission on Environment and Development
1987   *Our Common Future*, Oxford University Press, New York and Oxford.

CHAPTER 1

The Times
They Are A-Changin'

——

PHILIP DEARDEN AND RICK ROLLINS

Come senators, congressmen
Please heed the call
Don't stand in the doorway
Don't block up the hall
For he that gets hurt
Will be he who has stalled
There's a battle
Outside and it's ragin'
It'll soon shake your windows
And rattle your walls
For the times they are a-changin'.

Bob Dylan
The Times They Are A-Changin'
1963

INTRODUCTION

In December 1990, the government of Canada announced a comprehensive, $3-billion five-year environmental action plan for Canada. Known as *Canada's Green Plan* (Environment Canada 1990), the plan outlines over 100 initiatives involving more than 40 federal departments and agencies to 'secure for current and future generations a safe and healthy environment and a sound and prosperous economy' (ibid., 2). The plan was prompted by increasingly vociferous public concern for the environment, articulated through many different avenues. It was based upon recommendations emerging from public meetings held across the country. The plan was hailed as 'the most important environmental action plan ever produced in Canada . . . [It] is an investment in our planet, our nation and ourselves' (de Cotret 1990).

Irrespective of agreement or disagreement with the details of the plan, few would dispute the scale of the undertaking nor the effort that was invested in formulating the program. Furthermore, this is not to be a one-shot effort; there is a commitment that the plan will be updated annually on the basis of emerging issues and priorities. In sum, there are good grounds to argue that the plan, formulated at the beginning of the last decade of the second millennium, is a symbol of the changing attitudes and management approaches of society towards the environment in Canada. It represents, one hopes, a watershed in this relationship from which a more thoughtful and less abusive symbiosis will evolve.

The preservation of parks and protected areas is probably more symbolic of this changing relationship than any other single facet of environmental issues. At the regional and national levels, calls for the protection of wilderness ecosystems are often among the most highly profiled environmental campaigns. The initiative to designate South Moresby Island as a protected area took on national and international significance. At the global scale, a major environmental challenge has emerged for this generation. For the first time, humans have the capability to transform all natural ecosystems into human-controlled ecosystems. If the former are to survive and be passed on to succeeding generations, it will be largely because of the legislative decisions that we as a society have made to protect such areas from further human disturbance. This is a watershed of truly historical significance.

Society is at a critical juncture in terms of its relationship with environment, and parks and wilderness protection are an integral and significant symbol of this change. This book reflects these concerns, coupled with a frustration that no single source was available that articulated a Canadian perspective on parks and protected areas.

The book is intended to be a concise encapsulation of Canadian practices. It seeks to link philosophy, research, and management practices around a number of key themes. It does not eschew theory and approaches developed elsewhere but seeks to develop these within a Canadian perspective. We think it important to produce such a book now, not only to reflect historical and current approaches but also to provide a base against which to assess future developments. As such the book should be of use to students taking courses on the subject of parks and protected areas and for anyone interested in a Canadian analysis of this topic.

MAJOR INITIATIVES

Before going on to outline the contents of the book, we should briefly review some current developments in parks and protected area development in Canada. The National Parks Act was passed in 1930 and survived largely unchanged until 1988, when major amendments were passed. These amendments will not be described in detail here (see Chapter 4) but in general they strengthened the conservation mandate of the parks. For example management plans are now mandatory; a state-of-the-parks report must be tabled by the federal minister every two years; public participation is now required;

poaching fines have been increased substantially; and wilderness zones within parks will have legislated boundaries.

Furthermore, for the first time in the history of parks in Canada, a political and public commitment has been made to complete the national park system by the year 2000 (Environment Canada 1990). This commitment has been reinforced by a timetable calling for the establishment of at least five new national parks by 1996 and another 13 by the end of the decade. This will put some 3 per cent of Canada's land area under the protection of the national parks system. Perhaps more significant, however, is the stated goal to set aside 12 per cent of the country as protected space. It is likely that between 150 and 200 additional parks will be required to fulfil this commitment, coupled with enthusiastic co-operation from provincial jurisdictions. The signing of the Tri-Council Agreement (Canadian Council of Ministers of the Environment, Canadian Parks Ministers' Council, Wildlife Ministers' Council of Canada) at Aylmer, Quebec, in November 1992, is a major step in assuring such provincial commitment (see Appendix 1).

In addition to the two major developments mentioned above, a third influential initiative is also underway—a revision of the national parks policy. The last revision, published in 1979, was a landmark document that for the first time explicitly stated the primary conservation function of the national parks system and laid out the specific policy details through which this would be enacted (see Chapter 4). Following several revisions it appears as though the new policy will follow the lead of the new legislation mentioned above, and offer increased protection of natural elements in the parks.

Finally, it should be pointed out that all the new protected area initiatives are not restricted to the federal government. Most provincial governments are also actively developing systems plans and targeting future acquisitions (see e.g. Leduc and Smith 1992). For example, the British Columbia government announced in May 1992 a new protected areas strategy that would double the current area of protected parks and wilderness by the year 2000. The government would designate 23 new areas in 1992 and another 21 by 1993, and a further 140 areas would be assessed for possible designation by the year 2000. This would bring the province to its goal of protecting 12 per cent of the land area.

At present, there are some 2,945 conservation sites (70.8 million hectares) owned or managed by governments in Canada. This approximates some 7.1 per cent of the total land and freshwater area (Turner et al. 1992). However, less than half this amount lies in highly protective categories such as ecological reserves and national parks, and 80 per cent of these most highly protected areas are less than 1,000 hectares in size. The rest allow activities such as logging, mining, and hunting that many consider irreconcilable with protected area status. Nor are these areas distributed to maximize their conservation value. Of 177 ecoregions described by the Canadian Council on

Ecological Areas, over a quarter have no protected areas (Turner *et al.* 1992). Clearly much remains to be done.

The initiatives described above, although laudable, can hardly be described as proactive. Instead they are reactions to the rapidly changing social and biophysical environment of the times. The next section will outline some of these changes.

THE CHANGING ENVIRONMENT

Major worldwide changes are underway in both the biophysical and social environments. Rapid climatic change appears to be a certainty rather than a far-fetched hypothesis (see e.g. Hare 1991) and public attitudes toward the environment appear to be changing as well (see e.g. Gray 1985). The purpose of this section is not to review these changes, but to focus on their direct implications for parks and protected areas.

One such change (and one that helped to trigger the political responses outlined above) has been increased public interest in the well-being of our parks and park system. Although public polls consistently demonstrate the high level of concern amongst the general public, it is the so-called 'special interest' groups such as the Canadian Parks and Wilderness Society and the Sierra Club that have been mainly responsible for articulating this interest. At all scales, from lobby groups interested in the protection of a specific locale of regional interest through to national and generic concerns, these groups have been growing rapidly as a powerful influence on park designation and management. A potent symbol of the latter was recently demonstrated by the Canadian Parks and Wilderness Society, which took the federal Environment minister to court in a lawsuit to end logging in Wood Buffalo National Park. The society was successful and logging has now been eliminated from the entire national park system.

Another such initiative, notable both for its scale and the response it elicited, is the *Endangered Spaces* campaign. Launched by the World Wildlife Fund Canada and the Canadian Parks and Wilderness Society in September 1989, the specific goal of the campaign is to ensure that Canada sets aside at least 12 per cent of its land area in protected areas by the year 2000. The national campaign was initiated by the release of an authoritative text (Hummel 1989) on the topic that was distributed free to all federal and provincial politicians in the country, coupled with a high-profile media campaign. Shortly thereafter, the federal minister made the first public commitment to complete the national park system (letter to Canadian Parks and Wilderness Society, 20 November 1989). The campaign is now actively monitoring the progress on this and other commitments. Unfortunately wilderness appears to be disappearing at an ever-increasing rate (Figure 1.1).

Native peoples should certainly be mentioned here as a most rapidly evolving influence on park designation and policy. This has been recognized for some time in federal lands north of 60° (see e.g. Sadler 1989); but only

Figure 1.1
Canadian wilderness areas are disappearing at an ever-increasing rate. The WWF report on the status of efforts to protect wilderness in 1992 found that Canada was losing at least 1 sq. km of wilderness every hour. In the 10 provinces, nearly 60% of land has been claimed for development. Less than 3.8% of the country's productive forest lands are found in the national and provincial park systems. *Credit: Ole Heggen*

recently have Native peoples begun to exert their influence in southern Canada (see Chapter 12). Indeed it is virtually certain that without Native support, South Moresby/Gwaii Hanaas would now be substantially logged instead of being one of the most spectacular parks on the continent (Dearden 1988). Nor are all such developments strictly federal. In April 1992 the British Columbia government announced the first joint Aboriginal/provincial park (known as Anhlunt'ukwsim Laxmihl Angwinga'asanskwhl Nisga'a in the Nisga'a language) covering some 17,683 hectares in the Nass River valley in northern British Columbia.

However, Native aspirations are not always congruent with those of park advocates. For example, in two well-known provincial parks in Ontario, Algonquin and Quetico, Native bands are demanding and in some cases have received access to park resources, a move that many consider antithetical to the parks' purpose. At Algonquin, the provincial government has signed an agreement with the Golden Lake First Nation allowing hunting in and motorized access to the park. The Lac La Ojibway band got permission for motorized access to Quetico and are now seeking aircraft landing rights and access to the entire park for trappers using snowmobiles. This is in direct contrast to the wilderness park policy calling for 'substantial areas where the forces of nature are permitted to function freely and where visitors travel by non-mechanical means and experience expansive solitude, challenge and personal integration with nature' (Ontario Ministry of Natural Resources 1978).

The examples mentioned above in some ways illustrate the growing influence of bodies outside the normal decision making channels of park establishment and management. This represents a generic trend from a historically closed administrative system to one which is much more easily penetrated by outside influences. Dearden and Berg (1993) have suggested three main groups as being significant influences on park decision making: entrepreneurs, environmentalists, and Native peoples. Furthermore, they suggest that the relative influence of these three groups has changed over time (Figure 1.2) leading to a primacy of the influence of Native peoples on current national park decision making. This is due not only to Native peoples' historical control in the north over park designation related to land claims, but also to the emergence of a similar situation in southern Canada where land claims are in effect, as witnessed by events at South Moresby, the Mingan Archipelago and elsewhere. The increasing role of Native peoples may, in some instances, significantly improve the conservation mandate of some parks. In other cases this will not be so.

The same penetration by external influences is also occurring in a bio-physical sense in the parks themselves. As the Canadian landscape has come increasingly under human control over this century, the parks have become islands in this sea of change. Park agencies can no longer ignore what happens beyond their boundaries. They must be aware of these external influences and plan accordingly.

The scope of these external influences is vast, ranging from atmospheric changes (e.g., acid rain, climatic change) and hydrospheric changes (e.g., changes in incoming water quality) that might be generated hundreds, if not

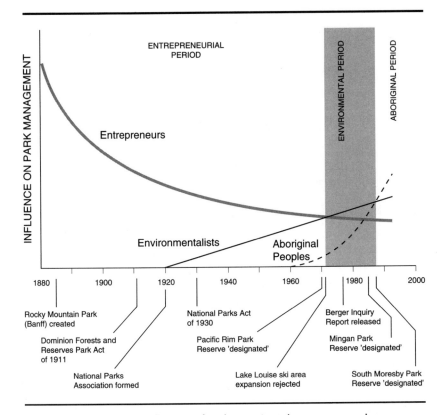

Figure 1.2 Suggested influence of various external groups on park management over time.

thousands, of kilometres away, through to changes occurring directly next to the park, such as logging activity or hunting on the boundaries (see e.g. Machlis and Tichnell 1987). Clearly the effects of these activities on park resources can vary enormously depending upon the nature of the activity and the nature of the park. Nonetheless they have something in common, and that is the need for park management to go outside its own administrative boundaries in order to protect the ecological integrity of park resources (see e.g. Zinkan 1992). This necessity will only increase in the future.

A graphic illustration of this trend is bear feeding on the boundaries of Riding Mountain National Park in Manitoba. There are some 70 bait sites on the boundaries of this park, many of which are baited on a continuous basis specifically to get the park bears to come to the sites to feed. This results in unnatural distribution of the animals, whose home ranges are vastly inflated to encompass the food sources. It may also result in the large size of the bears and irregularities in breeding behaviour. It also results in dead animals. Hunters pay to shoot the bears attracted by the bait. Annual average mortality

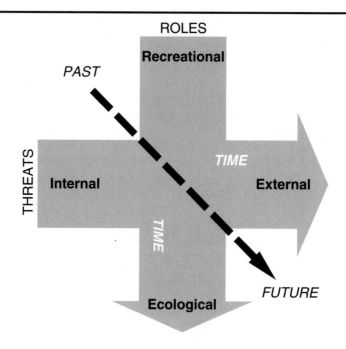

Figure 1.3 The changing emphasis in park roles over time.

is 122 animals, a figure that scientists conclude cannot be maintained if the population level is not to decline (Paquet 1991).

Clearly allowing bait stations for bears right on the park boundary by the Manitoba Department of Natural Resources is a significant detriment to the park ecosystem. Riding Mountain has no legislative mandate over activities outside the park and can use only persuasion to try to control the offending activity. As more parks become islands surrounded by land uses over which the park has no jurisdiction, the need to enforce regional co-operation by legislation will grow.

It is not the intention of this chapter to review the role of parks in society. Good literature on the topic exists elsewhere (see e.g. Nash 1971, Sax 1980, Bratton 1985, Sewell and Dearden 1989). Nelson (Chapter 3) and Eagles (Chapter 9) summarize some of these roles. It is, however, worth pointing out the apparent management implications of the changing priorities among these roles. One such change has been described above: the relative emphasis that must be put on activities within and outside park boundaries, with increasing attention being given to the latter. The second change in emphasis is a related one: the relative priority given to the conservation as opposed to the recreational mandate of the parks (see Figure 1.3).

The original Parks Act, although flawed in many ways, was also very forward-looking in one respect: its specific identification of intergenerational values. This has now become a prominent feature of much writing and policy regarding resource development (see e.g. Nelson 1991), largely due to the popularity of the 'sustainable development' concept as articulated by the World Commission on Environment and Economy (1987). However, the Parks Act back in 1930 called for parks to be left 'unimpaired for future generations'. This dictate survives until today but is becoming increasingly difficult to fulfil. Historically this mandate, especially through the rapid growth years in visitation of the last three decades, was addressed through control of the in-park activities of the visitors. Now, however, it seems as if the greatest threats may originate outside the parks and call for a vastly different set of management capabilities, rather than just a warden system that can control visitors.

One such capability is scientific: improved understanding of the functioning of the ecosystems that the parks are supposed to be protecting (see e.g. Willison *et al.* 1992). As the landscape becomes increasingly dominated by human processes, so the ecological roles of the parks will become more important. They may well be the *only* sites remaining where natural ecosystems can be studied, providing ecological benchmarks against which to assess change, and where populations retain some semblance of their interrelationships before humans arrived. Thus the future will witness a shift from a parks management philosophy that is almost exclusively internal and oriented toward recreational management to one that recognizes the significance of external influences and the necessity to invest resources in scientific understanding and management of biophysical systems. This increasing complexity of protected area management over time is illustrated in Figure 1.4.

This is not to say that the concepts and practices related to visitor management will be rendered redundant; but they too will need greater input from the scientific community, in particular from the social sciences, to make them more effective. Machlis (1992) has provided an overview of some of the roles of the social sciences in protected areas management, while authors such as Payne *et al.* (1992) and Rollins and Rouse (1992) provide recent case studies from Canada. Greater effort will also have to be given to formulating the bounds of the appropriate tourism experience that can be provided by parks. Interpretation, as described in Chapter 12, will increasingly focus on processes to educate and provide emotional responses of visitors in support of park values.

The foregoing outlined some of the elements of the rapidly changing field of park designation and management in Canada. The chapters in the remainder of the book help flesh out some of these details. Each author was asked to summarize one aspect of the current situation and to speculate on the future. The following section briefly describes each theme.

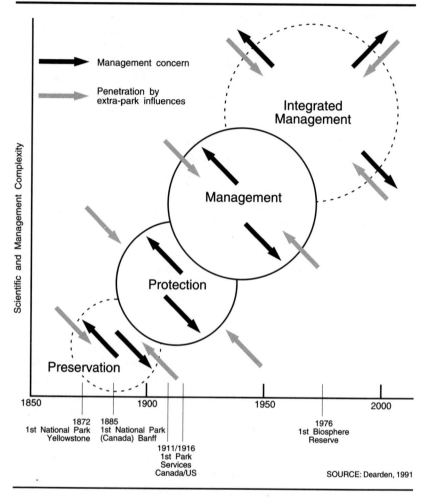

Figure 1.4 The evolving role of parks: from isolation to integration.

THE THEMES

The themes represented in this volume were chosen in consultation with the authors involved. Each author was approached with a theme suggested by the editors but was given the opportunity not only to respond to the suggested theme but also to add and subtract themes. Many suggestions were incorporated, new chapters added, and others discarded. The result is this collection.

Perhaps the most contentious issue was the question of what kinds of parks and protected areas to include. The book is not an attempt to include all aspects of park and protected areas in Canada. Other than the useful comparative legislative chapter by Paul Eagles (Chapter 4), little attention is given to regional and local parks. The bias is toward large, natural-area parks. Even at this scale, however, it should be noted that the emphasis is on formally designated *park* systems, rather than on other forms of protective designations such as national wildlife areas or on the details of wilderness preservation by provincial authorities. In the future we expect the latter to figure prominently in the protected area system in Canada. It is also likely that the private sector (see e.g. Filyk 1992) will play a larger role in the acquisition and management of conservation areas in the future, although little attention is devoted to this topic here.

In Chapter 2, Kevin McNamee presents an historical overview of the development of the protected area system in Canada. Focusing mainly on the national park system, McNamee traces the growth of the system, the main management issues, and the critical role that politicians and conservationists have played as the system has evolved. In Chapter 3, Gordon Nelson builds upon this historical overview and describes the recent evolution in thinking about parks and protected areas in terms of a less isolationist, more integrated approach. Strong public support is necessary and will depend on a better understanding of the various roles that protected areas play in society and of the range of protected area designations available to fulfil these roles. Nelson presents a model representing the relationships between land use, management, and institutional arrangements. Overall, he emphasises the growing need for a co-operative and co-ordinated approach to natural area protection in the future.

Paul Eagles, in the next chapter, provides a more detailed examination of the relevant parks legislation and policies in Canada. He rightly points out that designation and management practices ultimately depend on the legislative and policy base of the system in question. Four main levels of park systems occur in Canada: national, provincial, regional, and municipal. Eagles describes legislation and policies that govern national parks in some detail before going on to look at Ontario as an example of provincial park legislation and management. (Further descriptions of provincial systems can be found in Chapters 6 and 7.) He goes on to examine the regional and municipal levels using the examples of the Ontario Conservation Authorities and the Niagara parks regional systems and the Municipal and Public Parks Acts of Ontario. He concludes that the national parks system has the most progressive legislation and that provincial parks legislation in general leaves much to be desired. The major criticism of provincial park legislation is the degree of discretionary power ultimately resting on the bureaucracy and the lack of opportunity for formal public input. The regional systems are characterized in similar terms, but the municipal systems appear to be much more open to public scrutiny and input.

This overview is followed by a chapter by Rick Rollins on national parks and their management. This chapter forms the basis for more advanced discussions in later chapters and seeks to answer five main questions:

1. What is the purpose of national parks? What is the value of a national park, compared to the use of the same land for some other purpose? Who should benefit from national parks?
2. Where should national parks be located, and how many are needed? How large must they be, and how are boundaries resolved?
3. How are natural resources to be managed in national parks?
4. How is visitor use to be managed in national parks?
5. How are decisions to be made about management issues?

Following this assessment of national parks planning and management are two chapters dealing with provincial park systems. George Priddle points out that the 6.5 per cent of Ontario's land base in provincial parks is still well short of a proportional contribution to the 12 per cent goal articulated by the World Commission on Environment and Development (WCED 1987). Ontario has, however, a relatively sophisticated system for provincial park classification and zoning, arguably the most developed in the country. Priddle describes these policies and practices in some detail and concludes with several recommendations for future directions for the provincial park system in Ontario.

The other chapter illustrating the provincial systems is one on Alberta by Guy Swinnerton. Alberta has over 8 per cent of the land base in national parks, but the provincial park system is relatively modest compared with the size of the province, amounting to only 0.19 per cent of the land base. Initiatives are underway to expand the system, but progress is slow. There is also fundamental uncertainty regarding the role of the provincial park system in balancing conservation, heritage appreciation, outdoor recreation, and tourism. Clearly in Alberta 'the times they are a-changing' indeed, not only in the parks system, but in land-use strategy.

In Chapter 8, John Theberge examines the ecological base of our conservation and protected area strategies. He outlines some of the characteristics that make some species more vulnerable to human disturbance than others and therefore candidates for protective strategies. From this species-based approach, he moves on to look at the ecological principles for determining the site and size of protected areas, principles such as minimum viable population, island biogeography, patch dynamics, fragmentation, stress ecology, and catastrophe theory. Each approach is outlined and related to protected area management. He ends with the sobering conclusion that our parks are simply inadequate to fulfil the mandate of ecological protection. The latter demands care and attention to all things ecological throughout the landscape, not just in special areas set aside for that purpose. Thus Theberge sounds the trumpet not only for 'many more large parks and reserves' but also for 'strongly protective regional conservation strategies to buttress them'. For, as he points out, 'there isn't much chance that we will ever protect too much.'

Following this ecological theme is a chapter by Paul Eagles on the management of the environment within parks. Eagles reviews some of the main ecological roles of parks in society before getting into the details of environmental management. All management actions are based upon some explicit or implicit assessment of the value of particular environmental components by some influential group, whether local people, park bureaucrats, visitors, or lobby groups. He then explores the issues, management actions, and examples for components such as fire management, endangered species, vegetation, fish and wildlife, and paleontological resources within parks.

Bob Payne and Bob Graham warn of the need for input by social scientists in protected area management through a thorough examination of four related visitor planning and management frameworks. These frameworks, used both in Canada and the U.S.A., were designed to complement existing management processes that rely more upon natural science. They are the Recreation Opportunity Spectrum (ROS), Limits of Acceptable Change (LAC), Visitor Impact Management (VIM), and the Visitor Activity Management Process (VAMP). Each framework is described in terms of its development, purpose, and application and given a comparative critical analysis. The final section identifies the strengths and weaknesses of each framework and provides an assessment of the issues requiring attention if each framework is to reach its full potential.

Perhaps the most fundamental factor that will influence the destiny of our parks and protected areas into the future is the level of public support. Interpretation plays a fundamental role in this process and is the topic of Chapter 11. Jim Butler traces the antecedents of interpretation in parks in North America before going on to describe the definition and purpose of park interpretation. He points out that interpretation is not merely transferring information to others nor cataloguing things to see. It should instead 'fill the visitor with a greater sense of wonder and curiosity'.

We have much to learn from Native concepts about the 'wonder and curiosity' of our land. In Chapter 12, Berg, Fenge, and Dearden trace the evolving role of Native peoples in the designation and management of national parks in Canada. The authors outline the changing social and legal status of Native people before discussing relevant park policy and examples of northern and southern park initiatives. Park policy and practice must strive to keep up with Natives' changing legal and social position. Undoubtedly, this critical challenge will have a major impact upon how the national park system evolves in the future.

As land-dwelling animals, humans focus on the land, not the seas of our planet. It is only in the latter half of this century that policy makers have started to take serious note of the marine component. The establishment of protected areas is one such initiative; but, as Duffus and Dearden observe in

Chapter 13, our commitment is still nowhere near as significant as is the move to complete the terrestrial parks system. The national marine parks system plan defines 29 marine regions, but as yet, we have only one designated marine park and four marine additions to existing terrestrial parks. Several areas are under study, but Canada is only committed to add another six marine parks by the turn of the century. This is partially due to our lack of experience in establishing marine parks, to complicated jurisdictional matters, and to local opposition to some parks. Nonetheless, we question this somewhat tardy rate of establishment and the potential for further degradation of marine ecosystems in the meantime.

Hal Eidsvik, past chairman of the IUCN (World Conservation Union) Commission on National Parks and Protected Areas and a former senior policy advisor to the Canadian Parks Service, provides a chapter on the international dimensions of Canada's effort in the field of conservation and protected areas. Eidsvik quite rightly points out that this is not an easy task, since there is no one policy nor a single accounting system to help measure Canada's contribution. He goes on to outline some of the main international conservation initiatives, many of which have had significant input from Canadians either as individuals or acting on behalf of the country. From this broad base, Eidsvik goes on to describe two essential tools for assessing the international dimensions of protected areas: Udvardy's biogeographical classification system and the IUCN conservation area classification system. He concludes that Canada is probably second only to the U.S.A in terms of the conservation effectiveness of our protected area system.

The final chapter by the editors draws this material together: first, by illustrating the interaction between the role of theory and research, the role of legislation, policies, and plans, and the actions taken by resource managers; and second, by summarizing some of the key issues for the future.

These are exciting times for the evolution of the protected area system in Canada. Never has the need been greater; never have the challenges been stronger. What happens in this next decade, how capable we are of meeting these challenges, is critical. Hopefully this book can make one small contribution to advancing societal awareness and support for protecting the greatest resource of all.

REFERENCES

Bratton, S.P.
 1985 'National Park Management and Values', *Environmental Ethics* 7: 117–33.
de Cotret, Robert
 1990   News release, 11 December, Environment Canada, Ottawa.

Dearden, P.
1988   'Mobilizing Public Support for Environment: The Case of South Moresby Island, British Columbia', in *Effective Communication for Environmental Groups*, Alberta Environment Council, 62–75.

Dearden, P.
1991   'Parks and Protected Areas', in *Resource Management and Development*, ed. B. Mitchell, Oxford University Press, Toronto, 130–52.

Dearden, P., and L. Berg
1993   'Canadian National Parks: A Model of Administrative Penetration', *The Canadian Geographer* (in press).

Environment Canada
1990   *Canada's Green Plan*, Supply and Services Canada, Ottawa.

Environment Canada, Parks Service
1991   *Canadian Parks Service Proposed Policy*, Ottawa.

Filyk, G.
1992   'The Role of Private Stewardship in Habitat Conservation and Protection', in *Science and the Management of Protected Areas*, eds Willison *et al.*, 211–15.

Gray, D.G.
1985   *Ecological Beliefs and Behaviors*, Greenwood Press, Westport, Conn.

Hare, F.K.
1991   'Contemporary Climatic Change: The Problem of Uncertainty', in *Resource Management and Development*, ed. B. Mitchell, Oxford University Press, Toronto, 8–27.

Hummel, M.
1989   *Endangered Spaces: The Future for Canada's Wilderness*, Key Porter Books, Toronto.

Leduc, J.M., and A.D. Smith
1992   'System Planning for Protection-Oriented Provincial Parks in Nova Scotia', in *Science and the Management of Protected Areas*, eds Willison *et al.*, 139–44.

Machlis, G.E.
1992   'Social Science and Protected Area Management: The Principles of Partnership', in *Proceedings, Plenary Sessions and Symposium Papers*, 4th World Congress on National Parks and Protected Areas, Caracas, Venezuela, 126–38.

Machlis, G.E., and D.L. Tichnell
1985   *The State of the World's Parks*, Westview, Boulder, Colo.

Nash, R.
1971   *Wilderness and the American Mind*, Yale University Press, London.

Nelson, J.G.
1991   'Sustainable Development, Conservation Strategies and Heritage', in *Resource Management and Development*, ed. B. Mitchell, Oxford University Press, Toronto, 246–67.

Ontario Ministry of Natural Resources
1978   *Ontario Provincial Parks Planning and Management Strategies*, Government of Ontario, Toronto.

Payne, R.J., R.B. Rollins, S. Tamm, and C. Nelson
  1992 'Managing Social Impacts of Parks and Protected Areas in Northern Canada', in *Science and the Management of Protected Areas*, eds Willison *et al.*, 513–18.
Rollins, R.B., and J. Rouse
  1992 'Segmenting Backcountry Visitors by Setting Preferences', in *Science and the Management of Protected Areas*, eds Willison *et al.*, 485–98.
Sadler, B.
  1989 'National Parks, Wilderness Preservation and Native Peoples in Northern Canada', *Natural Resources Journal* 29: 185–204.
Sax, J.M.
  1980 *Mountains Without Handrails*, University of Michigan, Ann Arbor.
Sewell, W.R.D., and P. Dearden, eds
  1989 *Wilderness: Past, Present and Future*, special issue of *Natural Resources Journal* 29: 1–222.
Turner, A.M., C.D.A. Rubec, and E.B. Witien
  1992 'Canadian Ecosystems: A Systems Approach to Their Conservation', in *Science and the Management of Protected Areas*, eds Willison *et al.*, 117–27.
Willison, J.H.M., S. Bondrup-Nielsen, C. Drysdale, T.B. Herman, M.W.P. Munro, and T.L. Pollock, eds
  1992 *Science and the Management of Protected Areas*, Elsevier, Amsterdam.
World Commission on Environment and Development
  1987 *Our Common Future*, Oxford University Press, New York and Oxford.
Zinkan, C.
  1992 'Waterton Lakes National Park: Moving Towards Ecosystem Management', in *Science and the Management of Protected Areas*, eds Willison *et al.*, 229–32.

CHAPTER 2

From Wild Places to Endangere

A History of Canada's National Parks

────

KEVIN McNAMEE

INTRODUCTION

National parks are one of the oldest forms of conservation in Canada. They preserve more wilderness from industrial resource development activities than all other protected areas combined. Approximately 2 per cent of Canada's land is preserved by federal legislation within 35 national parks and national park reserves and one national marine park. Figure 2.1 shows the current distribution of national parks.

The evolution of the national parks system since its inception in 1885 has been influenced more by the nation's focus on economic development and prevailing social values and less by the need to preserve wilderness. Government, industry, and local communities emphasized the economic value of national parks as places of recreation and tourism destinations. However, as Canada's wilderness dwindles and efforts to implement national and regional conservation strategies increase, the essential role of national parks and protected areas in preserving important natural areas is being more broadly acknowledged. Parks are now viewed as places for conservation rather than recreation.

This chapter explores the evolution of the national parks system and some of the landmark events that have shaped it over the last century. The focus is on the expansion of the national parks system and on the range of management issues that have preoccupied governments and conservation groups for most of its history. Also featured is the critical role that politicians and conservationists have played in shaping the parks system.

BIRTH OF THE CANADIAN PARKS NETWORK (1885-1911)

The beginning of Canada's national parks system was relatively inauspicious. The impetus for Canada's first national park, Banff, was the discovery of the Cave and Basin mineral hot springs by two employees of the Canadian

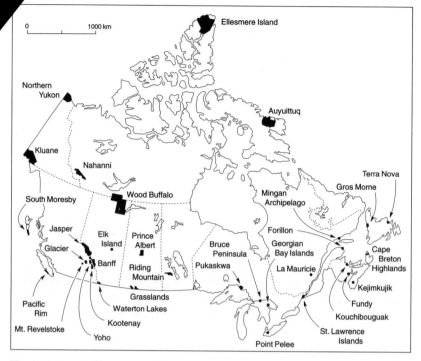

Figure 2.1 National parks in Canada.

Pacific Railway (CPR). They sought to establish a claim over the hot springs so that they could personally profit from its commercial development.

The federal government denied the claim. Instead, in November 1885, it established a 26 sq. km (10 sq. mi.) reservation around the Banff hot springs on the slopes of Sulphur Mountain. The hot springs were now public property and no longer available for 'sale, or settlement, or squatting'. The government, in partnership with the CPR, sought to exploit the economic benefits of the hot springs (Figure 2.2). The wording of the Order in Council that established the reserve reflected the value of the hot springs to the government: 'there have been discovered several hot mineral springs which promise to be of great sanitary advantage to the public' (Lothian 1976a, 1: 20).

Wilderness preservation had little to do with the establishment of the Banff hot springs reserve and other national parks around the turn of the century. The Banff hot springs were to become, as the deputy minister of the Interior stated in 1886, 'the greatest and most successful health resort on the continent.' To achieve this, he called for a plan 'to commence the construction of roads and bridges and other operations necessary to make of the reserve a creditable National Park' (Lothian 1976a, 1: 23). The hot springs, the clean

Figure 2.2
The first bathing establishment constructed at the Cave and Basin in Rocky Mountain Park (*c.* 1887-8). The architecture for the two bath houses is fashioned after Swiss-style buildings. In 1887, 3,000 availed themselves of the park's mineral hot springs. Cascade Mountain rises in the background.
Photo: Canadian Parks Service

air, and the mountain scenery would attract tourists to Banff on the newly constructed railway. They would stay at new hotels that were constructed within the new parks, such as the Banff Springs Hotel. Thus, both the government and the CPR, which constructed the hotels, would profit.

The First National Parks

The federal government moved quickly both to expand the Banff hot springs reserve and to establish other parks. A dominion land surveyor hired to complete a legal survey of the Banff reserve drew the government's attention to 'a large tract of country lying outside of the original reservation' with 'features of the greatest beauty'. The surveyor noted that these lands 'were admirably adapted for a national park' (Lothian 1976a, 1: 23).

Acting on the surveyor's find, Parliament passed the Rocky Mountain Park Act in June 1887 to establish the boundaries for a more extensive 673 sq. km (260 sq. mi.) park, which would later be called Banff National Park. The area was to be 'a public park and pleasure ground for the benefit, advantage and enjoyment of the people of Canada'. Under the legislation, the government could make rules for 'preservation and the protection of game and fish or of wild birds', and to preserve some of the park's natural features and to control the cutting of timber (Lothian 1976b, 4: 16). This was one of the first acknowledgements of the need to conserve park resources.

The creation of Rocky Mountain Park was partly modelled on earlier actions in the United States. Prime Minister Sir John A. Macdonald was advised to protect the commercial value of the Banff hot springs by establishing a reserve similar to the Arkansas Hot Springs Reserve in Arkansas, which was created by Congress in 1832. The Rocky Mountain Park Act used similar language to that contained in the legislation establishing Yellowstone in Wyoming as the world's first national park in 1872. The Yellowstone Park Act set land aside 'as a public park or pleasuring ground for the benefit and enjoyment of the people' (Lothian 1976a, 1: 24).

Herein the similarity to Yellowstone ends. While Yellowstone sat unattended for almost two decades, the Canadian federal government made sure that Rocky Mountain Park was made useful and contributed to the national economy (Figure 2.3). The prime minister confirmed this policy: 'the Government thought it was of great importance that all this section of country should be brought at once into usefulness' (Craig Brown 1969, 49). Timber cutting, mineral development, and grazing were allowed. Mineral claims were worked in Banff for almost half a century.

There was virtually no opposition to resource development activities within the park. The national policy of the Macdonald government in the 1880s stressed the need to develop and exploit natural resources as the means to developing a national economy. National parks that produced profits from tourism and resource development were simply viewed as an extension of that policy. The underlying assumption of the national policy was that there

Figure 2.3
The sleepy frontier town of Banff is pictured here in 1887, with Cascade Mountain rising over what is now Banff Avenue. Regulations passed under the National Parks Act in 1890 prohibited 'furious riding and driving on public roads' in the townsite. Cows were, however, permitted to graze on the main street. *Photo: Canadian Parks Service*

were plenty of natural resources to exploit, and that government and industry had a shared responsibility to develop those resources. The first parks were manifestations of that policy (Craig Brown 1969).

In addition to Rocky Mountain Park, several other parks were created under the national policy. In 1886, A.W. Ross, a member of Parliament from Manitoba, suggested the federal government examine the potential for more parks along the railway. As a result, Glacier and Yoho parks were established in 1888 to make the British Columbia and the mountain sections of the CPR as 'popular as possible'. And to ensure their popularity, the CPR constructed the Glacier Park Lodge and Mount Stephen House hotels within the two parks. The parks were also created 'to preserve the timber and natural beauty of the district' (Foster 1978, 31). Policies promoting both the exploitation and conservation of park resources were consistent because preserving natural scenery was central to retaining the first parks as tourist attractions.

Other parks were established outside the Banff area. F.W. Godsal, a local rancher from Cowley, Alta, spearheaded efforts to establish the Waterton Lakes Park despite the opposition of the federal bureaucracy. Godsal urged the government to protect the Crows Nest Pass and Waterton Lakes in a national park; 'otherwise a comparatively small number of settlers can control and spoil these public resorts' (Rodney 1969, 172). The bureaucracy, however, felt the government should focus on the three existing parks and manage them properly. One civil servant warned the deputy minister of the Interior: 'Don't you think it possible to overdo this park reservation business?' The comment was ignored. The Hon. T. Mayne Daly, minister of the Interior, established the Waterton Lakes Forest Park in 1895 (Figure 2.4), observing that 'Posterity will bless us' (Lothian 1976a, 1: 32).

By 1911, the federal government had protected a number of areas for posterity: Rocky Mountain Park, the Yoho and Glacier park reserves, and the Waterton Lakes and Jasper Forest parks. These areas were multiple-use parks, inspired by a profit motive and were not founded on any environmental ethic. Yet their creation was critical to today's legacy of wilderness reserves.

The first federal parks were also important because they stimulated provincial action. In 1893, the government of Ontario established Algonquin as the nation's first provincial park; Quebec established Laurentide Park in 1895. Both were multiple-use parks with an emphasis on the protection of water, fish, and wildlife, and with control over logging and recreation.

Through the establishment of the first federal and provincial parks, governments acknowledged that they had a responsibility to hold lands in trust for the public benefit, that there was a need to conserve natural resources, and that the creation and maintenance of parks was a government responsibility. Canadians continue to benefit from the farsighted decisions of Canada's early political leaders.

BRINGING THE PARKS TO CANADIANS (1911–57)

This period is characterized by government action to expand the national parks system beyond its initial Rocky Mountain focus to include natural areas in central and eastern Canada. In order to secure the political support for an enlarged network of national parks, federal civil servants promoted the recreational and tourism benefits of the parks. It is also during this period that some of the first examples of public advocacy for park values were exhibited.

In 1911, there was no system of national parks; instead, there was one park established by law and four created by Order in Council. There were parks, park reserves, and forest reserves. Each was run by a superintendent under the direction of the minister of the Interior with no real policy direction. It became clear to the government that there was a need for a separate branch of government to administer the parks.

The parks were also growing in popularity and proving to be a national asset. The success of the first parks convinced the government of the need to protect their scenery. The Hon. Frank Oliver, minister of the Interior, introduced legislation into the House of Commons in 1911 that shifted parks policy from promoting parks as 'primarily places of business' to places where 'there will be no business except such as is absolutely necessary for the recreation of the people' (Foster 1978, 75).

Figure 2.4
Visitors to Waterton Lakes Park pause beside their car at the park entrance
west of Pincher Creek, Alta, *c.* 1930. The Pincher Creek Automobile Club
began construction on the Pincher Creek-Waterton road in 1911. Only 64
visitors arrived in Waterton that year. In 1938, Ottawa imposed fees on
motor vehicles entering the Waterton Lakes parks: 25¢ for a single trip and
$1 for the season.   *Photo: Canadian Parks Service*

To this end, Parliament passed the Dominion Forest Reserves and Parks
Act in 1911. The Act accomplished several things. It created two categories
of conservation lands—forest reserves and dominion parks; it reduced the
level of development in the parks; and it placed the Dominion parks under
the administration of the world's first national parks branch, known over the
years as the Dominion Parks Branch, the National Parks Branch, Parks Canada, and (more recently) the Canadian Parks Service.

The legislation was a disappointment to the new parks branch because it
dramatically reduced the size of the Rocky Mountain, Jasper, and Waterton
Lakes dominion parks. Rocky Mountain, for example, was reduced by more
than half. The reductions occurred because the government concluded that
large parks were not required for recreation and providing access to natural
areas. Thus, land was withdrawn from the parks system and put in the forest
reserves, which focused on protecting wildlife.

The government's action to reduce the parks was not popular with James
B. Harkin, the first commissioner of the Dominion Parks Branch. The chief
civil servant in charge of the dominion parks from 1911 to 1936, Harkin left

an indelible mark on Canada's national parks system. He brought a philosophy to the position that was a mixture of reverence for the power of nature and a pragmatic view of the economic value of nature and the parks to society.

Harkin was heavily influenced by the writings of John Muir, one of America's foremost naturalists and national park advocates. Harkin believed that the national parks 'exist in order that every citizen of Canada may satisfy his soul-craving for Nature'. He believed the parks provided people with a chance for 'wholesome recreation that would physically and spiritually rejuvenate them' (Foster 1978, 81). In parks, people could experience nature and beauty, and absorb the peace of the forests.

To that end, Harkin believed that Canadians had a responsibility to safeguard Canada's wildlands by establishing more parks. He warned that 'future generations may wonder at our blindness if we neglect to set them aside before civilization invades them' (Foster 1978, 81). Harkin also believed that anything that impaired the natural beauty of the park or its peaceful tranquillity had to be excluded. Small wonder that under Harkin the national parks system expanded from its western base to eastern Canada, the number of parks increased from five to 16, and resource extraction activities were prohibited.

However, to get the political support and government finances to accomplish this, Harkin promoted very strongly the economic value of the national parks. He was particularly impressed by the tourism value of the parks (Figures 2.5, 2.6). In one annual report Harkin wrote that the 'National Parks provide the chief means of bringing to Canada a stream of tourists and a stream of tourist gold' (Marty 1984, 98).

The CPR agreed with Harkin because their calculations demonstrated that the Rocky Mountains generated $50 million a year in tourism revenue (Foster 1978). Harkin calculated the value of scenic lands to be $13.88 an acre, while wheatland was worth $4.91 (Marty 1984, 98). Armed with Harkin's statistics, politicians rose in the House of Commons over the years to defend government expenditures on the dominion parks.

Harkin's promotion of the tourism value of parks produced improved visitor accommodation, the provision of minor attractions to supplement natural features, and the construction of first-class roads (such as the Banff-Jasper Highway) and trails so that natural attractions could be reached in safety and comfort. The national park regulations were changed in 1911 to allow the first automobiles into the parks. It would not be for several decades that Harkin's work in developing the recreational potential of national parks would begin to cause their deterioration.

The Birth of a Public Constituency for Parks

Public protests against the reduction in size of some of the dominion parks in 1911 provide some of the first examples of how public pressure shaped

Figure 2.5
The bath house at the Upper Hot Springs in Banff National Park, *c.* 1935.
William McCardell claims to have discovered these springs on New Year's
Day in 1884. The first road for carriages to the spring, which was then
privately operated, was completed in 1886. The bath house pictured here
was constructed in 1932 by unemployed local men.

Photo: Canadian Parks Service

the national parks system. Organizations such as the Alberta Game and Fish
Protective Association, the Camp Fire Club of America, and the Canadian
Northern and Grand Trunk Pacific Railway lobbied for a return of the parks
to their larger size.

Backed by the Camp Fire Club of America and by other civil servants,
Harkin was able to get the government to expand the Waterton Lakes park
from 34 to 1,095 sq. km (13 to 423 sq. mi.) so that it would form a natural
continuation of the U.S. Glacier National Park in Montana. Howard Douglas,
chief superintendent of the national parks, informed Ottawa that 'the enlarge-
ment of this park is greatly desired by . . . the sportsmen here and on the
United States side' (Rodney 1969, 199). While the park was again reduced
by half in 1921, a core wilderness area had been protected because of public
pressure. Harkin was also successful in using public pressure to expand
Rocky Mountain Park to protect park wildlife.

Figure 2.6
Mountain guide Rudolph Aemmer is pictured here on the summit of Mount Victoria near Lake Louise in Banff National Park in 1931. In July 1954, four Mexican women and their male guide were killed after falling 600 metres in Abbot Pass. Three other women were rescued by a Swiss guide and Canadian Pacific Railway staff.   *Photo: W.J. Oliver*

The first organization to promote the value of national parks was formed in 1923 to oppose the Calgary Power Corporation's plan to dam the Spray River near Canmore, which was inside Rocky Mountain Park. The National Parks Association of Canada was formed to promote the conservation of national parks for 'scientific, recreational and scenic purposes, and their protection from exploitation for commercial purposes' (Bella 1987, 51). Arthur Wheeler, who led the fight against the dam, encouraged the association to 'protest against any actions that will create a precedent for commercial encroachment upon the integrity of the Canadian National Parks' (Johnston 1985, 9). Thus ensued a debate over the need to protect national parklands versus the need to develop their natural resources.

The Spray Lakes debate resembled a similar issue in the United States. A 1913 decision to flood the Hetch Hetchy Valley in Yosemite National Park was preceded by a tremendous national debate on the value of national parks and the need to preserve wilderness. While the valley was eventually lost, the fight promoted a broad swell of public support for the concept of national parks and wilderness. In Canada, while the Spray River cause was also lost, no large base of public support for the Canadian national parks emerged and the National Parks Association faded from view.

The Spray Lakes fight and other issues reinforced Harkin's efforts to further protect the dominion parks. Harkin was especially concerned that a 1926 agreement between Canada and Alberta to transfer control of natural resources to the province would have a negative impact on the parks. He convinced the Hon. Charles Stewart, minister of the Interior, to introduce legislation in the House of Commons in 1927 that would establish the principle of the absolute sanctity of the national parks.

Premier Rowntree of Alberta opposed the legislation because he did not want to lose control over the natural resources contained in the parks, citing the water power resources of the Upper Spray Lakes and the coal deposits in Rocky Mountain and Jasper parks as examples. Rowntree's opposition prompted a survey of the parks to identify and remove areas that had important industrial potential. This was an extension of the 'parks must be useful' philosophy. If resource development is to be prohibited, then useful resources should not be included within the park's boundaries. In 1928, the survey recommended that the Kananaskis and Spray Lakes watersheds, with their potential for hydro-electric power, and other areas suitable for grazing and for coal and timber extraction be withdrawn from the parks.

In 1930, control over natural resources was transferred to the governments of Alberta, Saskatchewan, and Manitoba. As part of the deal, the boundaries of the Rocky Mountain Park were changed to exclude the Kananaskis and Spray Lakes and areas now known as Canmore and Exshaw. However, in the process, it was agreed that the control of the national parks, such as the Rocky Mountain parks, Prince Albert National Park in Saskatchewan, and Riding Mountain National Park in Manitoba, would rest solely with the federal government. Despite this agreement, the provinces continue to pressure the federal government to develop these national parks to meet provincial economic development objectives.

The National Parks Act

Parliament also passed the National Parks Act in 1930 to provide a sweeping statement on parks that reflected Harkin's philosophy. No new parks could be established or existing parks eliminated or their boundaries changed without Parliament's approval. Mineral exploration and development were prohibited and only limited use of green timber for essential park management purposes was allowed. The parks were also confirmed as absolute game sanctuaries. The dominion parks were also renamed as national parks, and Rocky Mountain Park became Banff National Park.

Parliament did exercise its right to eliminate several national parks that were wildlife sanctuaries for species threatened with extinction. For example, Buffalo National Park at Wainwright was eliminated in 1947 because the buffalo had been saved with the establishment of Wood Buffalo and Elk Island national parks in the 1920s. The Nemiskan Park in Saskatchewan, established to protect the pronghorn antelope, was also abolished in 1947 because of the growth in antelope populations and opposition from farmers and ranchers who wanted to use the land for cattle grazing.

Harkin's efforts to promote the value of national parks resulted in more parks being established under the new National Parks Act. For example, Nova Scotia was the first province to agree to transfer provincial land to the federal Crown to create Cape Breton Highlands National Park in 1936. Prior to that, the national parks were established from lands administered by the federal government or that were purchased.

During Harkin's period, political support for national parks was high: Cape Breton Highlands was established because of the support of the Yarmouth Fish and Game Protective Association and the premier of Nova Scotia; a member of Parliament and the mayor of Dauphin, Man. lobbied for Riding Mountain park; and another member of Parliament wanted a park in Prince Edward Island. And while there was a decidedly commercial basis to this support, it clearly resulted in the preservation of large wilderness landscapes.

National parks were sometimes the product of more intricate political deals. The Prince Albert Liberal riding association presented a list of demands to Mackenzie King in 1926 before agreeing to nominate him as their candidate to the House of Commons. The list included a request for a national park. King defeated a young lawyer named John Diefenbaker in 1926, and as prime minister presided over the opening of Prince Albert National Park in 1928. Diefenbaker later referred to Prince Albert National Park as 'that mosquito park offered to Prince Albert as a reward for the election of Mackenzie King' (Waiser 1989, 43).

One year before he died at the age of 80 in 1958, Harkin lamented the lack of a public constituency in Canada for the protection of wilderness (Nash 1969). Perhaps if Harkin had lived into the next decade, he would have been pleased by the sudden growth in public citizens' organizations dedicated to promoting the value of national parks to all Canadians.

GROWING SUPPORT, DWINDLING WILDERNESS, NEW PARKS (1958-84)

The 1960s saw a dramatic growth in public concern for the environment. Rapid industrial and urban development, air and water pollution, threats to northern wilderness areas in Alaska and Canada, and the publication of

Rachel Carson's *Silent Spring* energized citizens to demand government action to protect the environment. Part of their agenda included a demand for more parks and less industrial and recreational development within the boundaries of existing parks.

The minister in charge of national parks generally has to make decisions on the establishment of new national parks and on the commercial uses to be permitted within them. Such decisions were generally *ad hoc* in nature. Although the parks were supposedly managed under the National Parks Act for the 'benefit, education and enjoyment' of Canadians, the public had little or no influence on those decisions.

Several parks ministers decried the lack of an organized public constituency for national parks. In 1960, the minister in charge of national parks, the Hon. Alvin Hamilton, made an impassioned plea in the House of Commons for help in defending national park values: 'How can a minister stand up against the pressures of commercial interests who want to use the parks for mining, forestry, for every kind of honky-tonk device known to man, unless the people who love these parks are prepared to band together and support the minister by getting the facts out across the country?' (Henderson 1969, 331).

Participants at the 1961 Resources for Tomorrow Conference in Montreal agreed with Hamilton. They concluded that there was a need for a non-government organization 'to perform a watchdog role over those areas now reserved for park purpose' (Henderson 1969, 332). The National and Provincial Parks Association of Canada (NPPAC; now the Canadian Parks and Wilderness Society) was formed in 1963 to perform this watchdog role by both promoting the value of parks and advocating the expansion of park networks.

The NPPAC subsequently lobbied successfully for the creation of Kluane and Nahanni national parks. It helped defeat proposals to hold the 1972 Winter Olympics in Banff National Park and to construct a multimillion dollar resort complex proposal in Lake Louise. These were major battles that focused public and political attention on the ecological value of national parks. They also marked the beginning of a policy shift away from a focus on the recreational value of national parklands to their ecological value. The NPPAC, along with other organizations such as the Alberta Wilderness Association and the Canadian Nature Federation, was instrumental in developing environmental standards for national parks to ensure that they were 'maintained and made use of so as to leave them unimpaired' as required by the National Parks Act.

National Parks Policy

Amongst the NPPAC's most important achievements was its successful advocacy for the first comprehensive national parks policy. In 1958 the government completed a broad policy statement to guide the use, development, and protection of the national parks. It sat, however, on the shelf for years. In response to the NPPAC's lobbying, the federal Cabinet adopted and released the policy in September 1964.

Until the adoption of the 1964 policy, the administration of national parks was done on a piecemeal basis. The National Parks Act, with its dual mandate for use and protection, left ample room for varying opinions as to what Parliament exactly meant when it passed the legislation in 1930. Parliament dedicated the national parks 'to the people of Canada for their benefit, education and enjoyment', and stated that they were to be 'maintained and made use of so as to leave them unimpaired'. What kind of benefits were the parks to provide to Canadians? What did 'unimpaired' mean? Where do the limits to recreational development end and requirements for conservation begin?

Each successive government and each minister in charge of the national parks had a different interpretation of these requirements. The National Parks Branch wanted a policy statement that would provide continuity for the management of the parks, one that would extend beyond the terms of office for any particular government and that was not in danger of being changed on a political whim (National and Historic Parks Branch 1969).

The 1964 policy established the preservation of significant natural features in national parks as its 'most fundamental and important obligation'. The provisions contained therein were to guide against private exploitation, overuse, improper use, and inappropriate development of parklands. The policy's focus was on drawing a distinction between urban-type recreation, which was to be discouraged, and recreation that involved the use and conservation of natural areas within the parks.

Cabinet approved a revised policy document in 1979 which adopted even stronger preservation oriented policies for the parks. The new policy put to rest the debate over the dual mandate contained in the National Parks Act by establishing the need to maintain the ecological integrity of parklands as a first consideration that must be regarded as a prerequisite to use. It also committed the government to setting legislative limits to the size of downhill ski areas and to the townsites of Banff and Jasper. Tourism facilities and overnight accommodation were to be located outside the parks wherever possible. The public was to be consulted on the development of park management plans, changes to the park zoning systems, and revisions to the policy. Finally, reflecting strong public concerns over the loss of parklands to development, the policy stated that the 'majority of national park lands and their living resources are protected in a wilderness state with a minimum of man-made facilities' (Parks Canada 1982, 40).

A Systematic Approach to Park Expansion

Progress on expanding the national parks system came to a halt after Harkin's resignation in 1936. Only two national parks were created between 1936 and

1968: Fundy in 1948 and Terra Nova in 1957. Moreover, the federal government's 1930 policy of establishing a national park in each province had not been attained because there were still no parks in Quebec. However, impetus was given to expanding the national parks system into Quebec and other areas when the Hon. Jean Chrétien took charge of the National Parks portfolio in 1968.

Chrétien immediately declared that, to achieve an adequate representation of Canada's heritage, 40 to 60 new national parks would be required to complete the national park system by 1985. He saw a need for urgent action: costs for new parkland were reaching 'prohibitive' levels, and potential national parklands could be quickly spoiled 'by different forms of economic and social development' (Chrétien 1969, 10).

Chrétien's statement was significant because it acknowledged the need for some criteria to guide the location of new national parks. The park establishment process was still largely an *ad hoc* process, with parks being created wherever there was political support or interest. In 1971, Parks Canada adopted a natural regions system plan to guide park expansion activities. The government's goal is to represent the characteristic physical, biological, and geographic features of each of 39 natural regions within the national parks system. While Chrétien had suggested completing the national parks system by 1985, the centennial of Banff's establishment, no target date would be confirmed until two decades later.

Chrétien did meet one target. The president of the NPPAC bet the minister $5 that he couldn't establish nine parks over a five-year period (anon., 1972). Chrétien won the bet handily, establishing 10 new national parks totalling 52,870 sq. km (18,500 sq. mi.). His successes included the first national parks in Quebec, including La Mauricie, located in Chrétien's riding of Shawinigan; the first new national park in British Columbia (Pacific Rim) in almost four decades; and the first national parks in northern Canada, Kluane, Nahanni, and Auyuittuq.

The political and local response to new national parks was different in the 1960s than during Harkin's era, particularly when it was now the federal government, and not local communities and politicians, that was initiating many of the new park proposals. Chrétien encountered strong opposition from local communities and Aboriginal people to new park proposals. The Association for the Preservation of the Eastern Shore successfully opposed the creation of the proposed Ship Harbour national park in Nova Scotia. Intense opposition from the Inuit and Innu in Labrador forced the cancellation in 1979 of federal-provincial negotiations for two new national parks in Labrador (Bill 1982). While this opposition stopped the creation of several national parks, it resulted in a vastly different park establishment process that is more sensitive to the social and economic concerns of local residents.

Local Communities Force Changes to Parks Policy

Government policy until the 1970s was to expropriate and remove communities located within the boundaries of proposed national parks. More than 200 families were expropriated to create Forillon National Park in Quebec (Figure 2.7). Some 1,200 residents and 228 households were also removed from their land and communities to complete the land acquisition process for Kouchibouguac National Park in New Brunswick.

Until the 1960s, there was little mass resistance to expropriations for national parks or other purposes. However, society began to reassess its relationship in the 1960s with those elements that exercised authority over daily life (La Forest and Roy 1981). This manifested itself in mass resistance by the residents affected by government plans to establish Kouchibouguac and Gros Morne national parks.

This resistance resulted in a number of actions. In 1980, Canada and New Brunswick commissioned a special inquiry into the violence and public controversy that surrounded the establishment of Kouchibouguac National Park.

Figure 2.7
Old fishing village along the Bay of Gaspé in Forillon National Park, Que., east of Grande-Grave, *c.* 1968-70. Park visitors can now bike or hike along the old road to the most easterly point in the park, Cap Gaspé. Most of the houses pictured here were removed after the Quebec government expropriated local residents to make way for the new federal park. In an ironic twist, the central theme of the park's interpretive program is 'Harmony between man, the land, and the sea'. *Photo: Canadian Parks Service*

The inquiry condemned the government's policy of requiring mass expropriations of lands required for national park purposes. And while it urged the government to proceed with developing the park, it recommended that area residents be allowed to continue commercial fishing and clam digging within the park, that Parks Canada emphasize bilingual staffing because the park resided in a predominantly French-speaking area, and that the history of the Acadian community be stressed in the park's communication programs.

The government began to change its approach to dealing with local people starting in Gros Morne National Park, Nfld. Under the Family Homes Expropriation Act, passed by the Newfoundland legislature in 1970, none of the 125 families affected by the park were forced to move. Few took up the offer to leave their outport communities. Today, there are seven communities located within several park enclaves; the park boundary is simply drawn around them. The National Parks Act was also amended in 1988 to allow local residents to continue to cut firewood and snare rabbits within the national park, thereby addressing two of their main grievances against the park.

The government also amended its policy in 1979 to prohibit the expropriation of private landowners in areas where it wants to establish new national parks. Private land can now only be acquired for parks purposes if the owner is willing to sell the land to the government. A case in point is the current land acquisition programs for the Grasslands and Bruce Peninsula national parks. Land is being acquired only from willing sellers.

Finally, the government must now ensure that there is local support for new national parks before they can proceed with park establishment. While this has lengthened the time it takes to successfully negotiate a national park, it ensures that local communities are now involved in the negotiations for new parks. The government is trying to ensure that new national parks are supported by local communities and that they make a positive contribution to the community's way of life.

Aboriginal Land Claims

In 1962 the federal government began to examine potential national park sites in the Yukon and Northwest Territories. Plans to mine the Kluane Game Sanctuary in the Yukon and to dam the Nahanni River in the Northwest Territories prompted public campaigns for their protection. The government of Prime Minister Pierre Elliott Trudeau announced plans to turn both areas into national parks in 1972.

Chrétien, Trudeau's parks minister, wrote that 'when I saw the Nahanni River in the Northwest Territories and the Kluane Range in the Yukon, I wanted to protect them forever and eventually did' (Chrétien 1985, 68). He was similarly moved to create Auyuittuq National Park after flying over Baffin Island. 'I was so excited that I said to my wife, "Aline, I will make this a national park for you" ' (Chrétien 1985, 68).

Legislation to create the three parks was, however, opposed by several Native organizations representing Aboriginal people who lived in the territories. For example, the Inuit Taparisat of Canada, who represented the Inuit of the eastern Arctic, contended that the government was acting unilaterally to establish the parks and was taking Inuit land. The Inuit charged that the government was, in effect, expropriating land from Aboriginal people and was in contravention of the Canadian Bill of Rights (Fenge 1978). The issue was resolved through amendments to the National Parks Act that designated the three parks as national park reserves pending the resolution of Aboriginal land claims. The Act also enshrined the rights of Aboriginal people to hunt, trap, and fish in northern national parks. In essence, Native people were not giving up their claim to lands over which they asserted Aboriginal title; they simply agreed to allow the federal government to administer a park on their land until such time their land-claim agreement was ratified by both Parliament and Aboriginal people. The claim itself would establish final park boundaries and management conditions.

The amendments to the National Parks Act established the precedent for all other national parks that are subject to Aboriginal land-claim agreements. To establish new national parks, the government must now negotiate agreements both with the provincial or territorial governments and with Aboriginal people. Hence, parks such as South Moresby, Pacific Rim, and the Mingan Archipelago in southern Canada are designated national park reserves pending the settlement of land claims.

Northern Canada and New Parks

Justice Tom Berger's Mackenzie Valley Pipeline Inquiry of 1974–5 set the tone for the establishment of new national parks for the next two decades. Among other things, Berger drew attention to the need to protect the northern wilderness and to 'do so now'. Berger argued that in northern Canada, 'Withdrawal of land from any industrial use will be necessary in some instances to preserve wilderness, wildlife species and critical habitat' (Berger 1977, 31).

To that end, Berger recommended the establishment of a national park across the north slope of the Yukon to protect the calving grounds of the Porcupine caribou herd from industrial development. He also recommended revisions to the National Parks Act to create a new statutory designation for use in northern Canada: a national wilderness park. Citing the level of development in the Rocky Mountain national parks, Berger concluded that the act was not adequate to preserve northern wilderness areas.

When the Hon. J. Hugh Faulkner became the minister in charge of parks in 1978, he acted on Berger's recommendations. In 1978, he withdrew the north slope of the Yukon from industrial development and announced plans to establish a national park in the area. He also announced the 'six North of 60' program to initiate public consultation on a plan to establish five new national parks in the territories and Canadian landmark status to protect the pingos of Tuktoyaktuk. To this date those ice-core hills remain the only site in Canada protected under the Canadian Landmark Program of the Parks Service.

Faulkner also proposed a revision to the national parks policy that would permit the government to establish national wilderness parks, as recommended by Berger. However, a number of national conservation groups objected to the proposal. Their concern was that national wilderness parks would downgrade the traditional national park designation by lessening its role in preserving wilderness and permitting greater tourism and recreation developments. Instead, the groups successfully pursued an amendment to the National Parks Act in 1988 that permits Cabinet legally to protect wilderness zones within national parks.

As the 1985 Parks centennial year drew close, announcements on new national parks were reduced to a trickle because of budget cuts, the onset of a recession, and an overall decline in public and political interest in both the environment and wilderness protection. The lack of local, Aboriginal, and provincial support for many of the planned parks was also an important factor.

New monies for park expansion were in short supply partly because of the need to spend money developing facilities in the newly established parks. Many of the new park agreements signed by Chrétien called for a large federal investment in the development of recreational and tourism infrastructure. For example, $22 million was spent to build a 62-km stretch of road in La Mauricie National Park (Lothian 1987).

But there was some progress. Two park agreements were signed between 1974 and 1984: Pukaskwa in 1974 and Grasslands in 1981, although the latter agreement failed to produce a park until a new agreement between Canada and Saskatchewan was approved in 1988. And in the dying days of the Liberal government of Prime Minister John Turner, two additional parks were established: the Mingan Archipelago National Park Reserve in Quebec and the Northern Yukon National Park.

The Northern Yukon National Park was the first park established as part of the comprehensive land-claims settlement process. Both the government of Canada and the Committee for Original People's Entitlement, representing the Inuvialuit of the Western Arctic, agreed to the park because it met their respective objectives: it represents natural regions 9 and 10 of the national parks system; and it prohibits any industrial development within the calving grounds of the Porcupine caribou herd, which supports the traditional way of life of Aboriginal people. The Northern Yukon established a precedent for the establishment of future national parks in northern Canada (see e.g. Sadler 1989).

Between 1968 and 1984, the Trudeau government and its short-lived successor led by John Turner made a substantial contribution to the preservation of Canadian wilderness, particularly in the creation of 13 new national parks and the protection of over 64,000 sq. km of wilderness lands, a land mass greater than Nova Scotia and Prince Edward Island put together. But with the election of Brian Mulroney's Conservative government in September 1984, park advocates wondered if the new government would work to finish and expand on the many Liberal park initiatives left uncompleted.

PARKS ON THE POLITICAL AGENDA (1984–PRESENT)

The centennial year of the national parks system should have been a time to celebrate the achievements of the past century and to plan for the future. Instead, it proved to be a low point in the history of the national parks. The new Conservative parks minister, the Hon. Suzanne Blais-Grenier, quickly angered Canadians when she cancelled all guided walks in national parks and suggested she would not rule out logging and mining in national parks. The spontaneous public outcry that followed was tangible proof that Canadians rejected the industrial exploitation of park resources and was cited as a major reason why she lost the portfolio in August 1985 (Bercuson *et al.* 1986).

The centennial year was also a disappointment because no new national parks were established, nor was any plan to complete the system adopted. But it was not for lack of trying that a plan was not produced. In the dying months of the Liberal government, Parks Canada was developing plans to expand the national parks system as its centrepiece for the 1985 centennial year. It was seeking Cabinet approval for a plan to complete the national parks system by the year 2000 and the allocation of $495 million to establish 20 terrestrial and 10 marine parks. Blais-Grenier gutted the plan and it never saw the light of day (McNamee 1992).

The public clearly demonstrated in 1985 the extent to which government action to protect wilderness was an urgency. Participants in the Canadian Assembly Project, a citizens' celebration of 100 years of heritage conservation, identified over 500 natural areas across Canada that were in need of protection. At the top of the list was a wilderness area on the far western shores of Canada that would increasingly dominate Ottawa's parks agenda: South Moresby.

Post-Centennial Action on New Parks

The Hon. Tom McMillan took over the parks portfolio in late 1985 and made it a high priority. Under McMillan, five new national parks were created, Parliament approved the first comprehensive amendments to the National Parks Act since 1930, the National Marine Parks policy was finally adopted, the first national marine park was established at Fathom Five in Ontario, and the federal Task Force on Park Establishment was appointed to examine new strategies that would facilitate the creation of new national parks.

Reporting in June 1987, the task force concluded that Canada must take decisive action to protect its disappearing wilderness. It also concluded that one of the major impediments to national park establishment was the federal government's requirement that the provinces transfer land for potential national parks to the federal Crown. The task force recommended the Canadian Heritage Lands designation as one way to break the impasse. If a province agreed to manage an area of national significance to national standards, the area would receive federal recognition as Canadian Heritage Land.

Parks Canada rejected the idea. The agency feared it would dilute the current national park model, particularly because some of the provincial governments were in the process of unilaterally alienating parklands and allowing industrial development within parks (*Protected Areas* 1991). The Canadian Heritage Land concept appeared to offer no legal protection to wilderness areas. However, if the traditional national park establishment proves to be unworkable in the coming years, the notion of managing provincial parks and protected areas to national standards may yet prove a useful tool in completing the representation of Parks Canada's 39 natural regions.

The task force also called on McMillan and Parks Canada to develop a strategic plan to ensure substantial progress by the year 2000 in completing the national parks system. Substantial progress was required because, in 1985, the national parks system was less than half complete (Dearden and Gardner 1987). McMillan, however, was not interested in developing a blueprint to complete the system (McNamee 1986). His focus was on the preservation of the South Moresby wilderness archipelago in British Columbia as a national park and on the completion of several unfinished park initiatives. Political negotiations were finally completed by McMillan to establish Ellesmere Island, Pacific Rim, Grasslands, and the Bruce Peninsula as national parks.

The success of McMillan and a cast of thousands of Canadians in preserving South Moresby may prove a turning point in the wilderness preservation movement (Dearden 1988). John Broadhead, a leader of the South Moresby lobby, observed that

> South Moresby had shaken the national tree. A profound moral dilemma had crystallized in the Canadian conscience, and it could no longer be ignored. It was this: which is more important—the integrity of the earth and the spiritual recreation of future generations, or short-term legal responsibilities to corporations and their shareholders? More to the point, what kind of system is this that renders the two mutually exclusive? (Broadhead 1989, 51)

In the political arena, the exploitation of wilderness areas was clearly the dominant ideology. While resource development was accelerating, there was no corresponding effort by governments to preserve special natural areas. Given the federal government's lack of interest in developing a plan to complete the job of representing each of its 39 natural regions, the conservation community would have to lobby for the political commitment necessary to achieve this goal.

The Endangered Spaces Wilderness Campaign

The launch of the Endangered Spaces campaign by the World Wildlife Fund Canada and the Canadian Parks and Wilderness Society in 1989 stimulated public advocacy efforts to expand the national parks system. The campaign's goal is to get the federal, provincial, and territorial governments to complete their parks and protected areas systems by the year 2000 in order to represent each of the nation's approximately 350 natural regions. Once this is achieved, the land protected should total approximately 12 per cent of Canada, a target recommended by the 1987 landmark report of the World Commission on Environment and Development (the Brundtland Commission).

The Endangered Spaces campaign was launched for several reasons. First, the Brundtland Commission called on all nations to complete a network of strictly protected areas that represent each of the earth's major ecosystems as part of its overall commitment to protecting their diversity of species and ecosystems and to implementing sustainable development.

Second, action was of the essence. The federal Task Force on Park Establishment concluded that if Canada did not act to preserve its wilderness areas with some urgency, opportunities to do so would have all but disappeared by the year 2000.

Third, the South Moresby issue demonstrated that the cost to governments and conservation groups of fighting for the protection of wilderness areas on an issue-by-issue basis was prohibitive. Instead, a national campaign that would firmly establish the need to preserve wilderness on the political agenda was required.

Finally, there was an emerging consensus amongst the public, scientists, and government officials that more wilderness had to be protected. The Endangered Spaces campaign was launched to translate this growing level of public support for wilderness protection into political action.

In 1989, the Hon. Lucien Bouchard, then minister in charge of national parks, announced that the federal government would complete the national parks system by the year 2000 because 'the very fragility of the planet compels the expansion of the national parks system' (McNamee 1992). The federal Cabinet confirmed this as a government-wide commitment when it released Canada's Green Plan, a federal environmental strategy, in December 1990. The Green Plan established targets to meet this commitment: at least five new terrestrial national parks are to be established by 1996, and agreements on an additional 13 parks that are required to complete the system will be achieved by 2000.

But the Green Plan goal remains a policy commitment that can be ignored by the federal government. For example, the federal government refused to make a legal commitment to complete the national parks system by the year

2000 within the new native territory of the eastern Arctic, Nunavut. The Tungavik Federation of Nunavut, representing the Inuit of the eastern Arctic, sought this commitment as part of its 1991 comprehensive land-claim agreement with the federal government (Fenge 1992). The federal government did, however, make a legal commitment to manage all existing and future national parks in Nunavut as primarily wilderness parks.

The land-claim agreement did produce the first step towards the Green Plan goal for new parks. In February 1992, the federal Cabinet withdrew 22,200 sq. km of arctic wilderness from industrial development for the proposed North Baffin Island National Park. The federal government was committed to this step under the terms of its 1991 agreement with the Tungavik Federation of Nunavut. Before the park is finally protected under the National Parks Act, the Inuit and the federal government must negotiate an agreement on employment, business opportunities, and park access.

National Parks as Endangered Spaces

While the loss of unprotected wilderness lands has captured public attention, there is growing concern over the degradation of existing parklands and their natural resources. In the 1960s and 1970s, the prevailing concern was over the impact of too many visitors and the inappropriate development of tourism facilities on park resources. In the 1980s, there was growing evidence that developments in and around national parks were isolating them, and causing a decrease in the environmental quality of national parks.

A 1987 report by the Canadian Parks Service concluded 'that the magnitude and frequency of transboundary concerns will increasingly become a problem because of continuing development and pollution' (Irvine 1987). Three years later, the first national state-of-the-parks report confirmed that none of the parks were immune to internal and external threats, citing water pollution, poaching, and logging on lands near park boundaries as some of the major threats to the integrity of parklands.

For most of their history, national parks were wild spaces located in even larger expanses of wilderness. More recently, industrial and agricultural development on nearby lands has moved right up to national park borders. The boundaries of Riding Mountain National Park are clearly visible from space because agricultural development has removed the boreal forest right up to the straight-line boundaries of the park. The 1990 state-of-the-parks report described Fundy National Park as 'an ecological island in [an] area of intensively managed forest land'. It also reported that Pacific-Rim National Park Reserve is a narrow strip of wilderness and predicted that 'logging adjacent to [the] park could adversely affect [park] resources [and] watershed'. In effect, human activities outside parks are reducing them to 'endangered spaces'.

The federal government can no longer ignore such threats to parks even if the lands in question are outside their jurisdiction. In 1988, Parliament amended the National Parks Act to state that 'Maintenance of ecological integrity through the protection of natural resources shall be the first priority when considering park zoning and visitor use in a management plan' (Bill C-30 1988).

This amendment is significant for two reasons. First, it clearly establishes that the priority of national parks is to protect natural resources. Second, in order to maintain the ecological integrity of the national parks, the government must now take action to define and eliminate the range of internal and external threats to park resources. Thus, the Act compels the government to act against threats to park resources that emanate from areas outside the parks.

However, meeting the provisions of the National Parks Act will be difficult as long as the government fails to allocate sufficient funding to natural resource conservation programs in the national parks. In 1988–9, for example, only 1.6 per cent of the government's national parks budget was actually spent on the prime mandate of protecting park resources. This caused the former director of the Natural Resources Branch of the Canadian Parks Service to conclude that 'the Canadian Parks Service is not a conservation organization, despite its legislative mandate and policy mandate' (Lohnes 1992, 22).

It was left to the Canadian Parks and Wilderness Society to determine if the National Parks Act could actually be used to force the government to adhere to its conservation mandate. The society took the government to court in 1992, alleging that logging in Wood Buffalo National Park was in contravention of the National Parks Act. Several months later, the Federal Court of Canada declared both a 1983 contract that allowed logging in the park and the Order in Council approving the contract to be 'invalid and unauthorized by the provisions of the National Parks Act' (Federal Court of Canada 1992). Once again, public advocacy groups proved a potent force in shaping the government's national parks policy and preserving the Canadian wilderness.

CONCLUSION

When Parliament passed the National Parks Act in 1930, it declared that the national parks are 'dedicated to the people of Canada for their benefit, education and enjoyment'. Administrators of the parks have, for many years, interpreted this as being support for a recreational mandate. Today, however, national parks benefit Canadians by providing environmental protection for shrinking wilderness and wildlife habitat, opportunities to experience wild places, and benchmarks against which to measure the impact of society's activities on the landscape.

In 1992, over 1,500 delegates to the Fourth World Congress on National Parks and Protected Areas in Caracas, Venezuela, declared that the establishment and maintenance of parks and protected areas is essential to sustaining human society and conserving global biological diversity. Decisions taken in this decade will largely determine both the size and the health of Canada's national parks system, and its ability to contribute to global conservation in the 21st century. The decisions the federal government must make in this decade are clear: 18 new national parks are to be established by the year 2000; and national parks and adjacent lands must be managed so as to maintain their ecological integrity. These are the milestones against which historians will measure the evolution of Canada's national parks.

History has shown that governments do not act in a benevolent fashion when it comes to wilderness protection. Politics and public pressure are what drive the park establishment process and will continue to do so, because there is no law requiring the establishment of parks or the preservation of wilderness areas. Therefore, we must understand more fully the political process and seek to influence it with better information on the full range of national park and wilderness values, so that politicians will act more decisively to preserve wilderness.

History has also demonstrated that wilderness preservation is a non-partisan political issue, and one that requires the commitment of the minister in charge of the national parks portfolio. Jean Chrétien of the Liberal party and Tom McMillan of the Conservatives shared a common determination to achieve political deals that together resulted in the creation of 15 national parks and the preservation of almost 100,000 sq. km of wilderness. It will require other politicians with the same determination to establish a further 18 national parks. Public advocacy groups will have to ensure that each successive parks minister takes action to create new national parks and to stop the incremental loss of national parklands to commercial development.

Perhaps Chrétien said it best when he opened Kejimkujik National Park in 1969 (Lothian 1976a, 1: 122): 'Our national parks are part of the original face of Canada, inviolable spots which provide sanctuaries for man as well as nature. But it is man who must extend and preserve them. This is the task that lies ahead.'

ACKNOWLEDGEMENTS

The author kindly acknowledges Jacinthe Seguin for her insight, comments, and help in editing this chapter into its final form.
Thanks.

REFERENCES

Bella, L.
1979   'Partisan Politics and National Parks North of 60', *Park News*, 15: 6–13.
Bella, L.
1987   *Parks for Profit*, Harvest House, Montreal.
Bercuson, D., J.L. Granatstein, and W.R. Young
1986   *Sacred Trust? Brian Mulroney and the Conservative Party in Power*, Doubleday Canada, Toronto.
Berger, T.
1977   *Northern Frontier, Northern Homeland: The Report of the Mackenzie Valley Pipeline Inquiry*, Supply and Services Canada, Ottawa.
Bill C-30
1988   *An Act to amend the National Parks Act*, Supply and Services Canada, Ottawa.
Bill, R.
1982   'Attempts to Establish National Parks in Canada: A Case History in Labrador from 1969 to 1979', M.A. thesis, Department of Geography, Carleton University, Ottawa.
Broadhead, J.
1989   'The All Alone Stone Manifesto', in *Endangered Spaces: The Future for Canada's Wilderness*, ed. Monte Hummel, Key Porter Books, Toronto, 50–62.
Canadian Parks and Wilderness Society
1988   *Park News*, 25th anniversary issue and final edition, 23.
Canadian Parks Service
1991   *State of the Parks 1990 Report*, Supply and Services Canada, Ottawa.
Chrétien, J.
1969   'Our Evolving National Parks System', in *The Canadian National Parks: Today and Tomorrow*, ed. J.G. Nelson and R.C. Scace, University of Calgary, Calgary, 7–14.
Chrétien, J.
1985   *Straight from the Heart*, Key Porter Books, Toronto.
Craig Brown, R.
1969   'The Doctrine of Usefulness: Natural Resource and National Parks Policy in Canada, 1887–1914', in *Canada Parks and Perspective*, ed. J.G. Nelson, Harvest House, Montreal, 46-62.
Dearden, P.
1988   'Mobilising Public Support for Environment: The Case of South Moresby Island, British Columbia', in *Need-to-Know: Effective Communication for Environmental Groups*. Proceedings of the 1987 Annual Joint Meeting of the Public Advisory Committees to the Environment Council of Alberta, 62–75.
Dearden, P., and J. Gardner
1987   'Systems Planning for Protected Areas in Canada: A Review of Caucus Candidate Areas and Concepts, Issues and Prospects for Further Investiga-

tion', in *Heritage for Tomorrow: Canadian Assembly on National Parks and Protected Areas*, ed. R.C. Scace and J.G. Nelson, Environment Canada, Ottawa, 2: 9–48.

Federal Court of Canada
1992 'Canadian Parks and Wilderness Society *vs*. Her Majesty the Queen in Right of Canada', Trial Division, Vancouver.

Fenge, T.
1978 'Decision Making for National Parks in Canada North of 60', working paper 3, President's Committee on Northern Studies, University of Waterloo, Waterloo, Ont.

Fenge, T.
1992 'National Parks in the Canadian Arctic: The Case of the Nunavut Land Claim Agreement', in *Environments* (in press), University of Waterloo, Waterloo, Ont.

Foster, J.
1978 *Working for Wildlife: The Beginning of Preservation in Canada*, University of Toronto Press, Toronto.

Harkin, J.B.
no date 'Forward to the Heart of the Rockies', Herbert R. Lawson Publishing, Victoria.

Henderson, G.
1969 'The Role of the Public in National Park Planning and Decision Making', in *Canadian Parks in Perspective*, ed. J.G. Nelson, Harvest House, Montreal, 329–43.

Irvine, M.H.
1987 'Natural Resource Management Problems, Issues and/or Concerns in Canadian National Parks', ms. on file, Natural Resources Branch, Parks.

Johnston, M.E.
1985 'A Club With Vision: The Alpine Club of Canada and Conservation 1906–1930', *Park News* 21: 6-10.

La Forest, G.V., and M.K. Roy
1981 *The Kouchibouguac Affair: The Report of the Special Inquiry on Kouchibouguac National Park*, n.p., Fredericton.

Lohnes, D.M.
1992 'A Land Manager's Perspective on Science and Parks Management', in *Science and the Management of Protected Areas*, Proceedings of an international conference held at Acadia University, Wolfville, N.S. 14–19 May 1991, eds J.H.M. Willison *et al.*, Elsevier, Amsterdam, 19–24.

Lothian, W.F.
1976a *History of Canada's National Parks*, vols 1 and 2, Parks Canada, Indian and Northern Affairs, Ottawa.

Lothian, W.F.
1976b *History of Canada's National Parks*, vols 3 and 4, Parks Canada, Indian and Northern Affairs, Ottawa.

Lothian, W.F.
1987 *A Brief History of Canada's National Parks*, Supply and Services Canada, Ottawa.

Marty, S.
1984   *A Grand and Fabulous Notion: The First Century of Canada's Parks*, Supply and Services Canada, Ottawa.

McNamee, K.
1986   'Tom McMillan: Our Friend in Court', *Park News* 21: 40–1.

McNamee, K.
1992   'Overcoming Decades of Indifference—The Painful Process of Preserving Wilderness', *Borealis* 3: 55.

Nash, R.
1969   'Wilderness and Man in North America', in *The Canadian National Parks: Today and Tomorrow*, ed. J.G. Nelson and R.C. Scace, University of Calgary, Calgary, 35–52.

National and Historic Parks Branch
1969   *National Parks Policy*, Queen's Printer, Ottawa.

Nicol, J.I.
1969   'The National Parks Movement in Canada', in *The Canadian National Parks: Today and Tomorrow*, ed. J.G. Nelson and R.C. Scace, University of Calgary, Calgary, 35–52.

Park News
1972   'Well Done, Mr. Chrétien!' *Park News* 8 (3).

Parks Canada
1983   *Parks Canada Policy*, Supply and Services Canada, Ottawa.

Protected Areas
1991   *A Protected Areas Vision for Canada*, Canadian Environmental Advisory Council, Supply and Services Canada, Ottawa.

Rodney, W.
1969   *Kootenai Brown: His Life and Times*, Gray's Publishing, Sidney, B.C.

Sadler, B.
1989   'National Parks, Wilderness Preservation and Native Peoples in Northern Canada', *Natural Resources Journal* 29: 185–204.

Waiser, W.
1989   *Saskatchewan's Playground: A History of Prince Albert National Park*, Fifth House Publishers, Saskatoon.

World Commission on Environment and Development
1987   *Our Common Future*, Oxford University Press, New York and Oxford.

CHAPTER 3

Beyond Parks and Protected Areas

From Public Lands and Private Stewardship to Landscape Planning and Management[1]

J. G. NELSON

HISTORIC ROOTS OF PARKS AND PROTECTED AREAS

In western society in the last 1,000 years we have developed some basic approaches to using and saving the land for sustenance and recreation. The idea of the park has been used since at least Norman times in England to signify a protected pleasuring ground, first for hunting by nobles and later for walking, sight-seeing, and enjoyment by the people (Rackham 1976). In the New World, the concept of the national park arose in the United States in the late 19th century. Such parks were set aside for tourism as well as to protect such geologic and scenic wonders like Yellowstone, Yosemite, and Glacier (Nash 1967). National parks were also created for similar reasons at Banff and other sites in Canada. The idea was to preserve special places from the mining, lumbering, grazing, and other activities which were transforming surrounding lands (Nelson 1970). The hot springs, picturesque rocks, awesome landforms, and (later) the vegetation and wildlife of these special places were to be protected to be seen and appreciated by locals and visitors.

Other types of protected areas have also been developed in the last several centuries, more or less in parallel with the idea of the park and especially the national park (Scace and Nelson 1986). Thus, forest reserves were set aside by kings and nobles and later by towns, countries, and citizens to protect trees and forests and to provide lumber and other products through coppicing and other forms of forest management. In the last century in particular, various types of special areas have proliferated considerably in response to land-use pressures and to different kinds of perceived human needs and conservation requirements. Thus we have wildlife refuges, scenic

[1]This chapter was originally published in *Environments: A Journal of Interdisciplinary Studies*, published by the Faculty of Environmental Studies, University of Waterloo, Waterloo, Ont., vol. 21, 1.

areas, water reserves, provincial or regional parks, and historic parks and their equivalents throughout the world.

THE DOMINANT ROLE OF GOVERNMENT

Most protected areas have been developed by government on public land, with such notable exceptions as the English national parks, which essentially are highly regulated private land (Poore 1987). Indeed the development of special conservation regulations for private land in the public interest has been a distinguishing feature of the approach in England and other parts of western Europe. In this sense, the western European protected areas have included lands used for agricultural pursuits as well as forests, heaths, moors, and fens. The focus has been on unusually scenic and historically valued landscapes produced (in large part) by human effort rather than (as in much of North America) on wilderness or wildlands where human impact is seen as transient (Pritchard 1985).

EMERGING PRIVATE APPROACH

In recent decades in Canada, especially in southern Ontario and the prairies where human settlement and its destructive effects on natural systems are most apparent, more stress has been placed on private or combined private-public approaches to conservation—what is now being called *stewardship*. In Ontario, evidence of this is to be found in systems of small Environmentally Sensitive Policy Areas (ESPAS), created by regional government such Waterloo or Halton to protect small areas with rare plants, forests, or other special features. The Ontario government is also promoting the creation of Areas of Natural or Scientific Interest (ANSIS) on private land.

An Act has been passed to create a special management regime for the predominantly private lands of the Niagara Escarpment, the magnificent landform that traverses west-central Ontario, in an attempt to conserve a forested and pastoral landscape for recreational and aesthetic use. The escarpment was accepted as a UNESCO Man and Biosphere (MAB) Reserve in March 1990, reflecting a recent trend to link individual protected areas to international programs intended to promote appropriate use and global conservation.

MAB areas reflect another change in thinking about parks and protected areas. The MAB areas are not intended primarily for recreation, tourism, and conservation, but rather for education, science, and monitoring environmental change. MAB areas contain natural as well as human-made landscapes where land use is seen to be in harmony with nature. Land use and natural changes in MAB areas are to be observed and the lessons used in providing for better resource and environmental management in future.

DISSATISFACTION WITH PROGRESS

Even with the development of this array of different types of parks and protected areas on public and private lands, disagreements seem to be growing over the status of special areas. Is sufficient progress being made in the appropriate use and conservation of our natural and cultural heritage? For example, many conservation organizations are dissatisfied with the progress being made to complete the national park system in Canada. This involves establishing of one national park in each of the 39 land and 29 marine natural regions that represent the ecological diversity that composes Canada. The World Wildlife Fund Canada (WWF) and the Canadian Parks and Wilderness Society have spearheaded a recent drive to have many endangered spaces in Canada set aside as national parks or other high level forms of protection and management (Hummel 1989: see chapter 2).

Similarly, many people and groups in settled parts of the country such as Ontario are dissatisfied with what is being done to protect the much smaller fragments of forest or other natural areas in a landscape now often more than 80 per cent developed (Balser and Nelson 1990). Even the ESPA area system in Waterloo Region, with its 68 existing special areas and 10 future areas, is seen as inadequate in the face of continuing development pressure on designated or undesignated forests and other natural areas in the region. There is also concern about the designation, protection, and appropriate use of archaeological, historic, and other cultural features and areas, although these will not receive much attention here.

RECOGNIZING THE IMPORTANT ROLES OF PROTECTED AREAS

In the case of both the large endangered spaces, such as the proposed Grasslands National Park in southern Saskatchewan, and the small forests and woodlots close to expanding cities such as Waterloo and Kitchener, many private and public agencies and groups—often with conflicting philosophies, aims, and approaches—must be dealt with to build a more generally acceptable approach and a better natural and cultural heritage system.

The first step in such an approach is gaining stronger public recognition of the many different functions that national parks and protected areas have come to play in land use and environmental management. Some people, especially in industries such as mining and forestry, still refer to parks and protected areas (and especially national parks) as 'single-use areas'. They do this in order to convey the impression that mining and lumbering are more diverse activities, part of a larger multiple-use package that offers jobs, income, and greater overall return to the community and the country. They continue to do this at their peril. It is now quite apparent that parks and protected areas offer a very wide range of services that are essential to the well-being of us all.

Twelve such functions were identified in a recent review of the roles of national parks and protected areas in various nations' national conservation strategies (Nelson 1987):

- Protection and appropriate use of forests, water, soils, and wildlife, as in the mountain parks and protected areas of western North America;
- Protection of genetic resources, as in national parks and protected areas in Central and South America;
- Research and monitoring of environmental changes or stresses such as acid rain, as in the Bavarian National Park, West Germany, and in Kejimkujik National Park, N.S.;
- Protection and appropriate use of lakes and rivers, for example through heritage rivers or wild and scenic rivers programs like those in Canada and the U.S.;
- Protection and appropriate use of marine and coastal resources, as in the Australian Great Barrier Reef Marine Park, in estuaries or other areas of importance for fish production in the U.S., and in shipwreck sites or other historic resources such as Fathom Five Provincial Park, now part of the Bruce Peninsula National Park, Ont.;
- Protection and appropriate use of cultural and archaeological resources, like the Head-Smashed-In Buffalo Jump site, Alta.;
- Protection and appropriate use of urban heritage resources, such as green spaces, rare plants, biologically diverse habitats, aquifers, wetlands, or other environmentally sensitive or significant areas, as in Waterloo Region, Ont.;
- Protection and appropriate use for education, as at Point Pelee National Park, Ont., or Everglades National Park, Fla.;
- Protection and appropriate use for various kinds and levels of recreation and tourism, as in Banff National Park;
- Protection and appropriate use by indigenous peoples, as in the Alaskan national and state parks and in Kakadu National Park, Northern Territory, Australia;
- Use in comprehensive and integrated regional planning and management for the effects of land protection on land use and the environment, as with the Man and Biosphere Reserve at Waterton, Alta., or Riding Mountain National Park, Man.;
- Use in comprehensive land management, using all possible methods toward the goal of sustainable development. Protected areas have recognized roles in this campaign, along with environmental impact assessment, development controls, tax incentives, laws, economic incentives, and other social guides, planning and management generally and in conservation strategies and sustainable development (Nelson 1987, 68–9).

Recognition of the comprehensive land management function of national parks and protected areas leads to another way of envisioning their importance to overall land use and environmental management. This is portrayed in Figure 3.1. This general model was prepared as part of research on northern Canada (Bastedo, Nelson, and Theberge 1984) and shows the institutions active in the Yukon and the Northwest Territories. A generally similar set of heritage institutions could be shown for the Canadian provinces.

Figure 3.1 also shows linkages between the general land use classes (preservation, protection, multiple use, and extractive use) and different sets of land uses and institutional arrangements. There are roles for protected areas in situations ranging from the least intensive to the most intensive or extractive types of land use. Moreover, the general management classes hold true whether the land or waters in question are publicly or privately owned or managed.

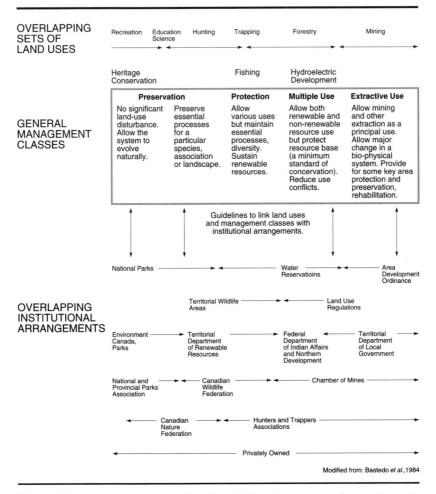

Figure 3.1 Land use spectrum showing relationship to general management classes and institutions.

THE NEED FOR CO-OPERATION AND CO-ORDINATION

One fundamental point conveyed by Figure 3.1 is that large national parks and smaller natural or environmentally sensitive areas are part of the same system. A second major point is that the ideas and principles pertaining to the general management classes apply to both public and private agencies and landowners, all being part of a balanced or sustainable land-use system. Federal agencies, provincial agencies, local governments, private organizations, non-government organizations, and private landowners should all recognize the roles of protected areas. All such agencies and groups should co-operate in developing an appropriate co-ordinated management regime.

Much of the justification for such co-ordination is provided by the inter-relationships among the many land uses shown in Figure 3.1. But there are several other compelling reasons for such co-operation and co-ordination, and these have become increasingly apparent in the last decade in particular.

Scientific research, notably in biology, has revealed that the character of wildlife and vegetation and water quality and other measures of ecological health in parks depend on natural processes in their surroundings, near and far. Animals, plant species, fires, pollution, and other phenomena cross the boundaries of parks and protected areas; the state of the system in these areas is therefore dependent on natural processes and cultural activities elsewhere.

Recent developments in ecological or biogeographic theory have also identified *the island effect* (Forman and Godron 1986): the tendency of species diversity in a protected area to decline with the decreasing size of the area. Associated with the island effect is the concept of *nodes* and *corridors*. This refers to the desirability of maintaining *connections* among natural areas in order to prevent species decline and maintain or enhance the biological richness of parks and protected areas. This approach is causing park and protected area managers and other concerned persons to move away from a focus on setting aside special sites toward the creation of interconnected systems linking various types of conservation areas along river valleys or other protected corridors. Figure 3.2 shows such a system as proposed in recent heritage river studies for the Grand River, Ont. Nodes, including important forests (Grand River Forest), wetlands (Dunnville, Luther Marsh), and other special features, are to be linked through various regulations applied to the floodplain and river valley by the Grand River Conservation Authority and other agencies. Such a nodes and corridors approach requires joint planning and management among managers of protected areas and owners of surrounding lands.

Another major reason for a growing interest in co-operation and co-ordination is the recognition that parks and protected areas are very much part of the socioeconomic region in which they are located. The economic and social activities that are encouraged in the protected areas clearly have an effect on surrounding lands, and vice versa. Tourism, transport and communications, and other activities often cross both areas. The concentration of

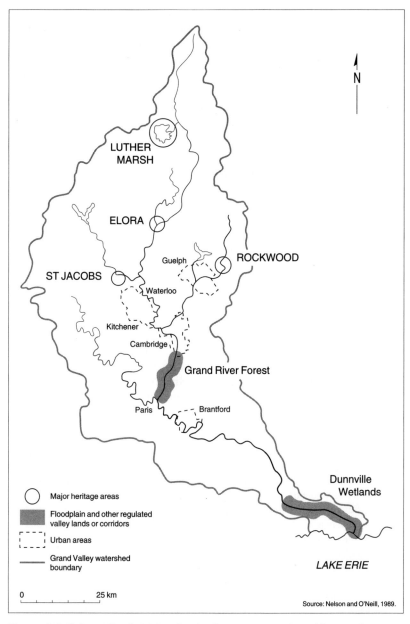

Figure 3.2 Schematic of outstanding heritage areas and corridors on the Grand River, Ontario.

tourist facilities along routes leading into national parks such as Kootenay or Gros Morne are good examples of this reality. In the interests of generating more compatible policies, programs, and benefits, the Canadian National Park Service has begun to place considerable stress on regional integration in park planning in recent years, requiring more joint efforts with surrounding agencies and landowners.

Another major reason for co-operation and co-ordination is the growing interest in the ideas of the World Commission on Environment and Development (1987) or Bruntland Commission, notably the concept of sustainable development. This concept calls for maintaining resources and environments for the future and on equity between present and future generations. A major means of planning for sustainable development is a *conservation* or *sustainable development strategy*. This involves identifying major issues such as wildlife depletion, soil erosion, and declining water quality and then developing a management approach to their improvement or solution. National parks and protected areas could form the core of a regional conservation strategy. They, like such ecological units as watersheds, are an ideal place to begin.

CO-ORDINATED PLANNING AND MANAGEMENT SYSTEMS

Some attempts have been made to develop ecologically based planning systems that require wide ranging co-operation and co-ordination among all interested parties. One of the leaders in this regard is Reed F. Noss of the Department of Wildlife and Range Sciences, University of Florida, Gainesville, Fla. In a 1987 article entitled 'Protecting Natural Areas in Fragmented Landscapes', Noss justifies a linked and co-ordinated approach in the following terms:

> The threats that impinge on the boundaries of a reserve, and often permeate much of the reserve, are a constant problem to natural areas managers. Smaller reserves with larger perimeter-area ratios have proportionately greater management problems resulting from interactions with the surrounding landscape and its human and nonhuman inhabitants. Exotic plants and other weeds, pesticides, domestic animals, off-road vehicles, and poachers often do not respect nature reserve boundaries. Furthermore, reserve boundaries themselves must change as climate changes. . . .
>
> A gradation of buffer zones around reserves can insulate natural areas from many problems. . . . Zoning also provides for the multiple uses stipulated by laws such as the National Forest Management Act, . . . mitigates effects of air and water pollution, and controls the impacts of visitors. . . . Ecological stewardship seeks to mimic the natural regime and represents a delicate balance between over-manipulation and laissez-faire neglect (Noss 1987).

Noss then presents examples of co-ordinated macroreserves or networks of protected areas and buffer zones for Florida and other states (Figure 3.3). Noss refers to such co-ordinated systems as Multiple Unit Modules (MUMs).

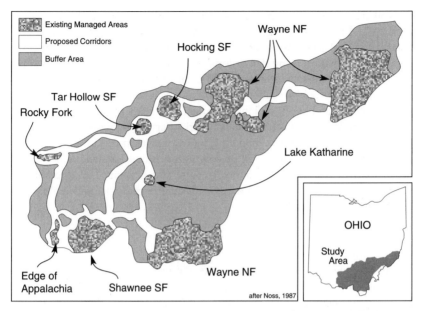

Figure 3.3 A proposed preserve network for southern Ohio. Note: NF=National Forest; SF=State Forest.

A somewhat similar approach has been taken by Theberge, Nelson, and colleagues through the use of the ABC resource survey, a method to identify and describe environmentally significant areas (Nelson *et al.* 1988). ABC stands for Abiotic (geologic), Biotic (biological), and Cultural categories in resource mapping. The term 'cultural' refers to land-use activities and to economic, social, and other human activities not usually included in such surveys. The ABC system has been applied at various scales through a set of overlays, the content of which has tended to change somewhat with funding, time, and other circumstances, including local ecology and land use.

The ultimate aim is to identify outstanding natural and cultural heritage resources and to link them to appropriate institutional or management arrangements. In other words, the natural and cultural attributes of the special areas are matched with management arrangements most likely to provide for their conservation and appropriate use. A network of interrelated parks and protected areas is often the result.

The Canadian Task Force on New Park Establishment attempted to build a co-ordinated approach to the management of environmentally significant areas into the concept of Canadian Heritage Lands (Environment Canada 1987). This concept was intended to break the log jam in the establishment of new national parks in long-recognized and outstanding large endangered spaces in Canada. Competition between provincial and federal governments, as well as among agencies and interest groups, coupled with insufficient funding and other problems, had hindered what many people saw as much-needed national park status for these areas. The task force worked to lessen disagreement by proposing that criteria be established for managing outstanding areas, and that one or more federal and provincial bodies combine to administer these areas, called Canadian Heritage Areas. This idea has received considerable discussion in the last few years but seems destined to die for want of support. The Canadian Parks Service in general seems reluctant to undertake initiatives favouring more co-operation and co-ordination. An example is the service's failure to create national landmarks, a type of protected area that would encourage federal and provincial co-operation in planning and managing smaller areas with unique geologic, archaeologic, or biological values.

SUMMARY

We are moving beyond the idea of parks and protected areas toward the idea of co-ordinated or integrated heritage area systems on both public and private land. We are moving from expecting government to look after heritage conservation and use toward a co-operative stewardship among different governments, private groups, corporations, and individuals. We are moving from a view of parks and protected areas as largely separate and distinct toward one emphasizing co-ordination and integration on natural, social, economic, and broadly human ecological grounds. Such trends are vital to and supportive of the strong current interest in sustainable development and conservation strategies. Technical or professional methods for developing co-ordinated planning and management systems are now available, although they can, of course, be improved.

The major challenge is to develop both the methods and the willingness to bring different government and non-government groups together to practice co-ordinated management in appropriately identified areas. The struggle for turf continues, with some promising exceptions such as the Natural Heritage League in Ontario or MAB areas around Riding and Waterton National Parks. The Ontario Natural Heritage League (ONHL) is an especially interesting institution, comprising 28 member agencies and associations, half from the public and half from the private sectors. Through the efforts of the ONHL, many new co-operative approaches have been tried by member groups, for example, the development of a landowner contact program for owners of key Carolinian Canada sites in southern Ontario. Most of these sites are small, fragmented, on private land, and not fully manageable through public ownership, even if funds were available for purchases. The landowner contact program is a way of informing private landowners of the value of Carolinian vegetation on their land and securing their co-operation in appropriately using and protecting it, mainly through informal or handshake agreements.

Other promising examples of co-operative management approaches are the Northwest Territories Caribou Management Boards, the co-operative arrangements for the management of the North Yukon National Park, and the recent joint stewardship council of the Ontario government and the Temi-Augami Anishnabai Indian Band. Half of this council will be appointed by each party and will plan for lumbering in a large part of the old-growth Temagami forest.

Another way of expressing the new direction is to say that we are moving from public parks and protected areas to public and private stewardship on an integrated landscape planning basis. Such planning builds upon the ideas of landscape and human ecology and the thrust toward sustainable development. A major need is to develop the attitudes and skills and organizational arrangements and behaviour that are necessary to implement these goals. Changes in planning objectives, interagency and intergroup management procedures, and staff reward systems are needed. The result would be an array of large and small interconnected natural and human heritage areas that will continue to make Canada a special place.

REFERENCES

Balser, David, and J.G. Nelson
1990   *Heritage Conservation Challenges at the Local Level: The Grand River Forest Area, Ontario. Nominating the Grand as a Canadian Heritage River*, Heritage Resources Centre, University of Waterloo, Waterloo, Ont., 141–56.

Bastedo, J.D., J.G. Nelson, and J.B. Theberge
1984   'An Ecological Approach to Resource Survey and Planning for Environmentally Significant Areas: The ABC Method', *Environmental Management* 8: 125–34.

Environment Canada
1987   *Our Parks—Vision for the 21st Century*, Minister of Environment's Task Force on Park Establishment, Environment Canada, Ottawa.

Forman, Richard T.T., and Michel Godron
1986   *Landscape Ecology*, John Wiley and Sons, New York and Toronto.

Nash, Roderick
1967   *Wilderness and the American Mind*, Yale University Press, New Haven and London.

Nelson, J.G., ed.
1970   *Canadian Parks in Perspective*, Harvest House, Montreal.

Nelson, J.G.
1987   'National Parks and Protected Areas, National Conservation Strategies and Sustainable Development', *Geoforum* 18: 291–319.

Nelson, J.G., P. Grigoriew, P.G.R. Smith, and J.B. Theberge
  1988   'The ABC Resource Survey Method: The ESA Concept and Comprehensive Land Use Planning and Management', in *Landscape Ecology and Management*, ed. Michael R. Moss, Polyscience Publications, Montreal, 143–75.
Nelson, J.G., and Harold Eidsvik
  1990   'Sustainable Development, Conservation Strategies and Heritage', *Alternatives* 16/17: 62–71.
Nelson, J.G., and Pauline O'Neill, eds
  1989   *The Grand as a Canadian Heritage River*, Heritage Resources Centre, University of Waterloo, Waterloo, Ont.
Noss, Reed F.
  1987   'Protecting Natural Areas in Fragmented Landscapes', *Natural Areas Journal* 7: 2–13.
Poore, Duncan, and Judy Poore
  1987   *Protected Landscape, The United Kingdom Experience*, Countryside Commission, Manchester, U.K.
Pritchard, Paul
  1985   *Views of the Green*, National Parks and Conservation Association, Washington, D.C.
Rackham, Oliver
  1976   *Trees and Woodland in the British Landscape*, J.M. Dent, London.
Scace, R.C., and J.G. Nelson, eds
  1986   *Heritage for Tomorrow*, Canadian Assembly on National Parks and Protected Areas, Supply and Services Canada, Ottawa.
World Commission on Environment and Development
  1987   *Our Common Future*, Oxford University Press, New York and Oxford.

CHAPTER 4

Parks Legislation in Canada

PAUL F. J. EAGLES

INTRODUCTION

In Canada, parks range from small intensively used green spaces in down-town metropolitan areas to large low-use wilderness areas with few facilities. Parks vary in the types of outdoor recreation and the degree of land protection that they provide. The various park types require different management strategies.

Park management in Canada is done through legislation at four levels of government: national, provincial, regional, and municipal. By doing a comparative analysis of the park legislation, it is possible to demonstrate the various priorities and approaches taken towards parks management in Canada.

This chapter discusses the governing park legislation at each of the four levels, with the following limitations:

1. Canada has two national park systems: national parks, including national historic parks; and national canals and national wildlife areas. Only the national parks are discussed.
2. Each province has a provincial park system, but only Ontario is discussed.
3. Canada has a series of regional park systems. As an example the oldest regional park agency is discussed, the Niagara Parks Commission. In addition, the unique conservation authority parks system in Ontario is covered in some depth.
4. Canada has a large number of municipal park systems. As an example the Ontario municipal park legislation is covered.

The chapter also contains an analysis of the National Parks Act and of Ontario legislation—the Provincial Parks Act, the Conservation Authorities Act, the Niagara Parks Act, the Municipal Act, the Public Parks Act, and the Parks Assistance Act.

It is important to recognize the difference between legislation and policy. Legislation is approved by a legislature, must be followed by the government and by the citizenry, and is enforced by an independent court system. Policy is simply a statement of government intent. It should be followed by the bureaucracy, but it is not enforceable by the courts. If policy is not followed by the bureaucracy or the government, the only recourse open to the citizenry is political action.

This chapter discusses the legislation, with only a few references to policy. One of the recurrent aspects of Canadian parks legislation is the fact that the legislation is written in very general terms. It provides a few broadly worded powers that are interpreted by government and bureaucratic policies. As one reviewer of this chapter commented: 'Our governing legislation provides guidance as to what we can do; it does not state what we actually do.' This is a telling statement.

THE NATIONAL LEVEL OF PARKS ADMINISTRATION IN CANADA

The National Parks Act

This Act, first established in 1930 and amended in 1988, provides the legislation for national parks in Canada. Before 1930, each national park had been established by an individual Act. The management of such a park was subject to the stipulations outlined in the establishing legislation. After 1930 the National Parks Act provided an organic set of rules for the operation of every national park. New park establishment then became simply a designation of the park's boundaries. In 1988 a major set of amendments was made to the Act. In this chapter, references are to the Canadian Parks Service official consolidation of the Act and the 1988 amendments.

Purpose of Parks The National Parks Act has a strongly worded purpose statement. Clause 4 of the Act states: 'The National Parks of Canada are hereby dedicated to the people of Canada for their benefit, education and enjoyment . . . and shall be maintained and made use of so as to leave them unimpaired for the enjoyment of future generations.'

There are noteworthy points in this purpose. First, the dedication of the parks is to the public. This suggests that even though the parks are directed and managed by government, their ultimate purpose is a public one. This section therefore implies that there should be some public say in the management of parks. Second, the intention of leaving parks 'unimpaired' gives a strong conservation message. Further protection for the natural environment in parks is outlined in section 5(1.2), which states: 'maintenance of ecological integrity through the protection of natural resources shall be the first priority when considering park zoning and visitor use in a management plan.'

Although there is some debate concerning the actual definitions of 'unimpaired' and 'ecological integrity', it is clear that the National Parks Act dictates that the protection of the natural environment is of primary importance.

The concept that national parks are there for 'enjoyment' provides direction for the development of leisure activities in parks. In the early decades of national parks, 'enjoyment' was interpreted very broadly so as to include a wide variety of activities. As attitudes changed, the range of activities started to be limited to outdoor recreation. Later still, only those outdoor activities were allowed that had minimum or non-consumptive impact on the environment.

The concept of 'future generations' suggests that national parks are to be around for a long time. Generally it is now recognized that once established, national parks are permanently in place.

Park Establishment   National parks are created and eliminated by the passage of legislation by the House of Commons and by the Senate (National Parks Act, section 14). This method provides for the strongest level of tenure of any park system in Canada. Any change to park boundaries involves legislative action by both the House of Commons and the Senate. Typically, the legislation docket of Parliament is full, with many bills vying for attention. Only those with highest priorities get action. This backlog mediates against changes that do not have strong government backing. If a piece of legislation containing a change to a national park does reach the House, it is then subject to full exposure by the national media. These two factors—the Parliamentary structure and media coverage—make both the creation and elimination of a national park a long, involved, and very public process.

Land can be added to an existing national park by Cabinet as long as: 'agreement has been reached with the province in which the lands are situated that the lands are suitable for addition' (section 3.1.1.b); notice of the addition has been published in the Canada *Gazette*; the Standing Committee on Indian Affairs and Northern Affairs has had hearings and made a decision (section 3.1.2 and 3.1.3); and the House of Commons agrees (section 3.1.5).

Policy Plans   Although each national park is required to have an official management plan, nothing in the legislation requires the minister to create an overall system policy. However, the Act implies that some form of policy statement exists, as it requires a biennial report on the state of the parks: 'The Minister shall report to Parliament every two years on the state of the parks and progress towards establishing new parks' (section 5.1.5).

The 'state of the parks' suggests that an overall benchmark or baseline exists to which park conditions can be compared. This probably requires an overall policy. It also requires that data on both ecological factors and visitor use must be collected for each and every park. In addition, if the establishment of new parks is to be systematic, then any measurement of 'progress' will be by reference to a systems plan. Fortunately, the Canadian Parks Service has both an overall policy statement and a systems plan now in place. What may be lacking is sufficient baseline information on ecological and visitor-use conditions.

Park Management In each park, management is the responsibility of the minister but is implemented by park staff. Management plans for each national park are required by law. In addition, the minister is legally required to table the management plan in the House of Commons within five years of the park's establishment (section 5.1.1). This plan must, as mentioned earlier, protect ecological integrity, and must also consider 'resource protection, zoning, visitor use and other appropriate matters' and must be reviewed every five years (sections 5.1.1, 5.1.2, and 5.1.3.). Therefore, each plan must be reviewed every five years and any amendments to the plan must be tabled in the House of Commons.

The National Parks Act is the only Canadian Parks legislation that requires the creation of a management plan for each park in the system. It is also the only Act that requires each management plan to be tabled in the legislature.

Public Access to Decision Making The public has a say in the management of the parks. Section 5.14 of the Act requires the minister to involve the public in many aspects of parks operations: 'The Minister shall, as appropriate, provide opportunities for public participation at the national, regional and local levels in the development of parks policy, management plans and such other matters as the Minister deems relevant.'

This section requires public participation in the development of parks policy, which is the overall governing statement of direction for the Canadian Parks Service and for the parks. In addition, each management plan for each park must be prepared with 'opportunities for public participation'. The minister can undertake this participatory activity in the method he or she chooses to define what is 'appropriate'. However, the word 'shall' implies that he or she must provide the opportunities and thus ministerial discretion is limited, probably to the method of application. The words 'public participation' provide strong direction to the minister. The public has the right to participate actively in decision making. The exact form and approach of this participatory democracy will be developed over time as the bureaucracy gains experience with this new legislative direction.

The National Parks Act is the only Canadian Parks legislation that requires the minister, and by implication, the bureaucracy, to allow public participation in policy, planning, and management decision making.

Park Regulations Regulations for national parks are made by Cabinet as outlined in section 7 of the Act. The regulatory powers are very broad and deal with many aspects of parks and the activities that are allowed in them. Examples of these regulatory powers include: the powers to make detailed rules governing the protection of flora and wild animals; public safety; management of fishing; public works; traffic; domestic animals; and control of fires, firearm discharge, and licensing. However, it should be noted that the presence of town sites in national parks, the use of parks by millions of visitors, and the provision of many services to both groups results in a complex set of regulatory needs.

Section 2 of the Act states that a park warden is an 'officer appointed under the Public Service Employment Act whose duties include the enforcement of this Act'. The wardens have the powers of peace officers in regards to violations of park regulations by residents or visitors. Section 8(1)a states that a person who violates the Act or any regulation is, upon conviction, subject to a fine 'not exceeding $2,000'. However, in the case of disturbance of certain listed species of wildlife the fine can be $10,000 or six months in jail or $150,000 or six months in jail, for endangered or other special species.

THE PROVINCIAL LEVEL OF PARKS ADMINISTRATION IN CANADA

Canada has a wealth of provincial parks. More extensive discussion on this topic can be found in Chapters 6 and 7.

The Provincial Parks Act of Ontario

The first park established by the provincial government was at Niagara Falls in 1885. Other parks such as Algonquin (1890) and Rondeau (1894) were established by individual acts of the legislature. In 1913 the establishment of the Provincial Parks Act provided for the development of a system of parks (Ministry of Natural Resources 1986). In 1954 the provincial government established a Parks Branch in the Department of Lands and Forests. In addition, the Provincial Parks Act was amended in the same year. The 1954 Provincial Parks Act did two things: it gave Cabinet the right to make parks and gave the minister the authority to operate them. The Act has not undergone major revisions since 1954. A detailed analysis of this Act was undertaken by Eagles (1984a). In the early 1970s the Department of Lands and Forests was renamed the Ministry of Natural Resources.

Purpose of Provincial Parks According to section 2 of Ontario's Provincial Parks Act: 'All provincial parks are dedicated to the people of the Province of Ontario and others who may use them for their healthful enjoyment and education.'

The parks are established for the public for 'healthful enjoyment and education'. This phrase implies that recreation is to be encouraged, but only if it is healthful. It also implies that education is to be a major focus. Outdoor education, where the parks resources are used for environmental learning purposes, is probably the intended focus.

Nothing is said or implied about environmental protection in section 2. In fact, natural resource protection is not mentioned in the Act until section 19, which states that the minister 'may take measures as he considers proper for the protection of fish, animals and birds and any property of the Crown in a provincial park.' This emphasis suggests that provincial parks exist mainly for recreational and educational use. Environmental protection is not in the legislative purpose for Ontario Provincial Parks.

Park Establishment   Creation of a provincial park in Ontario is a relatively simple process, as Cabinet passes a regulation regarding a piece of land owned by the Crown. Such a regulation need not be passed by or presented in the provincial legislature. Cabinet also has the authority as stated in section 3.2 to 'increase or decrease the area of any provincial park'.

The discretionary powers given to Cabinet have several implications. First, any action by Cabinet on parks will come through the minister of Natural Resources. Therefore, by default the power of Cabinet is transferred to the minister, who is therefore the key person in regards to parks establishment or delisting in Ontario. Second, theoretically, parks could be created or removed very quickly. No media or public disclosure or review is required. This happened in the mid-1980s when Holiday Beach Provincial Park was transferred to a Conservation Authority quietly and quickly. Third, major boundary changes can occur to a park in a similar secret and speedy fashion. It is, however, the political reality of potential backlash that makes most Ministers move slowly and openly in the creation or delisting of Provincial Parks in Ontario.

Ontario has a sophisticated systems plan that has been used to guide new park development in the last 15 years. This systems plan is not mentioned in the governing legislation.

Policy Plans   The Ontario Provincial Parks Act does not require the creation of or adherence to a policy plan. An overall policy statement has, however, been passed by Cabinet. This policy has four objectives: protection, recreation, heritage appreciation, and tourism. One useful feature of this policy is the designation of each park as belonging to one of six classes: wilderness, nature reserve, historical park, natural environment park, waterway park, or recreation park. Each class is designed to provide a particular type of outdoor recreation.

Interestingly, the park classes listed in the approved policy differ slightly from those listed in section 5 of the Act. Section 5 states that the minister, with the approval of Cabinet, may classify any provincial park and lists these classes. The Act mentions a 'natural environmental' class, while the 1978 policy mentions a 'natural environment' class. The Act and policy both discuss a 'nature reserve' class. The Act lists a 'primitive' class, while the policy lists a 'wilderness' class. The Act lists a 'recreational' class, which the policy calls a 'recreation' class. The Act lists a 'wild river' class, while the policy has a 'waterway' class. The Act makes no reference to a historical class, as does the policy; however, section 5 gives discretionary powers to create any 'such other class of park'.

The Provincial Parks Act does not define the purpose of park classes, nor define the words used for the park classes, and nor give any guidance on how these classes are to be used. Such definitions are left to the policy.

Park Management   Management within a provincial park is discretionary. The minister, in section 7(1), is given power over park control and management. If the minister wishes to prepare a management plan for a park, section 8 gives the authority to do this: 'The Minister may prepare a master plan in respect of any provincial park or proposed provincial park' (section 8[1]), and 'The Minister may review a master plan from time to time and make amendments thereto' (section 8[2]).

One of the methods of managing a park is to prepare a map showing zones, with each zone dedicated to a particular purpose. Section 7(2) gives the minister such power: 'in the management of a provincial park the Minister may from time to time define areas on maps or plans, designate such areas as zones, and classify any zone as an historic zone, multiple use zone, natural zone, primitive zone, recreational zone or otherwise as he considers proper.'

There is, however, no requirement of the minister to produce, table, review, follow, or inform anyone about management activities or about a management plan.

Public Access to Decision-making   The Ontario Provincial Parks Act does not suggest or require public involvement regarding any aspect of the parks.

Section 6 of the Act states that the minister may, with the approval of cabinet, appoint 'committees to perform advisory functions'. This implies that some members of the public will be asked to provide formal advice.

The minister has a standing advisory committee that is asked to collect and comment on issues referred to it by the minister. The minister often appoints local advisory committees to serve the role of collecting public opinions in regards to specific park management issues. In both situations, the minister typically appoints interested citizens.

Park Regulations   The minister has the power to create regulations concerning activities within a park. In section 7(2), the minister may designate and classify zones in a park; and in section 7(3) he may approve construction of facilities for outdoor recreation and 'the convenience of the public'. Section 21 of the Act gives cabinet the power to make regulations for such purposes as:

> regulating . . . staking out of mining claims . . . development of mineral interest or the working of mines in provincial parks; . . . controlling the use or keeping of horses, dogs, or other animals in provincial parks; . . . controlling . . . notices, signs, signboards . . . ; . . . controlling . . . fires; . . . controlling pedestrian, vehicular, boat or air traffic . . . ; for issuing permits to persons to enter and travel in provincial parks; regulating, controlling and licensing and requiring

the use of guides in provincial parks; prescribing the fees or rentals payable . . . ; prescribing the maximum periods of stay of persons, vehicles, boats, vessels or aircraft. . . .

Enforcement of these rules and regulations is carried out by district managers, superintendents, assistant superintendents, park wardens, and conservation officers who, in section 13, are given the 'power and authority of a member of the Ontario Provincial Police force'. With this authority, an official may seize private property and issue fines. Section 22(1) states that a person who is convicted of a contravention of the Act or the regulations is liable to a 'fine of not more than $500'.

THE REGIONAL LEVEL OF PARK ADMINISTRATION IN CANADA

The Conservation Authorities Act of Ontario

The Conservation Authorities Act was first passed by the Ontario legislature in 1946 (Higgs 1977). The Act has undergone numerous revisions since that time. It provides for the creation of public agencies called Conservation Authorities. These agencies are created by the Ontario cabinet upon the receipt of a request by two-thirds of municipalities in a particular watershed. The authority has jurisdiction over certain matters within a defined watershed of one or more rivers.

Conservation authorities are unique to the province of Ontario. Originally designed to control and manage the province's watersheds, conservation authorities have, due to public demand, begun to play an increasing role in providing park areas and outdoor recreation opportunities. There are now 39 conservation authorities in Ontario. Each is operated by a board, some of whose members are appointed by the province and some by local municipalities.

Purpose of Regional Parks   Section 20 of the Conservation Authorities Act states: 'The objectives of an authority are to establish and undertake, in the area over which it has jurisdiction, a program designed to further the conservation, restoration, development and management of natural resources other than gas, oil, coal and minerals.'

One of the methods of implementing this objective has been to establish parks. These are called conservation areas, presumably to differentiate them from provincial parks and municipal parks. The Conservation Authorities Act does not have a stated purpose for the parks that a conservation authority may create.

Policy Plans   The Conservation Authorities Act does not require the creation of an overall park policy. There is mention, in section 24, that 'before proceeding with a project, the authority shall file plans and a description thereof with, and obtain the approval in writing of the Minister.' Therefore, conservation authorities, upon the urging of the provincial government, have developed policy plans for their activities in the watersheds over which they have jurisdiction. Such plans usually refer to long-term conservation area development policies.

Park Establishment Section 21(m) gives a conservation authority the power to establish and operate parklands. It states that the authority has the power 'to use lands owned and controlled by the authority for park or other recreational purposes, and to erect, or permit to be erected, buildings, booths and facilities for such purposes and to make charges for admission thereto and the use thereof.'

This section means that land owned by an authority can be turned into a conservation area by a simple administrative decision of the governing board.

Park Management The management of a conservation area is discretionary. Basically, 'anything goes,' as no plans are required for the park lands. The minister of Natural Resources, who has some discretionary authority over certain actions of conservation authorities, has the power under section 24(1), to require the authority to 'file plans and a description thereof with and obtain the approval in writing of the Minister' before 'proceeding with a project'. This power is most often used when creating large water-control structures, such as dams. It is seldom used for conservation area development.

Public Access to Decision-making There is no role outlined in the Act for the general public to be involved in decision-making for conservation area planning or management. The conservation authority is, however, closely allied to local municipal governments. This fact usually dictates that public consultation be undertaken for conservation area development.

Park Regulations Section 29(1) states that an authority can make regulations in various areas, which must be approved by the Ontario cabinet. Regulations can be made for a broad range of measures including setting fees, regulating activities such as vehicular movement, lighting of fires, and use of areas by pets.

At present the provincial government is undertaking the development of an omnibus regulation to assist authorities in their management duties.

There is no specific person, or class of person, designated in the Act to enforce the regulations. However, park staff tend to use the Trespass to Property Act to enforce rules of behaviour.

The Niagara Parks Act

The Niagara Parks Act was originally passed for the establishment of Queen Victoria Park in 1887. The Act established the first park agency in Ontario, the Niagara Parks Commission. The parks controlled by the commission include Queen Victoria Park, Queenston Heights Park, Niagara River Parkways, Butler's Burying Ground, Drummond Hill Burying Ground, and Lundy's Lane Battlefield and Cemetery, as stated in section 1(c) of the Act.

Purpose of Parks   The Act lacks any statement of overall philosophy concerning the purpose of Niagara parks or the Parks Commission. However, section 4 of the Act states that 'It is the duty of the Commission to manage, control and develop the Parks' and goes on to give the commission specific powers. These include the powers to:

(a) lay out, plant and enclose the Parks;
(b) construct and pull down buildings and structures;
(c) construct and operate incline railways, aerial cars, lifts and works to assist the public in reaching and viewing the points of interest in the Parks;
(d) construct or acquire by purchase, lease or otherwise and operate bridges over the Niagara River . . . ;
(e) construct and operate golf courses, bowling greens and swimming pools;
(f) construct and operate restaurants, refreshment booths and stands for the sale of souvenirs and other wares;
(g) construct and maintain toilet and other facilities . . . ;
(h) acquire and operate buses and other vehicles . . . ;
(i) operate a school for apprentice gardeners;

It is clear from this section that the Niagara Parks Commission is very much in the business of operating scenic and recreational facilities in the parks of the Niagara area. The commission has assumed the role of providing a scenic recreation corridor along the length of the Niagara Peninsula from Fort Erie on Lake Erie to Niagara-on-the-Lake on Lake Ontario.

Park Establishment   Parks creation occurs as the commission, with Cabinet's approval, purchases, leases, or expropriates land. These powers are outlined in section 7 of the Act.

Policy Plans   The Niagara Parks Act does not require the development of any kind of overall policy. The parks commission has, however, developed many types of written policy in regards to activities such as long-range planning and individual site developments.

Park Management   The Niagara Parks Act does not require the commission to have any form of management plan. All management decisions are made by a commission composed of people appointed by Cabinet and by four nearby municipalities: Niagara Falls, Fort Erie, Niagara-on-the-Lake, and the Regional Municipality of Niagara.

Section 5 of the Act gives the commission power to borrow money and to issue securities. This section implies that the commission should be financially independent from the province. And this is what happens. D.W. Schafer, the general manager of the commission, points out that 'The necessity to raise our own funds, or course, influences the things we do, how we do them and much of our philosophy and policies' (Schafer, pers. comm.).

The operation of a School of Horticulture is a unique role of the commission. The school trains people in the skills of applied horticulture.

Public Access to Decision Making   Within the Niagara Parks Act, there is no requirement and very little opportunity for public involvement regarding park management. Individuals may be appointed to the commission, but their interests would likely reflect those of the municipalities or the province, rather than the general public. However, the commission has a policy of involving the general public in major decisions regarding the parks (Schafer, pers. comm.).

Park Regulations   The commission, as the managing body, may create and acquire facilities as stated in section 4 of the Niagara Parks Act. The Niagara Parks Commission can make regulations, but only with the approval of the Ontario Cabinet. Section 21(1) gives the power to create regulations for regulating public use, setting fees, and licensing guides and taxis, among other measures.

The Act does not state directly who has the power to enforce the Act or regulations. However, section 4(l) states that the commission has the power to 'appoint such auditors, officers, clerks, keepers, gardeners and other persons as may be required'. The general interpretation section of the regulations states that 'officer means a constable and any employee appointed by the Commission to enforce this Regulation.' The commission employs its own Parks police force.

THE MUNICIPAL LEVEL OF PARK ADMINISTRATION IN CANADA

According to the Canadian constitution, municipal affairs are a provincial power. All aspects of the operations of municipalities are governed by provincial legislation. The legislation governing municipal parks in Ontario has been chosen as an example. There is, however, a fair degree of similarity between provincial municipal parks legislation across the country.

Ontario Municipal Parks: The Municipal Act, the Public Parks Act and the Parks Assistance Act

Ontario was the first Canadian province to pass legislation governing the development and operation of municipal parks. The Public Parks Act was passed in 1883. This Act allowed cities and towns to establish parks, with the consent of the electors in that municipality, and provided for the establishment of boards of park management. The boards were given the authority to purchase land for parks up to 1000 acres in size for cities and 500 acres for towns. It appears that this Act was passed upon the request of the City of Toronto (McFarland 1982).

Municipal parks in Ontario are now governed by three Acts. The Municipal Act gives municipalities general powers, including management. The Public Parks Act allows for the establishment of a Board of Park Management to operate the parks. The Parks Assistance Act allows the Ministry of Natural Resources to provide financial and other forms of assistance to municipalities.

Purpose of Parks Within the three governing acts, there is no overall purpose given for a municipal park. Section 208 of the Municipal Act gives Ontario municipalities the power to pass by-laws for a variety of purposes. Section 208(57), which outlines certain by-law powers in regards to parks and recreation, has an introduction that outlines the purpose of these by-laws. The by-laws can be passed:

> For acquiring, erecting, altering, maintaining, operating or managing or granting aid for the acquisition, erection, alteration, maintenance, operation or management of monuments, memorial windows, tablets, parks, recreational areas, playgrounds, athletic fields, zoological or other gardens, natural history collections, observatories or works of art, or other places of recreation and amusement, arenas, auditoriums, health or community recreation centres, stadia, museums, including public historical museums and similar buildings, within or outside the municipality and any such undertaking may be for the purpose of commemorating or honouring persons or events.

The introduction to section 208(57) nicely outlines the very broad context of activities and facilities surrounding municipal parks. Since the first establishment of municipal parks as envisaged by the 1883 Public Parks Act, generations of people and ideas have influenced the leisure activities that occur in parks. Historically, the purposes for these parks have been more social and cultural than environmental.

In recent years, due to changing public attitudes, many municipalities are starting to acquire more parkland in natural ecological condition. The provision of storm water management facilities often results in green, passively managed parkland. The protection of environmentally sensitive areas (Eagles 1984) cause forests and wetlands to become parkland (Graham, pers. comm.).

Park Establishment Section 1(1) of the Public Parks Act gives municipalities in Ontario the power to establish parks: 'A park, or a system of parks, avenues, boulevards and drives, or any of them, may be established in any municipality, and the same, as well as existing parks and avenues, may be controlled and managed in the manner hereinafter provided.'

Section 208(51) of the Municipal Act gives municipalities in Ontario the power to pass by-laws 'for acquiring land for and establishing and laying out public parks'. Municipalities can obtain parkland by donation or purchase. In addition, under section 41(1) of the Planning Act, 1983, municipalities have the power to 'require that land in an amount not exceeding, in the care of land proposed for development or redevelopment for commercial or industrial purposes, 2 per cent and in all other cases 5 per cent of the land be conveyed to the municipality for park or other public recreational purposes.'

In many municipalities, this dedication of 5 per cent of land under development is the primary method of new park establishment.

These sections from three different Acts provide the basis for quite different methods for acquiring, establishing, and managing parks by the Board of Park Management and by municipal governments. Across Ontario municipal park management falls within both models. Typically, in recent years, larger municipalities have opted for having parks and recreation departments that operate the parks. Smaller municipalities tend to have parks boards, staffed by community volunteers.

Policy Plans   No legislation requires municipalities in Ontario to produce overall policy plans for their park system or for individual parks. Nevertheless, many do such planning.

The provincial government provides grants for many recreation and park activities. These grants are usually conditional upon the municipality having an overall policy plan. This 'carrot' approach is one factor in attracting municipalities towards the development of policy plans. Typically larger, more urban municipalities have sophisticated policy plans, while rural municipalities may have little or no overall park and recreation plan.

Park Management   Ontario has two basic means of parkland management: by the municipality directly or by a Board of Park Management. The Public Parks Act provides the rules for the establishment and operation of the board. When a board is established, the 'head of the municipality and six other persons' (section 4) are appointed by the municipal council. The board then has the responsibility and authority for all park management in the municipality. Municipal parks are not legally required to have a management plan. Generally, the municipality or the Board of Park Management has very broad discretionary powers as to how park management is carried out.

Public Access to Decision Making   The public can affect parkland decision making in several ways in municipalities. Municipal councils and municipal park management staff are usually readily accessible to the average citizen. Therefore, concerns can be taken directly to those in positions of influence.

Ultimately, the members of council are subject to the will of the electorate every three years. Second, if a Board of Park Management is in place in a municipality, the board must be composed of six citizens. Therefore, concerned individuals can play a direct role if appointed to the board. Third, there is a long tradition in municipal parks of public involvement in operation and management. This is often done by informal, voluntary arrangements. In addition, most municipalities have extensive public participation during parkland planning and management. However, in none of the relevant statutes in Ontario is the municipality *required* to involve the public in parkland decisions.

Parks Regulations Various sections of the Municipal Act give municipalities the power to set rules by the passing of by-laws. Section 208(42) states that by-laws can be passed 'for prohibiting . . . vehicles . . . in or upon any . . . park.' Section 234(1) states that by-laws may be passed for 'regulating or prohibiting the playing of bands or musical instruments in any highway, park.' However, most visitor behaviour is governed by using the Trespass to Property Act to remove offending persons.

The Public Parks Act gives the Board of Park Management, in section 11(1), the power to 'pass by-laws for the use, regulation, protection and government of the parks'. The board also has the power 'to attach penalties for the infraction' of the by-laws (section 11[4]). However, the maximum penalties are a fine of $20.00 or imprisonment of not more than 30 days (section 19[2]).

ABORIGINAL RIGHTS AND PARKS

The foregoing sections have dealt with legislation and related policies directly related to park designation and management. Other legislation and legal precedents may have important implications. For example, Aboriginal peoples often use natural resources of the area they live in for food, lodging and a cash income. Parks establishment in an area typically means that a government bureaucracy is given responsibility for the allocation of land and resource use. This has usually meant a restriction in use by *all* people for conservation and recreation purposes. Many Native bands argue that they are not bound by such restrictions.

Recent decisions by the Supreme Court of Canada have strengthened Aboriginal rights and the associated access to resources on crown land and in parks. Bartlett (1990) provides a succinct summary of the implications of the four most important decisions. Berg, Fenge and Dearden discuss the ramifications in greater detail in Chapter 12 of this volume.

In *Regina v. Horseman*, the Court ruled that the rights to hunt stated in Treaty 8 included the right to hunt commercially. However, the court also ruled that in the prairie provinces the Natural Resource Transfer Agreements of 1930 had removed some of these rights. Therefore in the Northwest Territories these commercial hunting rights still exist (Bartlett 1990). This decision could have strong implications for wildlife populations. It is unclear as of yet if such commercial killing could occur in national parks or migratory bird sanctuaries in the Northwest Territories.

In *Regina v. Sioui*, the Court ruled that the provincial parks legislation was not entirely in force because the Hurons' rights had not been extinguished by treaty. The most important finding was that the Huron people had been treated as a nation by Britain and therefore British policy had implied nation-to-nation relations that gave the Hurons considerable 'autonomy in their internal affairs' (Bartlett 1990). This implies that in areas with no treaty that extinguished Native resource rights, these rights still exist. This is particularly important in the parks field because the ruling dealt with the rights to resources in Quebec provincial parks.

In *Regina v. Sparrow*, the Court dealt with the right of a Native band in British Columbia to fish in contravention of the Federal Fisheries Act. The Court ruled that the Federal Fisheries Act had not extinguished an inherent Aboriginal right to fish and that the band could continue to exercise their fishing activities. This decision set the doctrine that constitutionally protected Aboriginal rights could only be infringed or extinguished with justification that is 'consistent with the honour of the Crown and the fiduciary or trust relationship to aboriginal peoples' (Bartlett 1990). The implications of this case in particular are more extensively discussed in Chapter 12 of this volume.

In *Mitchell vs. Peguis Indian Band* the Court ruled that Native property is immune from taxation and seizure (Bartlett 1990). Bartlett maintains that these four decisions have fundamentally altered the issue of aboriginal rights and law in Canada. He stated that these decisions may 'form the basis for the development of inherent aboriginal sovereignty which could dramatically change the structure of government as it affects aboriginal peoples and their lands and resources.'

The immediate impact of these decisions has been to open up many parks to destructive resource extraction by Natives. The controversy surrounding the hunting and fishing by natives in Algonquin Provincial Park in Ontario is but one example.

SUMMARY

In Canadian parks, all actions of the government agencies and of the citizens are governed by legislation. Agencies can do, and can only do, what the legislation allows. The park user is governed by the rules established under the legislation. Several basic principles are obvious from the Canadian park legislation reviewed in this paper; these will be summarised below.

The National Parks Act is fundamentally different from the other park legislation in Canada. Only at the federal level are parks established by the legislature. Only in national parks is an ecological factor given primary importance in parks management and is the minister required to prepare management plans for every park. Only in national parks must these management plans be tabled in the legislature, implying that they must be followed. Only at the national level is the minister responsible required to involve the public in decision-making in regards to park policy. The National Parks Act is the most progressive and ecologically conscious parks legislation in Canada.

The provincial Acts generally say very little about how the parks are to be managed. The Acts are written in very general language that is loose enough to allow a broad range of management actions. The bureaucracy appears to have extremely strong powers in management. These powers can be exercised in secret with no requirements for written statements of policy governing these actions and no requirements for public involvement in decision making. In essence, the ancient discretionary power of the Queen over her lands is passed on through the legislature, the Cabinet and the Minister to civil servants. Very few other civil servants have such immense discretionary powers.

In most provinces, provincial parks are established by regulation. However, there are exceptions. In British Columbia the older provincial parks cannot be removed or changed without an Act of the legislature. The Northwest Territories also requires territorial park deregulation to be confirmed by the legislature.

Eagles (1984) has documented the problem with the concept of *locus standii* or legal standing in regards to parks management. Canadian courts have held that with certain legislation, such as that governing parks, individuals are restricted from taking action in the courts unless they can show that they have been affected more than others. They must prove 'standing' before the court. This precedent virtually stops a citizen from taking a minister to court to force compliance with the law. Therefore, there is a remarkable lack of case law dealing with the interpretation of many park Acts in relation to their applicability to government management action.

The problem of standing, as well as the discretionary language of the provincial Acts, means that the parks business is really an incestuous relationship between a minister and the bureaucracy. There is very little room for the park user or for the average citizen in this tight interrelationship. The power of the bureaucracy is very closely guarded by the civil servants. Therefore, at the provincial level in Canada, public action must be political, with the most emphasis at the ministerial level.

Regional parks agencies such as the Niagara Parks Commission and the various conservation authorities operate in a legislative structure similar to that at the provincial level. The establishing legislation is loosely and powerfully written, the bureaucracy has strong discretionary power, the laws do not require public involvement in decision-making, the senior decision makers are usually all appointed, and no policy or management plans for parks need be created or followed if written. Park visitors must follow the rules that the agency promulgates.

The municipal level is quite distinct from the other levels of operation. Provincial legislatures make the rules in which municipalities operate. As a result the authority of municipalities is limited to that stipulated in legislation. And these laws are quite precise and detailed. For example, the Municipal Act for Ontario is 350 pages long and it is only one of several pieces of relevant legislation. The Provincial Parks Act, which governs almost 7 per cent of the province, is nine pages long. In addition many decisions of municipal councils can be appealed to an independent administrative tribunal, the Ontario Municipal Board, for a hearing. The board usually has the power to overrule municipal decisions. However, in Ontario provincial parks, bureaucratic or ministerial decisions are final and not appealable. It is clear the province keeps municipalities on a tight rein, while it gives itself broad discretionary powers.

Municipalities are quite different from other park agencies in that their methods of operation are comparatively open. Every major decision is open to public scrutiny. In the case of Boards of Park Management, citizens are given the authority of decision through membership on the board. No such board occurs at the provincial or national level, but they do occur at the regional level, such as the conservation authorities. And of course the municipal councillors must face the decision of the electorate every three years.

Municipal legislation is discretionary in that many land uses and activities are anticipated for the parks in the governing legislation. The mix of uses and activities is decided by the elected officials, usually after considerable public consultation.

Parks legislation varies widely in emphasis and scope in Canada. The recent important amendments to the National Parks Act may set a precedent for the upgrading of many of the provincial park Acts across the country in the future. Recent Supreme Court decisions on Aboriginal rights appear to give some Native groups in certain situations discretionary access to many park resources.

ACKNOWLEDGEMENTS

Special thanks to Liza Ordubegian and Richard Sherback of the Department of Recreation and Leisure Studies, University of Waterloo, to Mr Fred Graham of the City of Kitchener Department of Parks and Recreation, to Dr Guy Swinnerton of the Department of Recreation and Leisure Studies at the University of Alberta, and to Mr Dennis Schafer of the Niagara Parks Commission who commented on an earlier draft on this paper. Special thanks to Sandy Heise and Anne Ross who typed and retyped the many editions of this paper.

REFERENCES

Bartlett, R.
1990   'Indian Summer in the Supreme Court: The Sparrow Quartet', *Resources: Newsletter of the Canadian Institute of Resources Law* 32: 6–7.
Eagles, P.F.J.
1984a   *A Study of the Ontario Provincial Parks Act*, Recreation Series No. 1, Department of Recreation, University of Waterloo, Waterloo, Ont.
Eagles, P.F.J.
1984b   *The Planning and Management of Environmentally Sensitive Areas*, Longman, Harlow, U.K.
Higgs, K.
1977   'Land Use Planning Resources Management: Some Ontario Experiences', in *Land Use*, Special Publication No. 22, Soil Conservation Society of America, 329–41.
McFarland, E.
1982   'The Beginning of Municipal Park Systems', in G. Wall and J. Marsh, *Recreational Land Use Perspectives and its Evolution in Canada*, Carleton University Press, Ottawa, 257–71.
Ministry of Natural Resources
1978   *Ontario Provincial Parks Policy*, Provincial Parks Branch, Toronto.
Ministry of Natural Resources
1986   *Class Environmental Assessment for Provincial Park Management*, Draft, Provincial Parks Branch, Toronto.
Ontario, *Conservation Authorities Act, Revised Statutes of Ontario*, (R.S.O)
1980   C. 85, as amended by 1983, C. 8, section 20.
Ontario, *Municipal Act*, R.S.O.
1980   C. 302, as amended by 1981, C. 47, 23, C. 70, 23; 1982, C. 24, C. 40, 4.; C. 50, C. 5, 1; 1983, C. 8, 16, C. 41; 1984, C. 45, 18, C. 48, 20, C. 55, 222, C. 56, 23; 1986, C. 14, C. 24.
Ontario, *Niagara Parks Act*, R.S.O.
1980   C. 317.
Ontario, *Parks Assistance Act*, R.S.O.
1980   Chapter 367.
Ontario, *Planning Act*
1983   *Statutes of Ontario* S.O., 1983, C. 1, as amended by 1983, C. 82; 1984, C. 32, 21 and 1985, C. 16.
Ontario, *Provincial Parks Act*, R.S.O.
1980   C. 401, as amended by 1984, C. 45, 2.
Ontario, *Public Parks Act*, R.S.O.
1980   C. 417.
Schafer, D.W.
1990   Niagara Parks Commission, personal communication.

CHAPTER 5

Managing the National Parks

RICK ROLLINS

INTRODUCTION

Banff was established as Canada's first national park in 1885, following the example of the first national park at Yellowstone. Banff was seen as an opportunity to generate tourism revenues to offset the tremendous cost of building the Canadian Pacific Railway (CPR). People from all corners of the globe were encouraged to travel via CPR to visit the mountain resort community. The ensuing decades saw a rapid development of a tourism industry consisting of health spas, resorts, and outfitting, financed by the CPR and other private interests. All this had the blessing of the Canadian government, which saw railways and national parks as part of the nation-building strategy of the time.

People flocked to Banff to experience the scenery, the hot springs, and the sumptuous accommodations. Some adventured in the park by horseback or canoe; others came to hunt, fish, and climb mountains. At the same time, some logging, grazing, and mining activities were permitted in the park (Bella 1987). This was not viewed as inconsistent, since the prevailing view of government was that the park needed 'to be used'; conservation, as we use the term today, was yet to be defined (Craig Brown 1968; Bella 1987). The image was of an alpine resort town (see Figure 5.1), an image that continues to be portrayed in the tourism literature to this day.

This chapter deliberately begins with reference to Banff, not just as an historical curiosity but because Banff is a symbol of the controversy surrounding what national parks can and should be. Conservation groups have criticized the Canadian Parks Service for failing to provide adequate protection for natural resources in the park. The kind of urban growth in the park townsites of Banff, Lake Louise, and Sunshine Village poses threats to wildlife and ecological processes. Similar threats are posed by highway, pipeline, and railway construction in the park. Bears and other animals have changed their behaviour as a consequence of tourism. In the backcountry, many campsites and trails are over-used and degraded, and concerns have been raised about the presence of huts, lodges, and shelters (Environment Canada 1986a).

Figure 5.1
Horse-drawn carriages stand ready to whisk visitors from the Banff railway
station to hotels such as the Banff Springs (1913). Because it owned both
the hotel and the railway station, the Canadian Pacific Railway held
considerable influence over park visitors. Other hotels expressed resentment
over the CPR's influence during this period, particularly when they learned
the CPR was advising tourists that the Banff Springs was the only hotel in
town.   *Photo: Canadian Parks Service*

Many conservationists view tourism and recreation in Banff as serious
threats to what a national park should be: a place where natural landscapes
and processes are protected (Fuller 1977). Conservationists have been successful in preventing any more logging, mining, ranching or other resource
extraction activities in the park. As a consequence, however, many of the
resource industries in Canada have come to view national parks as a threat
to industrial development. Similarly, restrictions placed on tourism development in Banff, such as the refusal to hold the 1988 Winter Olympic ski
events in the park, have prompted concerns from the tourism industry.

The history and evolution of Banff illustrate the difficulties the Canadian
Parks Service has faced with the tourism industry, conservation groups,
resource managers, nearby land use, and the resource industries. The issues
can be reduced to the following kinds of considerations:

1. What is the purpose of national parks? What is the value of a national
   park?
2. Where should national parks be located, and how many are needed? How
   large must they be, and how are boundaries resolved?

3. How are natural resources to be managed in national parks?
4. How is visitor use to be managed in national parks?
5. How are decisions made about management issues?

This chapter describes how the Canadian Parks Service has answered these challenges. The commentary centres on the National Parks Act, the national park policy, and the systems plan for national parks. These documents were developed by the Canadian Park Service in part to address the sorts of issues identified here, and they represent one reality of how national parks are managed or should be managed. Two other realities also need to be considered. The second reality is found in the realm of science, a reality espoused by those who attempt to present conservation arguments in terms of ecological theory. Examples of this reality can be found in Chapter 9. Since theory and research into natural processes is incomplete and not always understood or believed, the reality of science is only partially reflected in the first realm of policy, legislation, and planning.

The third reality is much more difficult to define but can be summarized as the study of power, politics, and personality. When we notice inconsistencies between park policy and what actually occurs in a particular national park, the explanation can usually be found somewhere in this third reality. This chapter can be viewed as an effort to prepare people to be informed critics of the national park system. Therefore it is imperative to examine national park management from all three of these perspectives.

WHY NATIONAL PARKS

Millions of people explore the national parks of Canada each year. They clamber to lookouts, gaze from belvederes, and rest at scenic pull-offs that highlight special features. Parks staff and helpful fingerboards point out what should be seen. This is one of many types of national park experience. It follows that one way to approaching the management of national parks is to begin with people. National parks are for the use of the public, after all. They are usually established through high-profile political decisions. Public policy, sometimes hotly contested, is what guides park management, and parks, thanks to the tourism industry, are emotive public symbols.

Therefore the management of national parks cannot be construed as packing nature into some sort of giant home-preserve jar. Rather, parks are composed of the management of relations between people and the land. Park management includes the rationing of opportunities and benefits presented by parks to people.

The study of management practices in national parks needs also to consider diverse 'cultures' or stakeholders, as discussed in Chapter 9. For example, numerous studies have illustrated that park managers often hold views that differ from visitors' views on recreation impact and its management. Manning

(1986) summarizes how managers tend to be more sensitive to issues such as litter, vandalism, and visitor impact on trails and campsites. Other studies have shown that visitors differ somewhat among themselves regarding such management issues as the construction of shelters or tent pads in the back country (Lucas 1980; Hammit and McDonald 1983; Rollins and Rouse 1991).

The value that Canadians place on national parks is reflected in several polls conducted in recent years. For example, a 1990 Angus Reid poll revealed that 'six out of ten Canadians were in favour of at least doubling the amount of land protected as wilderness. Three-quarters of the respondents felt that governments were paying inadequate attention to the problem of threatened species and natural habitat' (Canadian Environmental Advisory Council 1991, 23).

Proposals for national park establishment are often opposed by the interests of major industries: agriculture (e.g., Saguenay Marine Park); forestry (e.g. La Vérendrye, Temagami, Carmanah Valley, South Moresby/Gwaii Hanaas); or water and hydroelectric power (e.g. Grasslands, French River). While industrial resource users and their lobbies are opposed to the creation of parks, other powerful interest groups such as Native people's associations may view the park management framework as appropriate to the protection of their way of life (see e.g. Dearden and Berg 1993). Park negotiations, Native claims, and the maintenance of traditional northern, rural, and Native lifestyles at times find themselves in political alignment (e.g. Ellesmere Island, Northern Yukon, and Gros Morne national parks). Indeed, parks negotiations in the 1980s were characterized more by this merging of consensus of local lifestyles and conservation concerns than was evident in the 1970s during the establishment of Kouchibouguac or Forillon national parks (Keogh 1989). These earlier negotiations were based more on environmental values than on prospects for local economies and lifestyles. For example, in Kouchibouguac, 228 households located within the park boundaries were compelled to leave, some by expropriation, when the new park was created.

Benefits

The benefits of national parks can be summarized as ecological, educational, scientific, economic, and cultural (Canadian Environmental Advisory Council 1991). Ecological benefits include the preservation of the genetic diversity of species and genetic variation within them. Educational benefits include the notion of outdoor classrooms where people have the opportunity to learn from firsthand experience with natural processes. Scientific benefits are numerous, but perhaps the most significant is the idea of parks as benchmarks that allow (for example) the chance to compare a natural forest ecosystem with a forest that has been managed for timber production. Economic benefits of parks range from tourism revenues to the identification of new medicines. Cultural benefits are evident in the works of such distinguished Canadian artists and writers as Robert Service, the Group of Seven, Emily Carr, Leonard Cohen, Margaret Atwood, and Gordon Lightfoot.

Direction Provided by the National Parks Act

A full discussion of national park legislation is provided in Chapter 4; however, amendments to the National Parks Act in 1988 are important enough to mention here. These amendments clarified the priority placed on ecological considerations through a number of measures, such as increasing the penalties for poaching and legislating the boundaries of wilderness areas in national parks. Prior to 1988, poaching fines were nominal and did little to deter some hunters from illegally hunting trophy animals such as bighorn sheep. The concept of 'ecological integrity' was made explicit as a guiding principle in the revised Parks Act.

Legislating the boundaries of wilderness has the effect of greatly increasing the protection of wilderness areas. Before 1988, wilderness was defined in the zoning system described in national park policy. With the 1988 amendment to the National Park Act, any proposed change in a wilderness boundary will require debate in the House of Commons.

Direction From National Park Policy

Policy guidelines provide extremely important direction for the day-to-day planning and management of national parks. However, policy is somewhat open to interpretation and does not carry the same clout as legislation. For example, any guidelines expressed in the National Parks Act can be enforced in the courts, whereas policy cannot.

As discussed in Chapters 3 and 4, the national park policy (Environment Canada 1979) describes the rationale for national parks and the philosophy for managing them. The stated purpose of national parks is 'to protect for all time representative areas of Canadian significance in a system of national parks, and to encourage public understanding, appreciation, and enjoyment of this natural heritage so as to leave it unimpaired for future generations' (Environment Canada 1979, 38).

Clearly, the notion of resource conservation implied here does not include any element of harvesting—no logging, mining, ranching, or the like. The challenge set out in this mission statement is to provide appropriate recreational facilities without compromising the priority of resource conservation. However, even relatively unobtrusive recreational activities such as canoeing, backpacking, or nordic skiing, will have some environmental impact (Hammitt and Cole 1987). Therefore, a general guideline for managing visitors' activities is provided by the notion of leaving parks 'unimpaired for future generations'.

The proper use of national parks is defined in the expression 'to encourage public understanding, appreciation and enjoyment'. Clearly, parks are intended to be used by people, but only certain kinds of recreational use will be encouraged. This priority is evident in several parts of the policy statement. For example:

> Parks Canada's primary concern is to protect and present heritage resources of national significance. Thus public demand for outdoor recreation opportunities in a particular locality is not justification for Parks Canada's participation. Provincial and territorial governments and their agencies, however, have a specific mandate for recreation. (Ministry of Environment 1979, 14)

WHERE TO LOCATE NATIONAL PARKS AND HOW MANY ARE NEEDED

One of the most controversial aspects of national parks is their location and number. Related considerations are the shape, configuration, and size of national parks.

The fierce debates over the establishment of a national park on South Moresby Island illustrate this point. Several stakeholders played a part in the final decisions about this park (Dearden 1987). Conservation groups realized the ecological significance of this area, a rare and unusual landscape, and they wanted to see a large national park established to provide maximum protection to it. Opposed to this notion was the forest industry, which wanted to see the old-growth forest logged. The tourist industry argued that the creation of a national park would serve as a focus for tourism. The Haida people wanted the area protected, but their concerns did not exactly mirror those of the tourism industry or the conservation community; they value the area for its spiritual significance in their culture. The provincial government was reluctant to give up any territory to the federal government as a national park and would have preferred some other solution.

The issue was resolved with the signing of a memorandum of understanding in 1987 between the federal government and the government of British Columbia. This was followed by the Canada-British Columbia South Moresby Agreement, signed in 1988, which provided compensation to the forest industry and other industries as well as funds for a regional economic initiative, based on tourism and small business development in the Queen Charlotte Islands (Environment Canada 1991). The Haida and the federal government are negotiating an agreement for co-operation in the planning and management of the park.

Every potential national park is established in this sort of context, with several stakeholders, some totally opposed to the concept of a park and others with varying visions of what a national park should be. For all of these reasons, it has become imperative to define a rationale for establishing new national parks.

Systems Planning

The creation of a systems planning framework was an effort to develop a rational basis for establishing national parks. In 1971, a national park systems plan was approved as a basis for deciding where national parks were needed (National and Historic Parks Branch 1971; Environment Canada 1990). The plan classified the landmass of Canada into 39 natural regions (Figure 5.2), each with its own characteristics—vegetation patterns, landforms, climate and wildlife. Natural regions were defined as:

> natural landscapes and/or environments of Canada which may be separated from other such landscapes and environments by surface features which are readily observable, discernible, and understandable by the layman as well as by scientists and others more familiar with the natural features of Canada. (National and Historic Sites Branch 1971, 3)

The identification of natural regions was heavily influenced by physiographic characteristics: the geology and topography of the country. This analysis of the Canadian landscape was guided by a belief that natural regions should be determined by factors that are readily observable by a layperson as well as an expert.

A second major influence on the development of natural regions was an analysis of forest regions of Canada. Forest regions, like physiographic regions, can be defined in a way that is obvious to anyone who can distinguish between (for example) prairie grassland, boreal forest, and west-coast rain forests.

The use of forest regions and physiographical regions to develop a natural region system approximates the diversity of Canadian landscapes. The rationale behind this exercise is that at least one national park should be located in each natural region. If each natural region is adequately represented in the national park system, then it can be reasoned that the diversity of life forms, natural features, and natural processes in Canada will also be protected. In this way, the identification of natural regions and the location of national parks will have significance to the largest number of Canadians. This in turn was expected to create the greatest level of public support for national parks.

Identifying, selecting, and establishing new national parks has proven to be a complex exercise, although the normal sequence of events can be summarized in five steps: identifying natural areas of Canadian significance (NACS); selecting potential parks; assessing park feasibility; negotiating a new park agreement; and establishing a new park in legislation.

NACS are identified in those natural regions that do not have a national park. Two criteria are important:

1. The areas must contain a good representation of wildlife, vegetation, geology, and landforms of the region; and
2. Human impact should be minimal.

The second step, the selection of potential national parks is influenced by the following considerations:

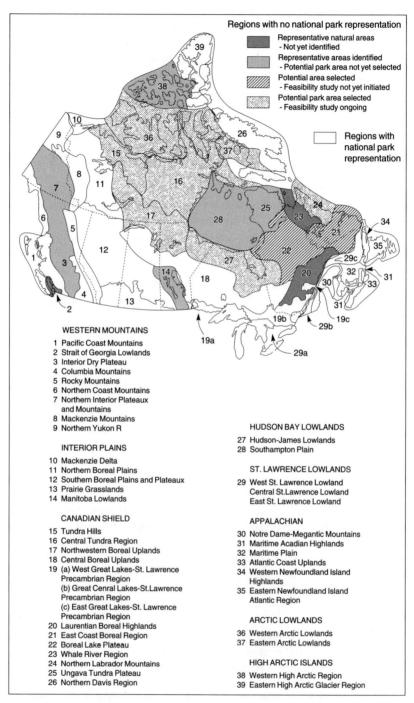

Regions with no national park representation

- Representative natural areas - Not yet identified
- Representative areas identified - Potential park area not yet selected
- Potential area selected - Feasibility study not yet initiated
- Potential park area selected - Feasibility study ongoing

Regions with national park representation

WESTERN MOUNTAINS

1 Pacific Coast Mountains
2 Strait of Georgia Lowlands
3 Interior Dry Plateau
4 Columbia Mountains
5 Rocky Mountains
6 Northern Coast Mountains
7 Northern Interior Plateaux and Mountains
8 Mackenzie Mountains
9 Northern Yukon R

INTERIOR PLAINS

10 Mackenzie Delta
11 Northern Boreal Plains
12 Southern Boreal Plains and Plateaux
13 Prairie Grasslands
14 Manitoba Lowlands

CANADIAN SHIELD

15 Tundra Hills
16 Central Tundra Region
17 Northwestern Boreal Uplands
18 Central Boreal Uplands
19 (a) West Great Lakes-St. Lawrence Precambrian Region
   (b) Great Cenral Lakes-St.Lawrence Precambrian Region
   (c) East Great Lakes-St. Lawrence Precambrian Region
20 Laurentian Boreal Highlands
21 East Coast Boreal Region
22 Boreal Lake Plateau
23 Whale River Region
24 Northern Labrador Mountains
25 Ungava Tundra Plateau
26 Northern Davis Region

HUDSON BAY LOWLANDS

27 Hudson-James Lowlands
28 Southampton Plain

ST. LAWRENCE LOWLANDS

29 West St. Lawrence Lowland
   Central St.Lawrence Lowland
   East St. Lawrence Lowland

APPALACHIAN

30 Notre Dame-Megantic Mountains
31 Maritime Acadian Highlands
32 Maritime Plain
33 Atlantic Coast Uplands
34 Western Newfoundland Island Highlands
35 Eastern Newfoundland Island Atlantic Region

ARCTIC LOWLANDS

36 Western Arctic Lowlands
37 Eastern Arctic Lowlands

HIGH ARCTIC ISLANDS

38 Western High Arctic Region
39 Eastern High Arctic Glacier Region

Figure 5.2 National parks' natural regions showing degree of representation.

1. Quality of natural region representation
2. Exceptional natural features
3. Cultural heritage features
4. Provincial/territorial government priorities
5. Opportunities for outdoor recreation
6. Accessibility
7. Educational value
8. Competing incompatible land uses
9. Actual and potential threats to the environment
10. Presence of other protected areas (e.g. provincial parks)
11. Land ownership
12. The implications of Aboriginal land claims and treaties
13. Potential for sustainable tourism development
14. National and local public support (Environment Canada 1990, 7).

In the feasibility step, consultations are held with provincial or territorial governments and with the public. In this step, alternative land uses are considered, as well as the feasibility of long-term protection as a national park. If a national park is not feasible, then other NACs in the region are considered.

The fourth step in establishing a new national park involves the transfer of the park lands from a provincial or territorial government to the federal government. A federal-provincial agreement is negotiated, which may involve the following considerations:

1. Final park boundaries
2. Cost-sharing for land acquisition
3. Timing of land transfer
4. Conditions under which traditional renewable resource harvesting may be allowed to continue
5. Co-operation in park planning and management
6. Regional integration
7. Economic benefits (Environment Canada 1990, 8).

Once these negotiations have been completed, the final step is to pass federal legislation establishing the new park. This allows the application of the National Parks Act, national parks policy, and various regulations (see Chapter 4) to the new park. For new national parks that involve the resolution of a Native land claim, a national park reserve is established until the land claim is resolved. Usually, traditional subsistence hunting, trapping, and fishing may continue during this period. Final park boundaries are confirmed when land claims are concluded.

It is clear from this discussion that the major rationale behind the systems plan has more to do with conservation than recreation or tourism (Dearden and Gardner 1989). Nevertheless it is important to note that actual decisions about the location and boundaries of national parks involve public debate as well as the systems plan.

The objective of the parks systems plan is to establish at least one national park in each natural region. As of 1991, 21 of the 39 natural terrestrial regions are represented by at least one national park. The most significant gaps are in the Northwest Territories, where seven regions are not represented, and in Quebec, where four regions are not represented (Figure 5.2).

This plan for Canada's landmass is paralleled by a marine systems plan discussed elsewhere in this volume (Chapter 14). The National Marine Parks Policy (Environment Canada 1986b) defines 29 natural marine regions, based on an analysis of the oceanographic, physiographic, and biological features of Canada's marine environment (Figure 5.3). The marine parks system has hardly begun; only one of 29 regions has an operational national marine

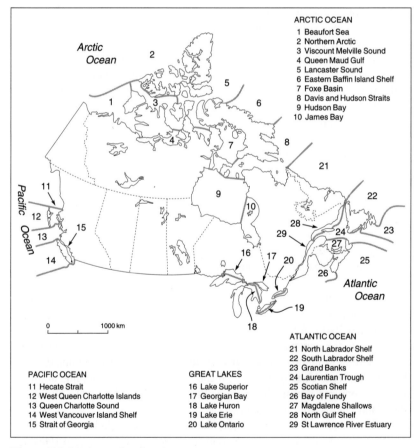

Figure 5.3 Marine natural regions.

park, Fathom Five in Lake Huron (Environment Canada Parks Service 1990). However, with the marine components of Pacific Rim National Park, Saguenay Marine Park, and South Moresby/Gwaii Hanaas National Marine Park Reserve, a total of five natural marine regions will be represented.

Direction Provided by National Park Policy

The national park policy identifies many of the critical considerations in the selection of new national parks, as follows:

1. The area must have experienced minimum modification by man or, if significant modification has occurred, it must have potential for restoration to a natural state.
2. The area will be of a size and configuration so as to:
   a) include a definable ecological unit(s) whose long term protection is feasible; and
   b) offer opportunities for public understanding and enjoyment; and
   c) result in minimum long term disruption of the social and economic life in the surrounding region; and
   d) exclude existing permanent communities.
3. The government of Canada will own all land and resources within national parks (Ministry of Environment 1979, 38–9).

These considerations are consistent with details described in the systems plan. Most important, these policies indicate that just because some natural areas are unrepresented does not mean that any area will be selected. While an area may contain features and processes representative of a natural region, it may fail to meet other criteria, such as being unimpaired in its natural qualities. Consequently, some areas which might fill gaps in regional representation can be rejected, even if there is public and provincial support for the designation of a new park.

Strict application of the criteria for selection would likely mean that no new national parks would ever be established in Canada's settled zones, particularly near major cities, as these areas are likely to be too disturbed to meet the policy selection criteria for national parks. In fact most parks are at a considerable distance from heavily settled areas (Burton 1976; Kreutzwiser 1989).

In addition, there are other less obvious criteria for selection of national parks during provincial or federal considerations of park proposals. For instance, national park policy states that national parks must be owned outright by the federal government. According to the Canadian Constitution and subsequent legislation, natural resources (land and minerals) fall exclusively under the jurisdiction of the provincial or territorial governments (Craig Brown 1968). This means that for any new national park to be established, the province or territory in question must agree to turn over the park area and all its resources in perpetuity to the federal government. Given the thorny history of federal-provincial relations, particularly in economic planning, provincial governments are traditionally extremely reluctant to surrender territory to the federal government. This explains why it has been somewhat easier for the federal government to establish new national parks in the Yukon and Northwest Territories in recent years.

The national park policy falls short of defining a minimum size for a national park, but a clear statement of ecological criteria is provided. In the past, many national parks have been established without considering such ecological specifics as watersheds or the range requirements of some important species (e.g. grizzly bears). The result is that park boundaries often do not include enough land to guarantee minimal protection. As Chapter 3 states, land-use practices in the areas surrounding a park are critical to the ecology of the park. Even when a park is very extensive, embracing all apparent ecological criteria, it is debatable how well such a reserve can function without a compatible conservation strategy in nearby territories. Further, while many conservation advocates have proposed the use of national parks as instruments for the management of watersheds (as at Nahanni National Park Reserve), industry and government often view the national park policy as too inflexible and too permanent a commitment for such a purpose. Other approaches, such as UNESCO's Man and the Biosphere Program, are discussed in Chapter 15.

MANAGING NATIONAL PARKS

Natural Resource Management

The principles of resource management in parks and protected areas are discussed in Chapter 9. What follows is a discussion of the national park policy (Ministry of Environment 1979) on this issue. The policy states (p. 41) that:

1. National parks are special areas which are protected by federal legislation from all forms of extractive resource use such as mining, forestry, agriculture, oil, gas and hydroelectric development and sport hunting.
2. In some new national parks, however, certain traditional resource uses by local residents may be allowed to continue ... [and] ... it is also essential that ... Parks Canada honour the treaties of Indian people which in some cases may involve hunting, fishing and trapping rights in national parks.

This latter approach to resource management is well developed in several of the northern parks that have been established in concert with the resolution of Native land claims. Such initiatives, however, have been strongly resisted in most of the national parks south of 60°, with the notable exceptions of

Pukaskwa and South Moresby/Gwaii Hanaas. This resistance may be attributed to the unofficial scepticism of federal bureaucrats about the ability of Native peoples to manage sustainable harvesting, or the perception of unfairness if non-Natives do not have the same privileges of hunting and trapping in national parks. (See Chapter 12 for further discussion of these issues.)

The policy also states (p. 41) that:

3. Manipulation of naturally occurring processes such as fire, insects and disease may take place only after monitoring has shown that:
    i) there may be serious adverse effects on neighbouring lands; or
    ii) public health or safety is threatened; or
    iii) major park facilities are threatened; or
    iv) natural processes have been altered by man and manipulation is required to restore the natural balance; or
    v) a major natural control is absent from the park; or
    vi) the continued existence of a plant or animal species, which is rare or endangered or which is critical to representation of the natural region, is threatened by a natural cause such as insects or disease; or
    vii) the population of an animal species or stage of plant succession which has been prescribed in the objectives for a park, cannot be maintained by natural forces.

Clearly, this list of exceptions is so large that, in fact, managers have considerable latitude to make management decisions that amount to interfering with natural processes. For example, virtually any naturally occurring forest fire could be perceived as a risk to visitors, park facilities, or nearby property. A manager could therefore justify actions geared at fire suppression on a large scale, even though such actions would interfere with natural processes.

For reporting, the policy (p. 42) states that:

4. All developments, plans and management activities occurring on national park lands, including those proposed by agencies other than Parks Canada, will be subject to an assessment and review process which ensures that the environmental implications are fully considered in decision-making. The process used will be consistent with the Federal Environmental Assessment and Review Process.

Adherence with the EARP protocol with proposed developments in national parks provides for public disclosure and debate concerning any likely impact that may result from development.

5. A zoning system for national parks will consist of five types of zones, reflecting resource conservation priorities and levels of visitor impact tolerated:
    i) Zone I—Special Preservation. Specific areas or features which deserve special preservation because they contain or support unique, rare or endangered features or the best examples of natural features. Access

and use will be strictly controlled or may be prohibited altogether. No motorized access or man-made facilities will be permitted.

ii) Zone II—Wilderness. Extensive areas which are good representations of each of the natural history themes of the park and which will be maintained in a wilderness state. Only certain activities requiring limited primitive visitor facilities appropriate to a wilderness experience will be allowed. Limits will be placed on numbers of users. No motorized access will be permitted. Management actions will ensure that visitors are dispersed.

iii) Zone III—Natural Environment. Areas that are maintained as natural environments and which can sustain, with a minimum of impairment, a selected range of low-density outdoor activities with a minimum of related facilities. Non-motorized access will be preferred. Access by public transit will be permitted. Controlled access by private vehicles will only be permitted where it has been traditionally allowed in the past.

iv) Zone IV—Outdoor Recreation. Limited areas that can accommodate a broad range of education, outdoor recreation opportunities and related facilities in ways that respect the natural landscape and that are safe and convenient. Motorized access will be permitted and may be separated from non-motorized access.

v) Zone V—Park Services. Towns and visitor centres in certain existing national parks which contain a concentration of visitor services and support facilities as well as park administration functions. Motorized access will be permitted.

These zones represent different levels of environmental sensitivity or importance, each with a different toleration for visitor use, to be paralleled by different management prescriptions. It is important to note however, that this zoning system does not really define the different types of recreation opportunities needed to manage people in national parks. This issue is taken up in the next section dealing with visitor management.

Threats to the ecological integrity of national parks can be defined as 'internal' or 'external'. Internal threats are those arising from visitor use or management actions, addressed in the following section dealing with visitor management. External threats originate outside a park boundary.

Common internal threats include the effects of camping and hiking on vegetation, soils, water quality, and wildlife, and such management decisions as the early suppression of natural forest fires. As the result of fire suppression policies, some forests have reached a stage of overmaturity in which they are extremely vulnerable to disease, insects, and devastating forest fires. This practice not only affects successional patterns but may also result in the buildup of fuel that will dramatically increase the severity of fires when they occur.

External threats include the introduction of mercury pollution, pesticides, acid rain, and the like, and are now seen to be one of the most serious sources of trouble for parks. Much of this literature has been reviewed and synthesized by Dearden and Doyle (1990). One complex example of an external threat is that of Wood Buffalo National Park, where the existing herd of hybrid bison (woods bison crossed with plains bison) carries bovine tuberculosis and brucellosis. Local ranchers and farmers worry that this herd will transmit these diseases to their livestock. One proposed solution is to eliminate all the diseased animals, but such a drastic course of action may irrevocably reduce the herd's gene pool (Canadian Environmental Advisory Council 1991, 53).

Since each park varies substantially from all other parks in the system, these policies serve only as guidelines for managers. The detailed interpretation and application of policies at the park level is developed in a Natural Resource Management Plan (NRMP) prepared by the Canadian Parks Service for each park. A summary of the NRMP is usually provided in the management plan for each park. The National Parks Act now states that a management plan must be prepared and presented to the House of Commons within five years of park establishment and reviewed at five-year intervals.

Visitor Management

Visitor management strategies are clearly described in legislation and policy. As discussed earlier, the use of national parks is guided by the principle of leaving them 'unimpaired for future generations'. The national park policy goes on to state (p. 43) that 'impairment by overuse, improper use, and inappropriate development must be avoided. As a general guideline, simplicity in facilities and self reliance on the part of visitors will be encouraged.'

How, then, can we reconcile policy with the facilities found in Banff and Jasper? The policy on towns (p. 45) states that:

1. Existing towns (Banff and Jasper) will be limited to the boundaries established by legislation; and
2. No new towns will be developed within national parks.

This policy views townsites as anomalies within the park system. The problem is how to manage existing townsites such as Banff, Jasper, and Village Lake Louise. The Canadian Park Service is under constant pressure to permit more growth and development in these sites. Further, their continued existence in very conspicuous locations creates a public perception that towns are meant to be part of the national park experience.

With regard to any new structures in national parks, the policy states (p. 44) that:

1. The scale, site, form, and character ... will be as unobtrusive as possible so that park architecture is in harmony with the natural surroundings. Further, essential facilities and services within national parks will normally be grouped together in visitor centres for public convenience, energy conservation and protection of park resources.

2. Within national parks, preference will be given to basic accommodation facilities such as campgrounds, hostels and shelters which enhance visitors' appreciation and enjoyment of the parks' natural values.

Once again there is considerable evidence that standards for park structures vary considerably. For example, some back-country areas have huts, shelters, lodges, developed campgrounds, and trail systems. Others are totally devoid of trails and buildings (Environment Canada 1986). Although all Canadians are invited to visit national parks, their mode of transportation will be limited in order to protect park resources, as follows: 'non-motorized means of transportation will be used in national parks wherever feasible. Where motorized transportation is required, preference will be given to public transportation' (Ministry of Environment 1979, 44).

The zoning system outlined in the previous section was developed as a way to protect park resources from indiscriminate use by park visitors. Clearly Zone I (Special Preservation) is the most restrictive, whereas Zones IV (Outdoor Recreation) and Zone V (Park Services) are the least. This system has been very effective in resource protection but has been found to be less ideal in defining and promoting appropriate visitor experiences. It conveys a message of restriction rather than opportunity. Further, few visitors are even aware that a zoning system exists in national parks and so cannot appreciate why the same facilities and services are not provided in all parts of a park.

With these concerns in mind, the Canadian Parks Service developed a specific visitor management strategy, the Visitor Activity Management Process (VAMP). VAMP is aimed at better understanding visitor needs, and providing and promoting appropriate facilities and services (Graham, Nilsen, and Payne 1988: see also Chapter 10). The process begins by defining specific visitor groups for a particular national park. Some types of visitor groups may be excluded at this stage. For example, people wanting to stay at a resort will not be encouraged to visiting Pukaskwa National Park because the management plan for Pukaskwa expressly states that resort facilities will not be provided in the park. Next, the strategy examines visitors' needs at each stage of their trip: at home, en route to the park, arriving in the park, during their stay in the park, leaving the park, and at the end of the trip. Appropriate information and other services and facilities are provided at each of these stages. An extension of VAMP is the monitoring of visitor needs and levels of satisfaction, now routinely undertaken through park surveys.

One aspect of the service provided to park visitors is facilitating visitor understanding, appreciation, and enjoyment of national park resources. While people can and do visit national parks without being aware of their special or unique natural features, the Canadian Parks Service is committed to helping the visitor experience and appreciate the park resources through such features as visitor centres, information signs, guided walks, evening programs in campgrounds, and printed brochures. As Butler describes in Chapter 11, park interpretation is also a way of conveying management policies to the visitor and promoting the objectives of the management agency.

The purpose of this chapter has been to examine national park policy and the systems plan for parks. Policy and legislation provide direction to the Canadian Parks Service in managing the national parks and provide for the Canadian public a framework for debating the purpose and rationale for various management actions. To fully understand how national parks are managed, we must, however, also understand the management culture: the bureaucracy of the Canadian Parks Service.

Jurisdiction

There is no collective Canada-wide policy for parks or environmental conservation equivalent to the national health policy. All levels of government (federal, provincial, regional, and local) operate park systems in Canada. With national parks, authority for park management emanates from the National Park Act. This Act gives clear authority to the minister of Environment. The minister, the director of the Canadian Parks Service, each park superintendent, and park wardens are cited in the legislation and are all involved in some way with the routine responsibilities of managing each park, regulating activities, leases, licenses, camping permits and so on. The assistant deputy minister (ADM), of course, has considerable authority, although this is not mentioned in national parks legislation.

While the National Park Act and the national park policy provide general direction and authority, most of the day-to-day management decisions in the park are directed by regulations passed as Orders in Council pursuant to the Act. Regulations have been developed for the following kinds of management activities: camping, domestic animals, fire protection, fishing; garbage, aircraft landings, highway traffic, timber and fire management, wildlife, licensing commercial activities, and so on.

Submission to Central Agencies

Although the Canadian Parks Service has sole jurisdiction over national parks, park managers are by no means completely autonomous. The Canadian Parks Service must also take direction from central agencies, including the Treasury Board, on such areas as program expenditures, personnel policies, and the management of real estate.

Like virtually all federal agencies, the Canadian Parks Service employs staff in financial administration, material management, and personnel administration to interpret and advise on these centrally conceived federal government policies. They provide constant management advice based on these policies and the underlying principles of economy, efficiency, effectiveness, and value for money.

Financial Management

The Canadian Parks Service manages its annual allocation on the basis of work plans and multi-year operational plans. In any given year, the Canadian Parks Service managers prepare or implementing over 9,000 capital projects such as the construction of visitor centres, parking lots, and new trails. Often these projects entail a total budget in the realm of a $100 million. Because park needs are inexhaustible and available funding is constrained, many projects and bright ideas cannot be funded. Decisions on operational funding and staff scheduling operations are made within each region and park and, at present, are less closely monitored nationally. Revenue management has been given special emphasis since 1984, but although park revenues have significantly increased, these revenues are turned over to Treasury Board. Subsequent budgets then are at the discretion of Parliament.

Decentralized Organization

The chief organizing principle of the Canadian Parks Service is decentralization. Program headquarters are based in Hull, Que., near Ottawa, but five regional offices, each headed by a director-general reporting to the ADM have been established: Western Region (head office in Calgary), Prairie Region and the north (Winnipeg), Ontario Region (Cornwall), Quebec Region (Quebec City), and Atlantic Region (Halifax).

Regionalism is intended to bring the parks closer to the public by maintaining a visible presence in each region of the country rather than locating the entire bureaucracy and decision making apparatus in Ottawa. These regional offices carry out park planning, and provide operational and developmental support to the parks.

Toward Greater Accountability

One of the most significant recent developments in the management of national parks is the increased level of accountability reflected in the 1988 amendments to the National Parks Act. Most of the originally proposed revisions (with the exception of the proposal to legislate park wilderness) were conceived as housekeeping measures: to stiffen fines for poaching, to limit the size of existing townsites and ski hills, and to eliminate some old provisions such as the authority to establish utility corridors in national parks. To the surprise of all watchers, the amended Act went much further. It required the minister to report to Parliament every two years on the state of the parks. This report shows progress towards completion of the systems plan, the state of protection of park resources, and the state of service to the public.

The bill's emphasis on ecological integrity implies a much higher level of stewardship than the notion of keeping the parks 'unimpaired for future generations'. This approach highlights the ecological priority of national parks and suggests some dissatisfaction with past performance. Taken as a whole, these changes gave renewed emphasis to ministerial accountability for managing national parks.

Renewed government and departmental emphasis on accords and partnerships with a wide variety of groups will also strengthen the public hand (or at least, the concerns of special interest groups) in national parks. National agreements have been signed with several groups, notably universities, some professional associations (like Interpretation Canada, an association of professional naturalists), and groups promoting access to parks for the disabled.

The national parks are entering a new era of shared decision making, not mere consultation. Any informed observer watching the negotiations for establishing a marine park in Quebec, or the South Moresby National Park, or parks in the north, can quickly see a contrast with the earlier model of authoritarian establishment practised in, for example, the establishment of Gros Morne National Park.

Multi-disciplinary Management Support and Reviews

Supporting this simple management structure is a complex interdisciplinary process of park management advice. It relies on staff for expertise in (among others) geography, biology, forestry, ecology, history, archaeology, planning, recreation, interpretation, sociology, economics, architecture, engineering, Native affairs, marketing, and visitor management. Each speciality has its own bias as well as specialized knowledge.

Among the best examples of this multi-disciplinary work is the process of planning park management and natural resources management. Park management plans take national direction and, following public consultation, apply it to individual parks. They thereby give an occasion every few years to consider the role and purpose of individual parks, to review park objectives, and to reassess park heritage values in the light of biophysical and socioeconomic situations.

CONCLUSION

Public opinion polls suggest that the Canadian public supports the concept of protecting wilderness and natural settings, yet the public appears to have little understanding of the special role and function of the national park system. This confusion can be attributed to conspicuous park practices that are inconsistent with current thinking about national park management, such as the existence of a townsite in Banff or logging operations in Wood Buffalo (now declared illegal and halted as a result of a lawsuit sponsored by the Canadian Parks and Wilderness Society). Furthermore, the debates over the scale of tourism development in the four mountain parks (Jasper, Banff, Yoho, Kootenay) illustrate the tension that exists between use and conservation of national parks.

This chapter also examined the process of determining where new parks should be located and how many are needed. The systems plan for national parks addresses this issue in a logical, easily understood manner. Notwithstanding the success of the endangered spaces campaign (Hummel 1989) in raising public awareness concerning wilderness protection, or the promises of Canada's Green Plan, the system of national parks is far from complete, particularly with regard to marine national parks.

A related issue is the size and configuration of national parks. No commitment has been made in defining a minimum size for national parks, although policy guidelines specify that new parks must contain definable ecological units whose long-term protection is feasible. In practice, many parks fail to meet this criterion. Pacific Rim illustrates this issue, in the debates over the protection of the critical Carmanah and Walbran watersheds, which are not within park boundaries.

Concerns about the management of natural resources in national parks are addressed both in legislation and in the National Park Policy. Ecological integrity is a major criterion guiding the management and planning of national parks, but visitor use and tourism are intricately bound up with it. Furthermore, the 1989 Auditor General's report comments that 'competing priorities have prevented the allocation of sufficient financial and other resources to national park resource conservation programs, resulting in many breaches of resource protection policy' (Canadian Environmental Advisory Council 1991).

Management of visitor use in national parks has been strongly criticized in the past (Fuller 1977), but the current policy seems to have addressed many of these concerns. The identification and development of appropriate visitor opportunities in national parks has become more sophisticated. Nevertheless, a Canadian Parks Service study concludes that both tourism and transboundary pollution are major issues still facing national parks (Canadian Environmental Advisory Council 1991).

The structures of decision making in the national parks system have been the source of past problems. Decision making—what actually occurs in national parks—must deal with two realities: the policy and legislation described in this chapter, and conservation science, discussed in other chapters. Each national park needs to be scrutinized for consistency with parks policy and legislation. Many national parks still fail to adhere to significant elements of park policy. Moreover, the parks policy itself needs to be scrutinized in terms of new developments in conservation science. Finally, the public needs to be apprised of the decision making process, so that it can affect decisions in a meaningful way.

ACKNOWLEDGEMENTS

Special thanks to Gary Sealey of the Canadian Parks Service for comments and suggestions on an earlier draft of this chapter.

REFERENCES

Bella, L.
1987   *Parks For Profit*, Harvest House, Montreal.
Burton, T.L.
1976   *Making Man's Environment Leisure*, Van Reinhold, Toronto.
Canadian Environmental Advisory Council
1991   *A Protected Areas Vision For Canada*, Supply and Services Canada, Toronto.
Clark, R.N., and G.H. Stankey
1979   *The Recreation Opportunity Spectrum: A Framework For Planning, Management, and Research*, USDA Forest Service General Technical Report PNW-98.
Craig Brown, R.
1968   'The Doctrine of Usefulness: Natural Resource and National Park Policy in Canada, 1987–1914', in *Canadian Parks in Perspective*, ed. J.G. Nelson, Harvest House, Montreal, 46–62.
Dearden, P.
1987   'Mobilizing Public Support For Environment: The Case of South Moresby Island, British Columbia', in *Need-to-Know: Effective Communication For Environmental Groups, Proceedings of the 1987 Annual Joint Meeting of the Public Advisory Committees to the Environmental Council of Alberta*, Environment Council of Alberta, 62–75.
Dearden, P., and L. Berg
1993   'Canadian National Parks: A Model of Administrative Penetration', *Canadian Geographer*, in press.
Dearden, P., and S. Doyle
1990   *Threats to National Parks: A Review of the Literature*, Canadian Parks Service, Calgary.
Dearden, P., and J.R. Gardner
1987   'Systems Planning For Protected Areas in Canada: A Review of Caucas Candidate Areas and Concepts, Issues and Prospects For Future Investigation', in *Heritage For Tomorrow: Canadian Assembly on National Parks and Protected Areas*, eds R.C. Scace and J.G. Nelson, Environment Canada, Ottawa, Vol. 2, 9–48.
Environment Canada
1986a   *In Trust For Tomorrow: A Management Framework for Mountain Parks*, Supply and Services Canada, Ottawa.

Environment Canada
1986*b* *Marine Park Policy*, Supply and Services Canada, Ottawa.
Environment Canada
1990 *National Parks Systems Plan*, Supply and Services Canada, Ottawa.
Environment Canada, Parks Service
1991 *State of the Parks: 1990 Report*, Supply and Services Canada, Ottawa.
Fuller, W.A.
1977 *Tragedy in Our National Parks*, National and Provincial Parks Association of Canada, Toronto.
Graham, R., P. Nilsen, and J. Payne
1988 'Visitor Management in Canadian National Parks', *Tourism Management* 9: 44–62.
Hammitt, W.E., and C.D. McDonald
1983 'Past On-site Experience and Its Relationship to Managing River Recreation Resources', *Forest Science* 29: 262–6.
Hammitt, W.E., and D.N. Cole
1987 *Wildland Recreation: Ecology and Management*, John Wiley, New York.
Hummell, M.
1989 *Endangered Spaces*, Key Porter Books, Toronto.
Keogh, B.
1989 'Social Impacts', in *Outdoor Recreation in Canada*, ed. G. Wall, John Wiley, Toronto, 231–76.
Kreutzwiser, R.
1989 'Supply', in *Outdoor Recreation in Canada*, ed. G. Wall, John Wiley, Toronto, 19–42.
Lucas, R.C.
1980 *Use Patterns and Visitor Characteristics, Other Wilderness Areas*, USDA Forest Service Research Paper INT-253.
Manning, R.
1986 *Studies in Outdoor Recreation*, Oregon State University Press, Corvallis.
Ministry of Environment
1979 *Parks Canada Policy*, Supply and Services Canada, Ottawa.
Ministry of Environment
1991 *Canadian Parks Service Proposed Policy*, Supply and Services Canada, Ottawa.
National and Historic Sites Branch
1971 *National Parks Systems Planning Manual*, Information Canada, Ottawa.
Rollins, R. and J. Rouse
1992 'Segmenting Backcountry Visitors by Setting Preferences', in *Science and The Management of Protected Areas*, eds J.H.M. Willison *et al.*, Elsevier, New York, 485–97.

CHAPTER 6

The Ontario Park System

Policy and Planning

—

GEORGE PRIDDLE

INTRODUCTION

Until 1954 Ontario had but eight (unclassified) provincial parks. By 1989 there were 270 parks, organized and managed according to sophisticated classification, zoning, and policy guidelines. Unfortunately, this still represents only 6.5 per cent of the Ontario landscape and falls well short of the Canadian Wilderness Charter (Hummel 1989), which envisions 'that the total area of Canada . . . protected comprise at least 12 per cent of the lands and water of Canada as recommended in the World Commission on Environment and Development report *Our Common Future*'.

The basic reason for establishing provincial parks has not fundamentally changed. Protection, recreation, heritage appreciation, and tourism are the objectives of the current provincial park system. These were the same reasons that were evoked in the 1880s for setting aside the first provincial parks in Ontario: Victoria Park, Algonquin Park, and Rondeau. Elsewhere in this volume (Chapter 4) Eagles has discussed the legislative and policy background to Ontario's provincial parks in more detail.

After the Second World War, rapid population growth and dramatic increases in the standard of living and mobility in North America produced an explosion in outdoor recreation. A massive demand for beaches, campsites, and access to natural areas resulted. The Ontario government responded by developing a network of provincial parks along the shorelines of the Great Lakes and at regular intervals along the northern tourism highways.

In response to these developments, environmental organizations began insisting on the need to protect natural areas as well to provide for outdoor recreation. The Federation of Ontario Naturalists, the Quetico Foundation, the Conservation Council of Ontario, and the Algonquin Wildlands League all joined the call. Throughout the 1960s tensions grew between the recreation, protection, and utilitarian emphases in parks policy. Conflicts surfaced between canoeists and motorboaters, between hunters and naturalists. Towards the end of the decade a major struggle developed between preservationists and loggers in Algonquin, Quetico, Killarney, and Lake Superior parks. Environmental groups like the Algonquin Wildlands League, the National and Provincial Park Association, and the Sierra Club of Ontario became forces to be reckoned with (Hackman 1989). These groups were able to galvanize the people of Ontario on the side of environmental protection.

In 1967 the Ontario government adopted a park classification system. The system recognized that there were different types of parks and that not all parks could be all things to all people. The system divided the parks along a continuum from highly protected natural resources to highly developed recreational parks. The forest industry resisted attempts to reclassify Algonquin, Quetico, Killarney, and Lake Superior as primitive parks. The result was a remarkable public crusade for the wilderness between 1968 and 1974 (Killan, forthcoming). The balance had shifted.

By 1978 the provincial Cabinet had approved a new parks policy, the Blue Book, a manual that provided a rationale for each class of park, details on how many of each type of park Ontario required, and specified activities permitted and not permitted for each zone and class (Ontario Ministry of Natural Resources [OMNR] 1978). According to Killan the Blue Book was highly touted by environmentalists and became known as 'the gospel relating to parks' (Killan, forthcoming).

The Blue Book develops a useful model for evaluating the provincial parks system as it now exists, as well as suggesting the needs and priorities that must be realized to have an effective park system in the future. The Blue Book contains a section for each type of park in the system: natural reserves, wilderness areas, natural environment parks, recreation parks, provincial waterways, and historical parks. These six types of parks are considered to be the components of a provincial park system. For each type of park, the following elements are defined:

1. The history, philosophy, and purpose of that particular type of park and a basic policy statement;
2. The relationship of that particular classification type to the overall park system and an approach towards determining the needs and locations for that park type, with an implicit method for actually evaluating an existing or proposed park in terms of that type of classification; and
3. Management considerations, in terms of planning, zoning, land and water management, forest and vegetation management, and fish and wildlife management, with consideration also given to visitor programs and to scientific research, and educational and cultural programs.

PARK TYPES

Nature Reserves

The basic philosophy underlying nature reserves is to preserve representative landforms and genetic materials. Nature reserves are seen as performing six major functions:

1. To preserve the original natural genetic materials found in Ontario;
2. To represent the geological and natural processes which have shaped the province;
3. To serve as benchmark areas against which to measure environmental conditions and change;
4. To contribute to scientific knowledge and to society through the application of this knowledge;
5. To provide for outdoor educational opportunities for individuals, groups, and institutions at all levels; and
6. To perform a recreative role for leisure activities.

The place of nature reserves in the park system is shown in Figure 6.1.

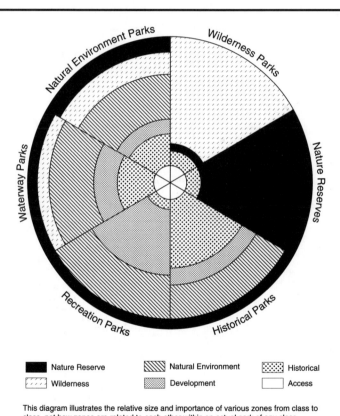

	Nature Reserve		Natural Environment		Historical
	Wilderness		Development		Access

This diagram illustrates the relative size and importance of various zones from class to class, not how zones are related to each other within an actual park of any class.

The absence of a particular zone within a class indicates that the zone in question is not compatible within the class.

Figure 6.1 How classes and zones are related within the Ontario parks system.

Angus Hill's site-region methodology (Hill 1990) provides a systematic approach for determining the representative landscape needed within the nature reserve program (Figure 6.2). It assumes that, through the systematic identification and representation of 150 potential vegetation types within each site region, the zoological elements will be effectively represented as well. The 150 vegetative site types are based on a 15-by-10 matrix of variables

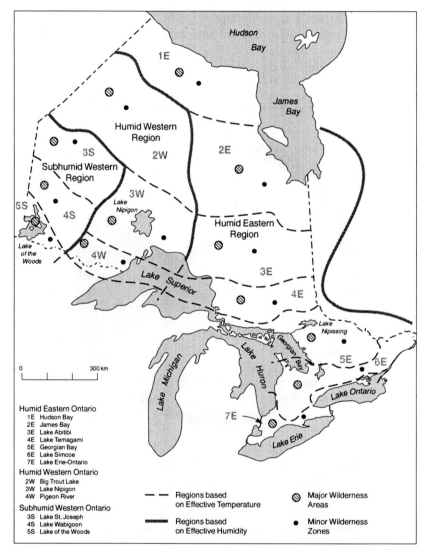

Figure 6.2 Map illustrating the site regions of Ontario and a theoretical distribution of wilderness areas.

that considers the moisture regime along one axis and microclimatic and substrate materials on the other axis. The method includes earth sciences by considering regional classifications of bedrock geology, geomorphology, and chronostratigraphy.

All nature reserves should have a management plan. Nature reserve zones would form the largest part of nature reserve parks. Furthermore, the Blue Book proposes two subclasses: *strict natural areas* would protect nature in an undisturbed state, whereas *managed nature areas* would be used to protect a species, a group of species, a biotic community, or physical features when these require special protection. *Wilderness zones* could exist for forms of recreation that would not in any way jeopardize the existence of individual animals, plants, and landforms.

The Blue Book discusses management in terms of the limited kinds of human activity that would be permitted, and under what conditions. The need for preservation is seen as paramount in nature reserves. The reserves are smaller than wilderness parks, and recreational considerations are not a high priority in their selection.

Wilderness Parks

The policy states that 'Wilderness Parks are substantial areas, where the forces of nature are permitted to function freely and where visitors travel by non-mechanised means and experience expansive solitude, challenge and personal integration with nature' (Ontario Ministry of Natural Resources 1978, Wi-1-3). Hill's 13 major site regions (Hill 1968) are again seen as the basis for establishing a system of wilderness areas (Figure 6.2). Each site region is an area of relatively uniform climate and represents an area of particular biological character. The relationship of wilderness areas to other components of the provincial park system is indicated in Figure 6.1.

Selection of areas to be set aside as wilderness parks is based on recreational, ecological, and historical criteria. Wilderness parks contain the greatest possible diversity of special and representative earth- and life-science features. The physiographic and ecological integrity of prospective areas is an important consideration. These parks are also supposed to contain the greatest possible diversity of heritage resources, and to be able to provide low-intensity isolated recreational experiences.

The size of a potential wilderness park is one crucial criterion. The average size for a major wilderness area is 247,000 acres (100,000 ha). The absolute minimum size should be not less than 124,000 acres (59,000 ha). This figure is based primarily on recreational considerations. The plan assumes that the average wilderness trip is 81 km (six days averaging 12–15 km/day) and that the trip is usually a loop through the area. Minimum and average park areas are computed both on the basis of circular trips and on the need to provide a buffer of up to 5 km around the perimeters of the park to protect the area from intrusive influences.

Four types of zones can be found in a wilderness park: wilderness, nature reserves, historical reserves, and access zones (Figure 6.1). Wilderness zones include the wilderness landscape of the park as well as a protective buffer. Access zones serve as staging areas with minimum facilities and services. Nature reserve zones are areas within the park requiring special protection, due to the presence of rare, unique, or endangered species or features. Historical zones contain any significant historical feature requiring special management attention.

In terms of resource management, the Blue Book states that: all lands in private ownership within the park are to be acquired; physical improvements will be removed; no leases will be issued; mining activity will be prohibited; and commercial timber harvesting will not be permitted. Native plants may be re-established when necessary. Natural fires may be allowed to burn depending on the management plan, and prescribed burns could also be used. Forest disease and insect management will be established in each master plan. Primitive hunting for sport might be allowed in some wilderness parks, whereas commercial trapping would be phased out. The basic objectives of fisheries management will be to provide a self-sustaining native population, and therefore stocking streams with sport fish will not be allowed. Fish should be caught and released and live bait would not be allowed.

Recreation management in wilderness parks is guided by the principle that the impact of humans ought to be unnoticeable. Therefore, the only means of travel is by non-mechanical means such as canoe. The wilderness experience is different from other outdoor experience, and so efforts are made both to limit group size and the number of visitors and to disperse people within wilderness zones.

In summary, the approach to management of wilderness parks in Ontario approximates the biocentric perspective articulated by Hendee *et al.* (1990, 19): the 'principal goal is to encourage management programs that most nearly approximate the natural energy flows within a wilderness ecosystem as they existed in the absence of human influence.'

Natural Environment Parks

Natural environment parks are seen as multiple-use parks. Sleeping Giant, Rondeau, and the new Frontenac Park are examples that would be classified as natural environment parks. The Blue Book envisages a system of such parks based on Hill's 65 site districts (Figures 6.3 and 6.4), with four major purposes:

1. To provide day-use and camping opportunities for recreation in a natural setting;
2. To preserve and maintain representative elements of Ontario's earth- and life-science features for scientific research and educational purposes;

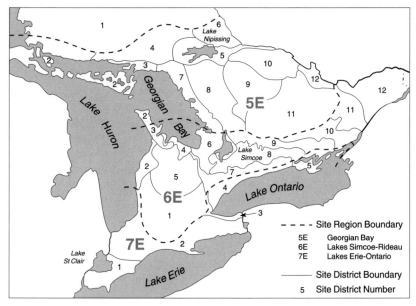

Figure 6.3 Theoretical distribution model for natural environment parks in Southern Ontario based upon natural heritage values.

3. To protect and maintain provincially significant prehistoric and historical resources for scientific and educational purposes, when these are found in conjunction with outstanding natural and outdoor recreational resources; and

4. To contribute to the economy of Ontario through tourism and its related industries.

A theoretical distribution map for natural environment parks in northern and southern Ontario is shown in Figure 6.3.

The Blue Book provides site evaluation methodology: to the extent possible, areas designated as natural environment parks in each site district will incorporate significant natural, cultural, and recreational features. All natural environment parks should contain at least one provincially significant feature. Six possible zones can exist in a natural environment park: nature reserve, wilderness area, access, development, natural environment, and historical reserves.

Resource management would be the same in nature reserve zones as in wilderness area zones (see above). In development and natural environment zones, water could be managed to enhance recreational opportunities and commercial forestry could be allowed if it enhanced the environmental and educational objectives. Similarly, agricultural practices such as tilling and

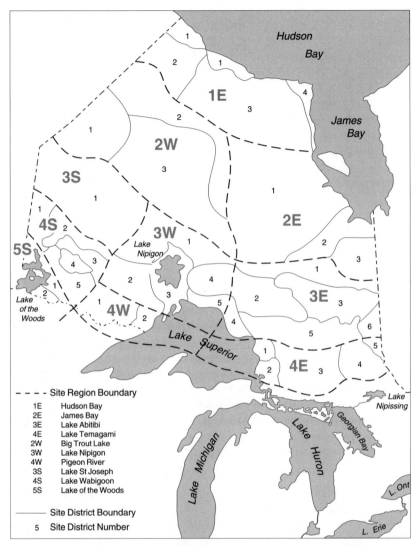

Figure 6.4 Theoretical distribution model for natural environment parks in Northern Ontario based upon natural heritage values.

grazing could be permitted. Fires would be extinguished immediately except in nature reserves and wilderness zones.

Stocking sport fish would be allowed in the development and natural environment zones. Motorboating would be limited to 10-hp engines and to designated waters. Snowmobiling and trailbike riding could take place in designated corridors.

Natural environment parks would in many cases be seen as wilderness areas by many park visitors. Algonquin Park and Lake Superior Park have a natural environment designation and yet provide a wilderness experience for a great many people. A natural environment park is a multiple-use park where resource extraction, be it logging or hunting, is allowed if it is perceived not to subvert natural and recreational values.

Recreation Parks

Recreation parks probably represent the most common public perception of what provincial parks are really all about. These are open-space lands that provide recreational opportunities for Ontario residents and visitors. Their total number and geographic location reflects the leisure needs of Ontario residents as well as the vacation trends of tourists. Craigleith on Georgian Bay and Wasaga Beach are examples of recreational parks. One objective of such parks is 'to provide an adequate and equitable distribution of year round, day use outdoor recreation opportunities for Ontario residents'. 'Adequate' is defined as: 'not less than the average per capita supply of outdoor recreation within two hours drive from home as supplied by public outdoor recreation agencies. The average per capita supply of day use outdoor recreation opportunities as measured in southern centres is 2.22.' A second objective of recreation parks is 'to provide an adequate and equitable distribution of camping opportunities for Ontario residents', defined as 'not less than the average per capita supply for camping opportunities within three hours drive from home as supplied by public outdoor recreation agencies. The average per capita supply of camping opportunities as measured in southern centres is 1.18 [visits per person per year].' A third objective of this type of park is 'to contribute to the economy of Ontario through tourism and its related industries'.

Five sub-objectives are used in considering the economic contribution of recreation parks:

1. To assist in the internal distribution of monies throughout the province;
2. To encourage out-of-province expenditure by tourists in selected areas of the province;
3. To provide local employment opportunities;
4. To assist in the development of leisure-related sales and manufacturing industries in the province; and
5. To encourage private recreation development.

The relationship of recreation parks to other components of the park system is shown in Figure 6.1. Not illustrated in this figure is the role of the conservation authorities; but it is recognized in the text of the Blue Book that the recreational facilities of the conservation authorities make a significant contribution in the provision of opportunities for this type of day use and camping. Chapter 4 in this volume describes the role of conservation authorities in greater detail.

In selecting sites for recreation parks, access, physical carrying capacity, and adequacy relative to population distribution are given high consideration. Zoning within recreation parks could include: development, natural environment, nature reserve, historical, and access.

In terms of management, some lands could be leased to (e.g.) food services or golf courses. Water management could involve dam construction and channel building. More native plant species can be used for landscaping. Public hunting opportunities can be provided. The objective of fish management would be to provide a maximum number of fishing opportunities. 'Put-and-take' operations could well be part of such a management strategy.

The selection and management of recreational parks is very much based on the recreational needs of campers and day users. If parks are seen as being on a continuum from extensive wilderness-type parks to places for intensive mechanized recreation such as motor camping and boating, then recreational parks are at the intensive end as far as Ontario's provincial parks are concerned.

Waterway Parks

The idea of waterway parks very much widens the concept of the 'wild river' designation that was established in the 1967 park classification system. Waterway parks are basically seen as three kinds: wild, historical, and recreational. The policy states that 'Waterway Parks incorporate outstanding recreational water routes with representative natural features and historical resources to provide high quality recreational and educational experiences' (Ontario Ministry of Natural Resources 1978, Wa-1-6).

Waterway parks are particularly important to Ontario because of their tremendous historical importance as transportation routes for the First Nations and for voyageurs. The exploration and settlement of Ontario were greatly facilitated by rivers. They also provided a critical source of power in the pre-electric days. In recreational and tourism terms, one of Ontario's big attractions is its rivers and waterways for canoe trips.

In terms of representation, the target is to have all of Hill's 65 site districts represented in waterway parks and heritage rivers. Heritage rivers are covered by federal-provincial agreements. The place of waterways within the system is illustrated in Figure 6.1.

All types of park zoning are theoretically permissible in these parks, but the zones and their proportionate size will vary dramatically depending on whether the waterway is primarily for low-intensity use or for medium- or high-intensity use. Waterway parks are usually linear, consisting of a narrow band of protected shorelines on both sides:

> . . . sufficient to maintain for the waterway user perceptual integrity appropriate to the waterway. This boundary will be determined on the basis of lines of

sight, contiguity of landform and natural and cultural features, and ecological integrity. The boundary shall be not less than 200 m from the shoreline . . . (and) shall normally not exceed 2 km from the shoreline except where nodes exist which include significant natural, cultural, or recreational landscapes or feature which are complementary to the park. (Ontario Ministry of Natural Resources 1978, Wa-111-3)

Management practices resemble those in wilderness parks: non-native species will not be introduced, natural fires will normally be allowed to burn out; and insects and disease will not be controlled. However, commercial fishing and sport hunting may be permitted. Motorized vehicles will not be allowed, and capacity standards may be introduced.

Historical Parks

'Historical Parks are areas selected to represent the distinctive historical resources of the province in an open space setting, and are protected for interpretive, educational and research purposes' (Ontario Ministry of Natural Resources 1978). The aim is to make sure that each of the 13 theme segments of the province's human history is included in the overall park system (Figure 6.5). These themes are not meant to represent all of Ontario's history but only those aspects that can best be represented in their original, outdoor non-urban setting. Historical, development, access, natural environment, and nature reserve zoning can be used in management plans for historical parks.

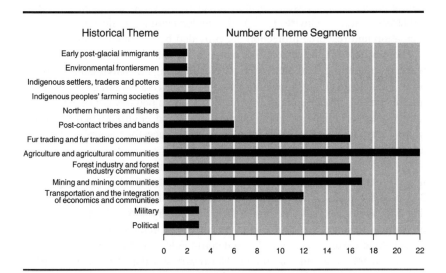

Figure 6.5 Themes and theme segments of Ontario history.

Little has really happened in Ontario with historical parks. At the time park policy was being drafted, the Historical Sites Branch of OMNR was transferred back to the Ministry of Culture and Recreation. Once the historical expertise had left the ministry, it was simply a matter of 'out of sight, out of mind'.

DISCUSSION

The Ontario park classification system resembles the Recreation Opportunity Spectrum (ROS) described by Payne and Graham in Chapter 10. ROS suggests that demand for outdoor recreation settings and experiences can be arranged along a continuum from modern developed campgrounds to primitive settings, where facilities are largely non-existent and visitors are dispersed. Within this ROS framework, Ontario's wilderness parks and nature reserves fall at the primitive end of the spectrum; recreation parks and historic parks would fit on the developed end; and natural environment parks and waterway parks belong in the middle.

The Ontario park policies as described in the Blue Book recognize this diversity in demand for outdoor recreation experiences, as well as the need for a variety of different levels of protection of natural landscapes. The target of representing the 13 site regions and 65 site districts in provincial parks is supported by the conservation community, although the size and configuration of some parks have been questioned.

The notion of wilderness is tackled effectively by the Blue Book. Wilderness is recognized as a unique type of recreation experience as well as a setting where entire ecosystems are protected. Planning and management of wilderness parks in Ontario reflects this understanding, while other forms of recreation and resource protection are provided by the other types of parks.

The real test for the Blue Book came in the late 1970s and early 1980s, when the Ontario government tried to execute comprehensive land-use planning. This exercise was known as Strategic Land Use Planning (SLUP). During this period, timber and mining interests, Native peoples with land claims, tourist operators, fish and game organizations, and environmental organizations were pitted against each other in a hectic race for resources and land allocation.

On 12 March 1982, the 'Report of the Task Force on Parks System Planning' (Ontario Ministry of Natural Resources 1982) was released. It suggested 245 possible parks. This was a reduction; Parks Branch had recommended that 335 additional parks be established. In January 1983, the then minister of Natural Resources, Allan Pope, had all the aforementioned stakeholders meet behind closed doors in order to determine land and resource allocations through negotiating and bargaining. The result was that the list was further whittled down from 245 to 155 candidate parks, many were reduced in size, and some of the management policies of the Blue Book were relaxed. Park management planning was exempted from the Environmental Assessment Act. At the end of 1983, Allan Pope announced the establishment of 150 new parks including the establishment of five new wilderness parks.

By 17 May 1988, the Tory dynasty was gone and the Liberal government, under pressure from park advocates, restored the protectionist essence of the Blue Book. This meant, for example, that such activities as fly-in camps and mineral exploration would not be allowed in wilderness parks.

Much is left to be done. Ontario still has only 6.5 per cent of its land in some kind of protected area status, provincial or federal. Alberta has 10.45 per cent (see Chapter 7) and even the Yukon has 7.9 per cent. Meanwhile in northern Ontario, the loggers are at the 'back of the farm' and will, within 20 years, experience wood shortages, a dramatic drop in demand for newsprint, and likely shortfalls in projected regeneration (Priddle 1991).

System planning for parks is now being totally neglected by the provincial government. Much can be done, for instance, on the two-thirds of the forested land that will probably not go back into commercial forest because of poor regeneration. Several recommendations can be made:

1. The original sizes envisioned for the parks should be reconsidered.
2. Large buffers with limited renewable resource use should be established around nature reserves, wilderness parks, and waterways.
3. The candidate parks that were rejected during the Strategic Land Use Plan and became known as Areas of Natural and Scientific Interest (ANSIS), should be reassessed as candidate parks.
4. Effective policies and management procedures should be established for ANSIS.
5. An honest attempt should be made to assure that at least 12 per cent of Ontario is in some meaningful form of protected area status.
6. Finally, a dramatic increase is needed both in provincial budget and personnel to address these needs.

In the mid-1970s the old Parks Branch in Toronto was well funded and well staffed and represented the best systems planning for parks anywhere in Canada. Since that time, the branch has been decimated in terms of budget and personnel. The result has been very little planning for the overall park system since the development of the Blue Book.

REFERENCES

Hackman, A.
1989   'Ontario's Park System Comes of Age,' *Endangered Spaces: The Future of Canada's Wilderness*, ed. Monte Hummel, Key Porter Books, Toronto.

Hendee, J.C., G.H. Stankey, and B.C. Lucas
  1990   *Wilderness Management*, Fulcrum Press, Golden, Colo.
Hill, G.A.
  1968   'The Physiographic Approach to the Classification of Terrestrial Ecosystems with Respect to Representative Biological Communities', manuscript on file, Provincial Parks Branch, Ontario Ministry of Natural Resources, Toronto.
Killan, G.
  in press *Ontario's Provincial Parks: Towards System and Balance*, Ontario Ministry of Natural Resources, Toronto.
Ontario Ministry of Natural Resources
  1978   *Ontario Provincial Parks Planning & Management Policies*, Government of Ontario, Toronto.
Ontario Ministry of Natural Resources
  1982   *Report of the Task Force on Parks System Planning*, 2 vols, Government of Ontario, Toronto.
Priddle, G.
  1991   'Forest Management in Ontario', in *Ontario: People, Economy and Environment*, ed. B. Mitchell, Waterloo Geography Series, University of Waterloo, Waterloo, Ont., 189–203.
The World Commission on Environment and Development
  1987   *Our Common Future*, Oxford University Press, New York and Oxford.

CHAPTER 7

The Alberta Park System

Policy and Planning

—

GUY S. SWINNERTON

INTRODUCTION

The origins of provincial parks in Canada coincided with the era of the establishment of this country's first national parks towards the end of the 19th century. During the ensuing 100 years, the gradual development of provincial parks has been characterized by an ambiguity of purpose. This ambiguity has largely revolved around the dual mandate of provincial parks: to provide opportunities for outdoor recreation, and to protect the natural heritage on which many of these experiences depend. Although this issue is also part of this country's national parks' legacy (Bella 1987; see also Chapters 2 and 5), the dilemma is even more strongly inherent in provincial parks legislation and practice.

Although provincial parks and other designated protected areas are frequently perceived as the last bastions of natural environments (Kostka 1976), many of these areas have come under increasing pressure to satisfy the demands for resource development and for the possible economic benefits from tourism and recreation (Swinnerton 1989). During the 1980s a number of provinces reassessed the role and function of their parks. This assessment has been evident through the preparation of policy statements and park system plans, as well as by the recognition of parks as components within a mosaic of protected areas. In addition, the preparation of provincial conservation strategies, following the guidelines provided by the World Conservation Strategy (International Union for the Conservation of Nature 1980), has provided a broader framework within which provincial parks should be considered (Swinnerton 1991a, 1991b).

This chapter examines provincial parks in Alberta, with particular emphasis on their role as protected areas. As such, it illustrates the development of provincial parks in a province with a relatively large land base, including a substantial amount of public land, but a relatively small population. Although each province's park system is unique, there is more similarity between Alberta and British Columbia, for example, than between Alberta and the

Atlantic provinces. The first part of the chapter examines the policy and legislative history of provincial parks in Alberta, and subsequent sections examine the current status of provincial parks in Alberta and their contribution to the protected land base of the province, as well as examining specific management issues relating to both the resource base and park use.

POLICY AND LEGISLATION HISTORY

The current pattern of provincial parks in Alberta and many of the attendant issues is the outcome of a 60-year legacy, which falls into three periods. The first phase, originating with the passing of the Provincial Parks Act in 1930, lasted until the end of the 1960s and was characterized by the establishment of the parks themselves. Phase two covers the period from the early 1970s to the early 1980s, with an emphasis on the development of a parks system. The current or third phase is characterized by a reassessment and consolidation of park development—by what Cline (1984) calls the 'maturing years' (see also Mason 1980; Morrison, Walls, and Bloomfield 1980; Swinnerton 1984, 1991a). Although this section focuses on the evolution of Alberta's provincial parks, many of the significant developments symptomize more widespread changes that influenced resource management and environmental issues in general over the same sixty years (see Swinnerton 1984).

Prior to 1930 the federal government retained jurisdictional control over natural resources in Alberta. As a result, the first extensive areas designated as protected areas were national parks (Banff, 1885; Waterton Lakes, 1895; Jasper, 1907; Elk Island, 1913; and Wood Buffalo, 1922). Although control over natural resources was transferred to the province in December 1929, the Alberta Natural Resources Act was not formally enacted until October 1930. However, the government of Alberta took advantage of this impending legislation to pass its own Provincial Parks and Protected Areas Act in March 1930 (see Harvie 1969; Mason 1988; Morrison, Walls, and Bloomfield 1980). The Act set out the purposes of provincial parks as follows (Morrison, Walls, and Bloomfield 1980, 8):

1. for the recreation and general benefit of the inhabitants of the province;
2. for the propagation, protection and preservation therein of wild animal life and wild vegetation; and
3. for the protection and preservation therein of objects of geological, ethnological, historical, or other scientific interest.

From a legislative perspective, the intended purpose of provincial parks in Alberta has remained essentially unchanged for the last 60 years. However there have been important changes in policy and practice during the evolution of provincial parks.

The initial provincial parks were small and primarily served the recreation needs of nearby towns or cities. A trend of incremental growth set the pattern until the early 1950s and resulted in a legacy of smaller parks, with little attention given to protecting heritage resources or to the systematic representation of important landscapes and resources. During the decade from 1951 to 1960 the number of provincial parks increased from eight to 34 (Morrison, Walls, and Bloomfield 1980). This period also witnessed an increase in the size of new parks and a gradual recognition of the conservation and preservation role of parks.

A Provincial Parks Act in 1964 with the comprehensive title of *An Act Respecting Provincial Parks, Historical Sites, Natural Areas, and Wilderness Areas* signified the broadening of the Parks Division's mandate. Three years later, in 1967, a provincial parks policy statement drew attention to the resource protection function of parks while acknowledging their role for education and public enjoyment (Harvie 1969).

Phase two in the evolution of Alberta's provincial parks signified the growing recognition of the need for a more comprehensive and systematic approach to the planning and management of parks and related areas (Swinnerton 1984). The limitations of the 1967 policy statement resulted in a new provincial parks policy in 1973. This document, usually referred to as 'Position Paper No. 13' (Alberta Department of Lands and Forests 1973), recognized a number of shortcomings in the existing parks, including conflicting approaches to resources and deficiencies in location and size. To counteract these shortcomings, the new policy set forth the government's position on seven major program areas: expansion, natural ecology, people, resource development, private enterprise, large parks, and integrated planning.

In 1974 the Provincial Parks Act was rewritten. The mandate for conservation, preservation, and enjoyment for outdoor recreation remained consistent with the original Act of 1930. But the new Act made specific provision for 'recreation areas', which would be distinct from provincial parks. Section 7 of the 1974 Provincial Parks Act made reference to the powers of the minister to establish, develop, and maintain a system and classification of provincial parks. This provision permitted progress towards the establishment of a provincial parks system which was to become more evident by the end of the decade.

The need for a systematic approach to park development was elaborated on in a report titled *Putting the Pieces Together: An Alberta Provincial Park System Plan* (Alberta Recreation, Parks, and Wildlife 1977). Recognition was given to the fact that a provincial park system should contain representative areas of Alberta's natural landscapes. For this purpose, Alberta was considered to include five natural regions (grassland, parkland, foothills, boreal forest, and Rocky Mountains). This framework was subsequently modified to include a sixth natural region, the Canadian Shield.

A park classification scheme was also proposed in order to ensure a balance between recreation and heritage resource protection within the park system. Four provincial park classes were proposed (preservation, wildland, natural environment, and recreation), together with a reserve land designation.

These classes were formally established in 1979 but were subsequently rescinded in 1983. Complementing the park classification scheme was a proposed zoning system comprising six zones (natural, cultural, primitive, outdoor recreation, facility, and restricted resource use) (Alberta Recreation and Parks 1979a). Despite the application of some aspects of the systems plan, the failure to implement the plan in a more comprehensive manner has been criticized (Swinnerton 1984).

By the end of the 1970s, the *Provincial Parks Five Year Plan 1980–1985* (Alberta Recreation and Parks 1979b) revealed both substantial shortfalls in the representation of natural regions and serious deficiencies in resource-based recreation opportunities. The report also referred to the increasing difficulty of designating and establishing appropriate areas because of competing land-use interests.

The optimist and expansionist phase of provincial parks, which was reflected in the five-year plan, extended into the early years of the 1980s. A new Provincial Parks Act was passed in 1980 and amended in 1983. Of particular significance to conservation was the passing of the Wilderness Areas, Ecological Reserves, and Natural Areas Act in 1980. This Act is jointly administered by Alberta Recreation and Parks and the Department of Forestry, Lands, and Wildlife. The minister of Recreation and Parks is ultimately responsible for wilderness areas and ecological reserves, whereas the minister of Forestry, Lands, and Wildlife administers the natural areas program. These three designations are distinct from provincial parks. The relationship between provincial parks and protected areas is discussed in more detail below (see also Table 7.2).

Phase three in the evolution of Alberta's provincial parks dates from approximately 1982. The eighth annual report of Alberta Recreation and Parks for the fiscal year 1982/3 drew specific attention to the downturn in Alberta's economy and the direct implications this would have for the management and direction of departmental programs and services (Alberta Recreation and Parks 1984). This recession resulted in a focus on fiscal restraint and improved cost-effectiveness, together with a search for ways in which government departments could contribute to the economic recovery of the province.

Early in 1984 Alberta's Minister of Recreation and Parks announced the preparation of a recreation and parks policy statement. A comprehensive process, involving substantial public participation, reassessed the existing park system and recreation programs and developed policy directions for the future (see Swinnerton 1987). The outcome of the process was a *Policy Statement for the Ministry of Recreation and Parks: Revised Draft* (Alberta Recreation and Parks 1986) which subsequently resulted in a document titled *Foundations for Action: Corporate Aims for the Ministry of Recreation and Parks* (Alberta Recreation and Parks 1988a).

Although the ministry initially intended to publish this policy, this has never occurred. The *Foundations for Action* report has not become an officially sanctioned public document, although it serves as an internal reference point for the ongoing work of the ministry. As such, it provides the basis for the review of the current provincial park system and its management in subsequent sections of this chapter.

In 1988 the Parks Division of Alberta Recreation and Parks (1988*b*) produced a document called *Parks in the 1990s* with the intended role of integrating long-term policy and short-term direction. The mission statement included in the document reiterated the dual mandate for parks as 'special natural places developed, maintained and preserved for public use and enjoyment' (Alberta Recreation and Parks 1988*b*, 4).

More recent developments, which will inevitably have significant implications for the future of the Alberta Parks Service, include a reduction in the number of divisional staff and a process of decentralization which has redeployed some of these staff to the four regional provincial park offices (Alberta Recreation and Parks 1990). One of the implications of restructuring and staff cuts has been the loss of specialist positions in areas such as visitor services, resource management, systems planning, and long-range planning.

ALBERTA'S PROVINCIAL PARKS: THE LAND BASE

Provincial parks in Alberta comprise only one category of protected area within Alberta Recreation and Parks' conservation-outdoor recreation system.[1] In addition, a number of other provincial departments, as well as the federal government through national parks and national wildlife areas, make significant contributions to the protected areas landbase of the province (see Swinnerton 1984, 1991*a*). A brief overview of this broader picture is appropriate before focusing on provincial parks.

Protected Areas in Alberta

Both the designation of lands with protected status and patterns of outdoor recreation depend heavily on the availability of public land (Swinnerton 1982, 1991*a*). Approximately 28 per cent of Alberta is privately owned land; the

---

[1]Both the *Policy Statement for the Ministry of Recreation and Parks: Revised Draft* (Alberta Recreation and Parks 1986) and *Foundations for Action: Corporate Aims for the Ministry of Recreation and Parks* (Alberta Recreation and Parks 1988*a*) refer to the ministry's conservation-outdoor recreation system and its four distinct classes established by legislation: ecological reserves, wilderness areas, provincial parks, and recreation areas. Despite the fact that the Alberta Parks Service refers to these four classes as comprising a 'parks system', the term 'conservation-outdoor recreation system' is used throughout this chapter to avoid confusion and ambiguity.

balance consists of public lands under federal or provincial jurisdiction. Table 7.1 provides an overview of Crown lands with protected status in Alberta. Provincial parks account for 1.8 per cent of the land under legislated protection in Alberta, or 0.19 per cent of the province's total area. In contrast, national parks account for 78.3 per cent of Crown lands with protected status

Table 7.1 Crown Lands with Protected Status in Alberta (1991)

Program	Number of Sites	Area (sq. km)	% of Province
Legislated Sites			
National parks	5	54,084	8.18
Wilderness areas	3	1,010	0.15
Ecological reserves	13	271	0.04
Willmore wilderness park	1	4,597	0.70
Provincial parks	62	1,277	0.19
Provincial historic sites	2	5	0.00
National historic parks	1	2	0.00
Natural areas	118	357	0.05
National wildlife areas	3	4	0.00
Migratory bird sanctuaries	4	142	0.02
Provincial wildlife areas	1	58	0.01
Provincial bird sanctuaries	7	506	0.08
Wildlife habitat development areas	2	30	0.00
Forest land use zones	10	5,501	0.83
Provincial recreation areas	131	155	0.02
Forest recreation areas	173	1,214	0.18
Total		69,190	10.45
Under Protective Zoning			
In Eastern Slopes			
Prime protection		6,524	0.99
Critical wildlife		6,635	1.00
Within integrated resource plans outside the			
Eastern Slopes		2,728	0.41
Total		15,887	2.40

Source: Alberta Forestry, Lands and Wildlife (1991) and subsequent revisions based on information from Alberta Recreation and Parks and Alberta Forestry, Lands and Wildlife

Note: Area of Alberta (land and water) 661,185 sq. km (426,270 sq. km public lands; 184,915 sq. km privately owned land). In addition to the protected land included under legislated sites and protective zoning, approximately 4,400 sq. km of the province is under protective reservation.

in Alberta and 8.2 per cent of the province's total area. Table 7.1 also illustrates the importance of Alberta Forestry, Lands, and Wildlife as an agency responsible for protected lands in the province through its involvement with natural areas, forest land-use zones, forest recreation areas, and provincial wildlife areas. Detailed reviews of this agency's responsibilities in terms of protected areas and outdoor recreation have been undertaken by Pachal (in press), the Renewable Resources Subcommittee (1989), and Swinnerton (1984, 1991a). A number of mechanisms facilitate provincial government co-ordination and provincial-federal co-ordination for protected areas in Alberta, including the Deputy Ministers' Heritage Resources, the Recreation and Tourism Committee, the Natural Resources Advisory Council/Committee and the Federal-Provincial Parks Council (see Alberta Recreation and Parks 1986, 1988a).

Alberta Recreation and Parks' Conservation-Outdoor Recreation System

Over the last 60 years the Ministry of Recreation and Parks and its predecessors have created a number of different classes of protected lands and related programs. In addition, an incremental approach to park establishment has been gradually replaced by a systematic one. This course has been directed towards two broad objectives: first, providing of outdoor recreation opportunities; and second, protecting examples of Alberta's natural regions. In recognizing that individual areas cannot provide a complete range of functions, a classification framework has gradually developed to provide planning, management, and operational guidelines for each class. The classification system is also intended to help the public choose the right place for the recreation they want (Alberta Recreation and Parks 1988a).

At the present time the conservation-outdoor recreation system administered by Alberta Recreation and Parks incorporates four distinct classes, established by legislation: ecological reserves, under the Wilderness Act and Natural Areas Act; wilderness areas, under the Wilderness Areas Act; provincial parks; and recreation areas, both under the Provincial Parks Act (Alberta Recreation and Parks 1988a). Overall, the system has four program objectives: protection, outdoor recreation, heritage appreciation, and tourism (Table 7.2). Although the four classes emphasize these objectives to different extents, provincial parks are considered to 'contribute significantly to all four program objectives' (Alberta Recreation and Parks 1988a, 29).

Ecological reserves are areas selected as representative or special natural landscapes and features of the province, with two subclasses: representative ecological reserves, and special ecological reserves. Thirteen ecological reserves have been created to date and a further three are being considered. The three wilderness areas, all in the Rocky Mountain natural region, are given strong legal protection and are substantially larger in size than virtually all of the 62 provincial parks in Alberta.

Table 7.2 Principal Contributions of the Classes to the Objectives of Alberta Recreation and Parks' Conservation-Outdoor Recreation System

	Ecological Reserves	Wilderness Areas
Legislation	Wilderness Areas, Ecological Reserves and Natural Areas Act	Wilderness Areas, Ecological Reserves and Natural Areas Act
Purpose	Areas selected as representative of special natural landscapes and features of the province, which are protected as examples of functioning ecosystems, as gene pools for research, and for education and heritage appreciation purposes.	Large areas of undeveloped land retaining their primeval character and influence without permanent improvements or human habitation. Natural processes in these areas continue relatively unaffected by human influences, and visitors travel by foot to experience solitude and personal interaction with nature.
Objectives		
Protection	Protects a system of provincially significant representatives and special natural ecosystems and features to ensure the perpetuation of genetic materials and natural ecological units.	Protects provincially significant wilderness landscapes.
Heritage Appreciation	Provides opportunities for unstructured individual exploration and appreciation of the natural resource heritage of Alberta to the extent that is compatible with protection of natural resource features. Provides opportunities for exploration and appreciation of natural environments through formal interpretation and education programs in certain ecological reserves to the extent that is compatible with the protection of natural resource features.	Provides opportunities for unstructured exploration and appreciation of the wilderness heritage of Alberta to the extent that it is compatible with the preservation of wilderness environments. Provides opportunities for exploration and appreciation of natural environments through informal interpretation programs which provide opportunities to learn and experience the meaning and purpose of wilderness within Alberta's society.
Outdoor Recreation	Non-consumptive, nature-oriented recreational use may be permitted subject to management guidelines. (Not a priority objective.)	Provides wilderness travel and camping opportunities; the recreational experience is characterized by solitude, challenge, and personal interaction with the natural environment.
Tourism	Provides ecologically based opportunities for visitors, subject to management guidelines. (Not a priority objective.)	Provides opportunities to experience wilderness environments. Attracts visitors to Alberta to experience wilderness environments.

Provincial parks are defined as follows: 'Provincial parks integrate and protect outstanding recreational landscapes and provincially significant natural, historical and cultural landscapes and features to provide quality recreational and educational experiences' (Alberta Recreation and Parks 1988a,

Table 7.2 (continued)

	Provincial Parks	Recreation Areas
Legislation	Provincial Parks Act	Provincial Parks Act
Purpose	Areas to integrate and protect outstanding recreational landscapes and provincially significant natural, historical, and cultural landscapes and features to provide high quality recreational and educational experiences.	Areas which provide and/or support a wide diversity of extensive and intensive outdoor recreation opportunities in natural, modified, or man-made settings.
Objectives		
Protection	Protects a system of provincially significant representative landscapes or environments which incorporate the greatest possible diversity of provincially significant biophysical resources and landscape-related prehistorical and historical resources.	May protect provincially or regionally significant natural landscapes and/or significant or unique natural features.
Heritage Appreciation	Provides opportunities for exploration of natural, historical, and cultural landscapes and features through a full range of interpretive and educational programs and features. Provides opportunities for unstructured individual exploration and appreciation of natural, historical, and cultural landscapes and features to the extent that is compatible with the protection of the heritage resources.	Provides opportunities for unstructured exploration and appreciation of natural landscapes and features. Provides opportunities for exploration and appreciation of natural, historical, and cultural environments through interpretive and educational programs reflecting the diversity of resources and features. (Primarily in the Integrated subclass.)
Outdoor Recreation	Provides day-use, facility-based camping, and associated opportunities in areas of outstanding recreational potential in a natural, historical, and cultural setting. Provides opportunities in selected provincial parks for back-country travel and camping where the recreational experience is characterized by solitude, challenge, and personal interaction with nature.	Provides day-use, facility-based camping and associated opportunities in natural, modified, or man-made settings. In an integrated resource management setting provides opportunities for a variety of dispersed outdoor recreation opportunities, including both mechanized and non-mechanized activities and consumptive and non-consumptive uses.
Tourism	Provides a variety of natural environment-based recreation opportunities and services conducive to tourism development and promotion. Provides Albertans and visitors with opportunities to explore and experience the distinctive natural, historical, and cultural landscapes and features of Alberta. Encourages private sector involvement in the supply of complementary facilities and programs within, or in association with, provincial parks.	Provides a variety of recreation opportunities and services conducive to tourism development and promotion. Supports and encourages the development of private sector involvement in supplying complementary facilities and programs within, or in association with, recreation areas.

Source: Alberta Recreation and Parks (1986, 6–9) with subsequent revisions based on information supplied by Alberta Recreation and Parks.

19). Two subclasses of provincial parks were envisaged in *Foundations for Action*: heritage provincial parks, and natural environment provincial parks. More recently these two subclasses have been replaced by a natural environment provincial park subclass and a recreation provincial park subclass (Alberta Recreation and Parks 1989*a*). The former emphasizes heritage resource protection, whereas the latter provides a wider range of outdoor recreation and nature-oriented learning opportunities. Further changes to subclassification within provincial parks are pending.

The 62 provincial parks in Alberta cover an area of 127,696 ha, and range in size from the 50,000 ha of Peter Lougheed Provincial Park to the 0.9 ha of Twelve Foot Davis. The five largest parks (Peter Lougheed, 50,142 ha; Cypress Hills 20,451 ha; Notikewin 9,697 ha; Lesser Slave Lake, 7,557 ha; and Dinosaur, 6,622 ha) account for three-quarters of all provincial parkland (Figure 7.1). Dinosaur Provincial Park is also a designated World Heritage Site. In contrast, many of the remaining parks are too small for some forms of outdoor recreation or for natural heritage protection.

Provincial recreation areas are similar in size and function to many of the smaller provincial parks. The 131 recreation areas (52 managed by the Alberta Parks Service and 79 managed by Kananaskis Country) accommodate a wide range of extensive and intensive outdoor recreation opportunities in natural, modified, or manmade settings. Although *Foundations for Action* identified four subclasses of recreation areas (integrated recreation areas, provincial recreation areas, regional recreational areas, and wayside recreation areas) only two of the subclasses (access/wayside recreation areas and integrated recreation areas) were subsequently recognized by the ministry (Alberta Recreation and Parks 1989*a*). The existing two subclasses of recreation areas are being reconsidered at the present time.

The access/wayside recreation areas include areas which provide access to land- and water-based recreation and heritage features, as well as rest stops or stop-over activities. Integrated recreation areas are intended to be quite large and to accommodate both dispersed and concentrated recreation using integrated conservation management. The Cooking Lake-Blackfoot Grazing Wildlife and Provincial Recreation Area east of Edmonton is the only example of this subclass at the present time. Kananaskis Country (424,038 ha), which was established in the late 1970s, demonstrates many characteristics of an integrated recreation area but is managed as a separate unit by the Ministry of Alberta Recreation and Parks. An integrated recreation area has also been proposed for the Lakeland area northeast of Edmonton. This initiative involves the establishment of Lakeland Provincial Park and Provincial Recreation Area (Alberta Recreation and Parks 1991*a*).

The establishment of new parks and protected areas in the last decade has largely resulted from the initiation of the ecological reserves program. Since its inception in 1980, when the Wilderness Areas, Ecological Reserves, and Natural Areas Act was passed, 13 ecological reserves have been designated

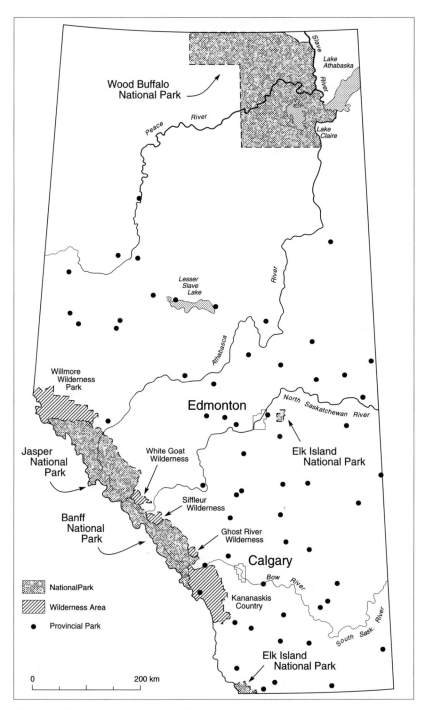

Figure 7.1 National and provincial parks and wilderness areas in Alberta.

with a total of 26,190 ha. In contrast, no wilderness areas have been designated since the three existing areas were established in the 1960s. No new provincial parks have been designed since 1982, when two provincial parks were established. An important addition to the system will be the proposed Lakeland Provincial Park and Provincial Recreation Area (Alberta Recreation and Parks 1991a). Provincial recreation areas have been enlarged but the actual area of land involved is relatively small. Moreover, these additions have largely been a result of transferring existing recreation areas from other provincial government agencies to Alberta Recreation and Parks.

One recent initiative that may increase Alberta's protected land involves the private sector. The Park Ventures Fund, established in the late 1980s under the auspices of the Recreation, Parks, and Wildlife Foundation, allows land, money, and other assets to be donated for conservation and recreation opportunities. From January 1989 to the end of 1991, $2.6 million had been committed or donated to the Park Ventures Fund in land and financial donations.

A Representative System of Protected Areas

The Brundtland Commission (World Commission on Environment and Development 1987) implicitly recommended that at least 12 per cent of a nation's land area should be fully protected. This figure has been endorsed in the Canadian Wilderness Charter (Hummel 1989) and by the government of Canada (Environment Canada 1990). The fact that approximately 10.5 per cent of Alberta's area is protected by legislation has been used to imply that Alberta has an enviable record in establishing parks and other categories of protected land. This contention is, however, misleading. A more critical yardstick for evaluating protected areas programs is the extent to which a park system incorporates a representative sample of a country's or province's natural diversity (see Hackman 1990; IUCN 1980; Swinnerton 1984, 1991a; World Wildlife Fund Canada 1991).

In Alberta, six natural regions are further subdivided into 17 biogeographical zones (Figure 7.2). Representation of these regions and zones through a protection-oriented provincial park system has been a long-standing objective of Alberta Recreation and Parks (see Alberta Recreation, Parks, and Wildlife 1977; Alberta Recreation and Parks 1979b, 1988a, 1988b, 1989b), although a systems plan has yet to be completed (Alberta Recreation and Parks 1989a). A natural history theme matrix, developed by Achuff, Godfrey, and Wallis (1988) will provide the basis for protecting representative areas (Alberta Recreation and Parks 1989a). According to Alberta Recreation and Parks (1989a) the park system is approximately 40 per cent complete. Five of the 17 biogeographical zones are not represented at all, while representation of the remaining 12 biogeographical zones is approximately two-thirds complete (Morrison 1989). However, considerable discussion has taken place about the

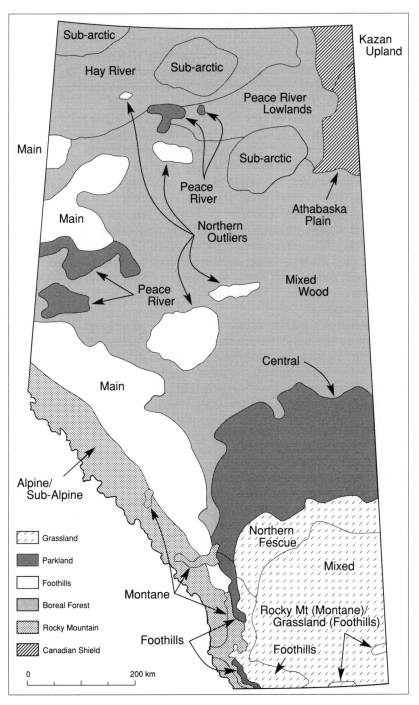

Figure 7.2 Natural regions of Alberta.

current level of representation of biogeographical zones, given different inter-pretations of the data (Hackman 1990; Pachal, in press; World Wildlife Fund Canada 1991). The World Wildlife Fund Canada (1991) has suggested that only three of the 17 zones are adequately represented. These are the Peace River lowlands of the boreal forest and the alpine and subalpine biogeograph-ical zones of the Rocky Mountain natural region.

Looking only at whether the zones are represented within the system as a whole (aside from the question of protection), only seven zones are thought to have more than half the appropriate representation. These are: central park-land, main foothills, mixed-wood boreal forest, Rocky Mountain montane, Rocky Mountain subalpine, and Rocky Mountain alpine (Morrison 1989). In the past, underprotection of the grassland and parkland natural regions has been of particular concern because of economic pressure on these areas and the limited number of suitable and available land (Alberta Recreation and Parks 1989a). More recently, new and proposed forestry projects involving large areas of the boreal forest natural region have been allocated under forest management agreements (Renewable Resources Subcommittee 1990). This has serious implications for the future establishment of protected areas in this region (Swinnerton 1991a).

Complementing the six natural regions and 17 biogeographical zones is a system of natural history themes that classifies the natural phenomena of the province by physiographic and biological standards. Twenty natural history themes have been identified, and these have been grouped into five broad categories: non-sandy upland, sandy upland, valley/ridge, wetland, and gla-cier/snowfield. Each natural history theme within a biogeographical zone is called a sectional theme. Proper representation of physiographic and biolog-ical features of the province may therefore be considered on the basis of the 20 natural history themes, either throughout the province or in each bioge-ographical zone. At the provincial level only five of the 20 natural history themes are considered to have more than half the desired representation in the system as a whole (Morrison 1989). Although the expansion of the eco-logical reserves program has addressed some of these deficiencies, important gaps continue to exist.

THE MANAGEMENT OF PROVINCIAL PARKS IN ALBERTA

Park designation is a critical first step towards the achievement of a park system, but this indicator is to a large extent illusory unless individual parks meet their intended goals and objectives. The purpose of this section is to provide an overview of selective aspects of park management in Alberta.

Management Plans and Related Mechanisms

The ministry has said that it intends to prepare a general management plan for each site in the system, and that public involvement will be an important component of the planning process (Alberta Recreation and Parks 1988*a*). The purpose of management plans was defined as follows:

> General management plans will: identify the area's role in the ministry's conservation-outdoor recreation system; identify its purpose and management objectives; identify strategies for achieving the area's purpose and management objectives; establish guidelines for the long-term protection, development, management and use of each site; and present a zoning strategy for the site. (Alberta Recreation and Parks 1988*a*, 35)

Few such plans currently exist. In the interim, policies have been prepared for a number of program elements, including bear-human management, prescribed burning, and water quality. A standards manual for resource management was also prepared in 1989 (Alberta Recreation and Parks 1989*b*). Although resource management plans have been or are being developed for a number of areas, including provincial parks, less than 10 per cent of those needed for the system as a whole have been approved (Alberta Recreation and Parks 1989*b*). More recent guidelines will provide a framework for preparing management plans (see Landals 1991).

One component of most management plans is zoning, a management tool that complements park classification schemes and provides additional direction in balancing protection and use. An integral part of planning, management zoning identifies areas according to their special characteristics and functions within each park. Alberta Recreation and Parks (1989*a*, 4) has proposed a system of seven zones, as follows:

1. *Preservation zones* protect representative or special landscapes or features for their intrinsic, educational, or scientific values.
2. *Historical/cultural zones* include lands or features of significant historical, prehistorical, or archaeological value, and areas with landscapes created by agricultural or pastoral activities that are culturally significant.
3. *Wildland zones* are extensive areas suitable for wilderness recreation and representing natural regions and natural history themes.
4. *Natural environment zones* encompass natural and manmade landscapes that allow people to appreciate and enjoy natural values through outdoor recreation, education, and interpretation opportunities.
5. *Integrated management zones* include areas designated for extractive and consumptive resource uses. This zone will only apply to integrated recreation areas.
6. *Facility zones* provide, support, or accommodate a range of intensive outdoor recreational opportunities, facilities, and services.
7. *Access zones* give access to outdoor recreation opportunities and include roadways through a site or specific zone.

Preliminary work has been done on the relationship between classes and zones and their proper facilities and activities. *Foundations for Action*

(Alberta Recreation and Parks 1988*a*) discusses appropriate opportunities for recreation and heritage appreciation and associated facilities for park classes. It does not, however, examine the relationship between classes and zones.

Table 7.3 shows the activities permitted in each class. A substantial number of activities and facilities which may be allowed or encouraged in ecological reserves on wilderness areas. Provincial parks occupy a middle ground, and as a result, ambiguity continues to exist regarding their primary role (Swinnerton 1987). Some of the more contentious uses which may be allowed in provincial parks include cottages, accommodations, and resort complexes. One problem is that considerable diversity exists within provincial parks and even within the two subclasses of provincial parks. Consequently, planners recognize that whenever a recreational activity or facility may be permitted or encouraged (see Table 7.3), the appropriateness of the activity must be determined case by case through management plans.

Resource Management Practices

Although one role of provincial parks is to protect heritage resources, the level of this protection varies from province to province. In addition, resource management often involves other agencies with mandates for managing (e.g.) wildlife and timber. Watkins (1990) has prepared a comprehensive review of the situation across Canada. Table 7.4 summarizes the main findings of this study and provides a means of comparison. While Alberta is not as restrictive as some jurisdictions, neither is it as permissive as others. However, Table 7.4 considers only each park system as a whole. Consequently, specific land-use policies are not indicated for the four classes in Alberta's conservation-outdoor recreation system. For example, while sport fishing is prohibited in wilderness areas and ecological reserves, it is permitted in provincial parks and provincial recreation areas.

In Alberta, the Provincial Parks Act gives the minister substantive power over the development and maintenance of parks and recreation areas (Duffin 1990). In essence, the minister has control over the management of these lands in order to maintain their resources. Where other acts and regulations exist for a particular resource (e.g., the Wildlife Act), they would also apply and, in some instances, take precedence. As a result, the administering agency (Alberta Forestry, Lands, and Wildlife in the case of the Wildlife Act) would be involved in planning some management programs. The degree to which outside agencies become involved depends on both the legislation and the complexity and sensitivity of the programs being considered.

Alberta Recreation and Parks (1988*a*, 38) has stated that its principal aim in resource management is 'the unimpeded interaction of ecosystem processes'. The ministry, however, recognizes that intervention may be necessary when a special resource is in question. In such instances active resource

Table 7.3 Possible Recreational Activities and Facilities Ecological Reserves, Wilderness Areas, Provincial Parks, and Recreation Areas*

	Ecological Reserves	Wilderness Areas	Provincial Parks	
			Heritage	Natural Environment
Camping				
Auto access	N	N	Y	Y
Hike-in, boat-in	M	Y	Y	Y
Group	N	N	Y	Y
Equestrian	N	N	M	M
Picnicking				
Auto access	N	N	Y	Y
Primitive	Y	Y	Y	Y
Sport fishing	N	N	Y	Y
Sport hunting	N	N	N	N
Boating				
Powered	N	N	Y	Y
Sailing	M	Y	Y	Y
Cycling	N	N	Y	Y
Hiking	Y	Y	Y	Y
Equestrian use	N	N	M	M
Nature appreciation	Y	Y	Y	Y
Photography	Y	Y	Y	Y
Crosscountry skiing	M	Y	Y	Y
Downhill skiing	N	N	M	M
Playgrounds	N	N	Y	Y
Play fields	N	N	M	M
Court games (e.g., tennis)	N	N	M	M
Snowmobiling*	N	N	N	N
Off-highway vehicle use	N	N	N	N
Golf courses	N	N	M	M
Resort complexes	N	N	M	M
Restaurants	N	N	M	M
Back-country shelters	N	N	M	M
Cottages	N	N	N	N
Housekeeping cabins	N	N	M	M
Motels	N	N	M	M
Concessions				
Food	N	N	Y	Y
Equipment rentals	N	N	Y	Y

Source: Alberta Recreation and Parks (1986, 79) with subsequent revisions based on information supplied by Alberta Recreation and Parks.

Notes:

Y   Permitted/encouraged in this class

M   May be permitted/encouraged in selected units of the class where the activity/facility enhances program objectives

Table 7.3 (continued)

	Provincial Parks Integrated	Recreation Areas Provincial	Regional	Wayside
Camping				
Auto access	Y	Y	Y	Y
Hike-in, boat-in	M	M	M	N/A
Group	Y	Y	Y	M
Equestrian	M	M	M	N/A
Picnicking				
Auto access	Y	Y	Y	Y
Primitive	Y	Y	Y	M
Sport fishing	Y	Y	Y	Y
Sport hunting	M	N	N/A	N/A
Boating				
Powered	Y	Y	Y	M
Sailing	Y	Y	Y	M
Cycling	Y	Y	Y	Y
Hiking	Y	Y	Y	Y
Equestrian use	M	M	M	N/A
Nature appreciation	Y	Y	Y	Y
Photography	Y	Y	Y	Y
Crosscountry skiing	M	Y	Y	M
Downhill skiing	M	M	M	N/A
Playgrounds	Y	Y	Y	M
Play fields	Y	Y	Y	M
Court games (e.g., tennis)	M	M	M	N/A
Snowmobiling*	M	M	M	N/A
Off-highway vehicle use	M	M	N	N
Golf courses	M	M	M	N/A
Resort complexes	M	M	M	N/A
Restaurants	M	M	M	N/A
Back-country shelters	M	N/A	N/A	N/A
Cottages	M	M	M	N/A
Housekeeping cabins	M	M	M	N/A
Motels	M	M	M	N/A
Concessions				
Food	Y	Y	Y	Y
Equipment rentals	Y	Y	Y	N/A

N   Not permitted in this class as it is incompatible with class objectives; if the activity now exists, it will be phased out if possible, or a specific management strategy prepared

N/A   Not applicable

*   Subsequent changes to the provincial park and recreation areas subclasses are discussed in text.

Table 7.4 Comparison of Resource Extraction and Land Use Policies in Canada's Park Systems

Activity	CD	BC	AB	SK	MB	ON	PQ	NB	NS	PE	NF	YT	NWT
Forestry practices													
Commercial harvest	P	M	M	M	A	P	P	A	M	—	P	—	—
Firewood, etc.	P	P	P	A	A	P	P	P	M	P	P	—	—
Fisheries management													
Sport	A	A	A	A	A	A	A	A	A	A	A	A	A
Commercial	P	P	P	A	A	*	P	P	P	—	P	—	—
Bait fish harvest	P	P	P	—	A	A	P	—	P	—	—	—	—
Fish farming	P	P	P	P	P	—	P	P	P	—	P	—	—
Mining													
Sand and gravel	M	A	P	A	A	P	P	M	M	A	P	—	—
Other	P	A	P	A	A	P	P	P	P	P	P	—	—
Trapping	P	*	*	A	A	*	P	P	P	P	P	A	—
Hunting	P	A	M	A	A	A	P	P	P	P	P	A	A
Wild rice harvest	P	—	—	*	A	*	P	—	—	—	—	—	—
Cottages	A	*	A	A	A	*	P	—	P	—	P	—	—
Commercial development													
General service	A	A	A	A	A	A	A	A	A	A	A	—	—
Lodges and outcamp	A	A	A	A	A	A	P	P	P	—	P	—	—
Water control structures	A	—	A	A	A	A	P	A	A	A	A	—	—
Utility transportation corridors	A	A	A	A	A	A	P	A	A	A	A	—	—
Agriculture													
Crops	P	P	M	*	M	M	M	A	M	M	P	—	—
Hay/grazing	P	M	M	A	A	M	M	A	M	A	P	—	—
Mechanized travel													
Off-road vehicles	P	A	P	A	A	A	P	A	P	P	P	A	A
Motor boats	A	A	A	A	A	A	A	A	A	A	A	—	—

Source: Watkins (1990, 18) with subsequent revisions based on information supplied by Alberta Recreation and Parks.

Notes: A = allowed generally or in some park classes/zones
M = allowed for park management purposes only
* = to be phased out
— = not applicable

management is expected to duplicate natural processes as much as possible. *Foundations for Action* also states that 'where conflict occurs between conservation and facility development, the integrity of the resource features will receive priority consideration' (Alberta Recreation and Parks 1988a, 38; see also Alberta Recreation and Parks 1989b).

Management also required consideration of incompatible and nonconforming land uses and activities. Normally, such consumptive activities as Commercial mineral, oil, and gas exploration and extraction and commercial timber operations are not allowed in provincial parks (Alberta Recreation and Parks 1988a). In addition, new utility lines, highways, or other major rights of way will not normally be developed (Alberta Recreation and Parks 1988a). Other prohibited activities in provincial parks include sport hunting, trapping, and commercial fishing. Selected resource management practices may, however, be permitted to conserve certain natural features or to sustain and enhance recreation opportunities, as long as they do not conflict with conservation.

Park Visitors

Alberta's provincial parks provide a variety of recreation opportunities for both day users and campers. Trends in visitor use over time are difficult to track with any real accuracy because of changes in data collection and presentation. During the 1989/90 fiscal year, Alberta's provincial parks and recreation areas recorded more than 1.3 million campers and 6.1 million day users. Compared to the previous season, day-use visitation increased by just over 3 per cent, while camping decreased by slightly over 4 per cent (Alberta Recreation and Parks 1990, 1991b). Further increases were recorded for 1990/1, with 1.4 million campers and 6.8 million individual day users.

Based on a survey carried out in 1984 by Alberta Recreation and Parks, over 80 per cent of the visitors came from Alberta itself (Swinnerton 1986). Of the respondents, 87 per cent considered that the protection of plants and animals was a very important role of provincial parks, whereas only 64 per cent felt the same way about the provision of facilities for outdoor recreation. These figures tend to show that visitors see heritage resource protection and recreation as not mutually exclusive. A more recent survey of Alberta households shows that 66 per cent of the respondents considered the protection of areas of natural interest very important and 52 per cent felt the same about outdoor recreation opportunities (Alberta Recreation and Parks 1988c).

The 1984 park visitor survey also showed strong support by park users for activities and programs that help them to understand and appreciate the park's intrinsic features or that depend to a large extent on its natural features. Respondents clearly opposed most mechanical forms of outdoor recreation, resource extraction, and commercial development of any sort (Swinnerton 1987).

Provincial Parks and Privatization

Although involvement by the private sector in aspects of the operation of Alberta's provincial parks goes back to the early days of park establishment, more active encouragement of private-sector involvement began in the early 1980s (Servos 1989). Provincial government directives encouraged privatization on the grounds of economic efficiency and on the more political argument of reducing the government's portion of the gross provincial product (see Servos 1989). Alberta Recreation and Parks (1988a, 41) has indicated that it 'will encourage the commercial sector and private groups to provide facilities and services, where appropriate'. These arrangements are meant to stimulate the economy, provide attractions and services without drawing on the ministry's limited resources, create jobs, and promote the province's tourism industry (Alberta Recreation and Parks 1988a, 1989a).

Only limited information exists on the contribution that Alberta's park system makes to the provincial economy. Camping fees accounted for over two-thirds (69 per cent) of the ministry's total revenue of $3.7 million in 1989/90. Concession revenues and disposition fees accounted for a further 16 per cent each. A study undertaken in 1986 (DPA Group Inc. 1986) calculated that the government spent approximately $43 million on replacing, maintaining, and operating facilities and services in provincial parks and recreation areas in fiscal 1984/5 and that over 3 million visitors spent $49.3 million.

CONCLUSION

This review of the evolution of provincial parks in Alberta and their current status illustrates issues and concerns that are to be found in other jurisdictions across Canada. A number of points are worth emphasizing. First, the conservation-outdoor recreation system provides the framework for the ministry's involvement in the protection of heritage resources and the provision of outdoor recreation opportunities. Concern has been expressed about achieving a completed system in a reasonable length of time, particularly with increasing pressures on both public and private land in the province (Swinnerton 1991a; see also Canadian Environmental Advisory Council 1991). Except in the ecological reserves program, the ministry's activities in the last 10 years have largely been to upgrade and redevelop existing sites, not to acquire new ones or to diversify its programs.

Second, provincial parks continue to have an ambiguous role in the system. On the basis of the *Foundations for Action* document (Alberta Recreation and Parks 1988a), provincial parks are expected to make significant contributions to protection, heritage appreciation, outdoor recreation, and tourism. Past experience has shown that these objectives are not always mutually compatible. Although the two subclasses of provincial park (natural environment and recreation) partly solve this problem, further direction will have to be provided through the application of the zoning system and careful consideration of the activities and facilities permitted in each class. The failure of the Alberta Parks Service to put into practice a proper classification framework and associated policies to show how each class and subclass contributes to program objectives continues to be a shortcoming of the agency's approach.

The decision not to release *Foundations for Action* (Alberta Recreation and Parks 1988a) as a public document was extremely unfortunate. Although the report is being used within the agency, the government lost an opportunity to make Albertans aware of the purpose and direction of the conservation-outdoor recreation system. This situation is in marked contrast to recent approaches in other provinces, including British Columbia, Saskatchewan, and Nova Scotia. Consequently, the potential for strengthening and broadening public support outside specific interest groups has also been largely dissipated. In the absence of a public policy document, preparing management plans for individual units in the system will be a crucial opportunity for public involvement.

Third, privatization, and commercialization in particular, have been contentious in other provinces when heritage resources are involved (see Servos 1989). The extent to which these arrangements will be pursued in Alberta is an open issue. It is, however, clear that the ministry intends to actively encourage private-sector involvement.

Fourth, it is premature to assess the impact of decentralization and staff reductions in the Alberta Parks Service. As noted above, the service has lost specialist positions in areas such as visitor services and long-range planning. The rationale for decentralization without the benefit of a formal policy document or systems plan is questionable, given the need for consistency in planning and management decisions among the four regions.

Finally, the conservation-outdoor recreation system proposed by Alberta Recreation and Parks has to be seen in the larger context of resource development, economic growth, and heritage protection, involving of agencies at all levels of government as well as the private sector. Of particular significance in this regard will be any pertinent recommendations by Alberta's Round Table on Environment and Economy. The Round Table has already noted that its vision for the future encompasses the preservation of Alberta's biological diversity (Alberta Round Table on Environment and Economy 1991). Parks and other protected areas have an important contribution to make in demonstrating the principles and practice of sustainable development. As Sax (1985, 207) observed, 'parks are not only, and not even most importantly, resources in their own right, but indicators of the general well-being of the society in its management of natural resources.'

ACKNOWLEDGEMENT

The author thanks the Alberta Parks Service for its input and comments on an earlier draft of this chapter. The opinions and views expressed in the chapter are those of the author.

REFERENCES

Achuff, P., J. Godfrey, and C. Wallis
  1988   *A Systems Planning Natural History Framework and Evaluation System for Alberta Recreation and Parks*, Alberta Recreation and Parks, Edmonton. 4 vols.
Alberta, Department of Lands and Forests
  1973   *Provincial Parks Policy for Alberta*, Position Paper No. 13, Alberta Department of Lands and Forests, Edmonton.
Alberta, Forestry, Lands and Wildlife
  1991   *Annual Report 1989–90*, Alberta Forestry, Lands, and Wildlife, Edmonton.
Alberta, Recreation and Parks
  1979a   *Alberta Provincial Parks—A Zoning Framework*, Provincial Parks Division, Alberta Recreation and Parks, Edmonton.
Alberta, Recreation and Parks
  1979b   *Provincial Parks Five Year Plan 1980–1985*, Provincial Parks Division, Alberta Recreation and Parks, Edmonton.
Alberta, Recreation and Parks
  1984   *Eighth Annual Report 1982–1983*, Alberta Recreation and Parks, Edmonton.
Alberta, Recreation and Parks
  1986   *Policy Statement for the Ministry of Recreation and Parks, Revised Draft*, Alberta Recreation and Parks, Edmonton.
Alberta, Recreation and Parks
  1988a   *Foundations for Action: Corporate Aims for the Ministry of Recreation and Parks*, Alberta Recreation and Parks, Edmonton.
Alberta, Recreation and Parks
  1988b   *Parks in the 1990s*, Provincial Parks Division, Alberta Recreation and Parks, Edmonton.
Alberta, Recreation and Parks
  1988c   *1988 General Recreation Survey*, Alberta Recreation and Parks, Edmonton.
Alberta, Recreation and Parks
  1989a   'State of the Nation Address, Alberta 1988/89 and Status of Park System Planning', in *Federal-Provincial Parks Council Annual Conference, 1989*, Federal-Provincial Parks Council, Regina.
Alberta, Recreation and Parks
  1989b   'Resource Management in Alberta: Influencing Factors and Current Programs: March 1989', in *Developing the Tools for Natural Resource Management in Parks*, Federal-Provincial Parks Council, Alberta Recreation and Parks, Edmonton.

Alberta, Recreation and Parks
1990   'State of the Nation Report: Alberta', in *Parks, Protection and Sustainable Development: Proceedings, Federal-Provincial Parks Council Annual Conference*, Federal-Provincial Parks Council, St John's, Nfld., 71–5.
Alberta, Recreation and Parks
1991a   *Lakeland: Foundation Document*, Alberta Recreation and Parks, Edmonton.
Alberta, Recreation and Parks
1991b   *Fifteenth Annual Report 1989–90*, Alberta Recreation and Parks, Edmonton.
Alberta, Recreation, Parks and Wildlife
1977   *Putting the Pieces Together: An Alberta Provincial Park System Plan*, Alberta Recreation, Parks and Wildlife, Edmonton.
Alberta, Round Table on Environment and Economy
1991   *Alberta: Working For a Sustainable Future*, Environment Council of Alberta, Edmonton.
Bella, L.
1987   *Parks for Profit*, Harvest House, Montreal.
Canadian Environmental Advisory Council
1991   *A Protected Areas Vision for Canada*, Environment Canada, Ottawa.
Cline, D.
1984   'The Alberta Park System', in *Proceedings, Thirteenth Annual Joint Meeting of the Public Advisory Committee on the Environment and the Environment Council of Alberta*, Environment Council of Alberta, Edmonton, 15–20.
DPA Group Inc.
1986   *Economic Evaluation Framework for Parks Planning and Economic Impacts of Alberta's Provincial Parks. Vol. II. Economic Impact of Alberta's Provincial Parks*, DPA Group Inc., Calgary.
Duffin, B.
1990   'Legislated "Wilderness" in Alberta', in *Wilderness Management*, eds J.G. Nelson, J.A. Carruthers, and A.R. Woodley, Occasional Paper 14, Heritage Resources Centre, University of Waterloo, Waterloo, 87–94.
Environment of Canada
1990   *Canada's Green Plan: Canada's Green Plan for a Healthy Environment*, Supply and Services Canada, Ottawa.
Hackman, A.
1990   'Endangered Spaces: Ten Years for Wilderness in Canada', *Borealis* 1: 27–9.
Harvie, C.H.
1969   'The Provincial Parks of Alberta', in *The Canadian National Parks: Today and Tomorrow*, eds. J.G. Nelson and R.C. Scace, University of Calgary, Calgary, 461–72.
Hummel, M., ed.
1989   *Endangered Spaces: The Future for Canada's Wilderness*, Key Porter Books, Toronto.
International Union for Conservation of Nature and Natural Resources (IUCN)
1980   *World Conservation Strategy: Living Resource Conservation for Sustainable Development*, IUCN, Gland, Switzerland.

Kostka, M.D.
1976   'Parks—The Last Bastions of Environment', *Parks and Recreation* 11: 33–5, 51–3.
Landals, A.
1991   *Management Plan Format: Provincial Park and Outdoor Recreation Areas*, Provincial Parks Service, Alberta Recreation and Parks, Edmonton.
Mason, A.G.
1988   'The Development of Alberta's Provincial Parks', M.A. thesis, Department of Recreation and Leisure Studies, University of Alberta, Edmonton.
Morrison, K.
1989   *Alberta Recreation and Parks' Conservation-Outdoor Recreation System: An Evaluation of the Protection Program Objective—Biophysical Resources Component*, Alberta Recreation and Parks, Edmonton.
Morrison, K., T.R. Walls, and J. Bloomfield
1980   'The Alberta Provincial Park System: A Look at Its Development', *Parks News* 16(3): 8–12.
Pachal, D.L.
(in pre- *Wilderness*, Sector Report for an Alberta Conservation Strategy, Environ-
para-   ment Council of Alberta, Edmonton.
tion)
Renewable Resources Subcommittee, Public Advisory Committees to the Environment Council of Alberta
1989   *A Place for Wildlife*, Sector report for an Alberta Conservation Strategy, Environment Council of Alberta, Edmonton.
Renewable Resources Subcommittee, Public Advisory Committees to the Environment Council of Alberta
1990   *Our Dynamic Forests: The Challenge of Management*, Sector report for an Alberta Conservation Strategy, Environment Council of Alberta, Edmonton.
Sax, J.L.
1985   'A Rain of Troubles. The Need for a New Perspective on Park Protection', in *Parks in British Columbia: Emerging Realities*, ed. P.J. Dooling, Department of Forest Resource Management, University of British Columbia, Vancouver, 205–14.
Servos, P.E.
1989   'Alberta Recreation and Parks Privatization of Parks Operation and Maintenance Services', M.A. thesis, Department of Recreation and Leisure Studies, University of Alberta, Edmonton.
Swinnerton, G.S.
1982   *Recreation on Agricultural Land in Alberta*, Environment Council of Alberta, Edmonton.
Swinnerton, G.S.
1984   *Conservation in Practice in Alberta: An Examination of the Role of Alberta Recreation and Parks*, report prepared for Alberta Recreation and Parks, Department of Recreation and Leisure Studies, University of Alberta, Edmonton.
Swinnerton, G.S.
1987   'The Role of Alberta's Provincial Parks: A Government and Park Visitor

Perspective', Paper presented at the 5th Canadian Congress on Leisure Research, Dalhousie University, Halifax, Nova Scotia.

Swinnerton, G.S.
1989   'Recreation and Conservation', in *Understanding Leisure and Recreation: Mapping the Past, Charting the Future*, eds E.L. Jackson and T.L. Burton, Venture, State College, Pa., 517–65.

Swinnerton, G.S.
1991a   *People, Parks, and Preservation: Sustaining Opportunities*, discussion paper for the Alberta Conservation Strategy Project, Environment Council of Alberta, Edmonton.

Swinnerton, G.S.
1991b   'Parks and Outdoor Recreation: Components of a Conservation Strategy', paper presented at the Canadian Parks/Recreation Association Annual Conference, Regina, Sask.

Watkins, W.G.
1990   *A Survey of Resource Extraction and Land Use Policies in Canada's Park Systems*, prepared for Federal/Provincial Park Council, Queen's Printer, Victoria, B.C.

World Commission on Environment and Development
1987   *Our Common Future*, Oxford University Press, New York and Oxford.

World Wildlife Fund Canada
1991   *Endangered Spaces Progress Report Number 2*, World Wildlife Fund Canada, Toronto.

CHAPTER 8

Ecology, Conservation, and Protected Areas in Canada

———

JOHN B. THEBERGE

INTRODUCTION

Increasingly, a more environmentally conscious society views parks and other protected areas less as playgrounds and more as green spaces that perform vital ecological functions. Green spaces modulate water cycles, absorb pollutants, regulate atmospheric gases such as oxygen and carbon dioxide, buffer the spread of crop and livestock diseases, capture energy, stabilize populations, act as gene pools, and provide for wildlife species. In other words, they balance our assaults on the biosphere. *Maintenance of ecological integrity* now stands as the primary goal of Canada's national parks and takes priority over human use and enjoyment, by virtue of a 1988 amendment to the National Parks Act. Globally, protected areas have doubled over the last decade. Much of the increase took place in Third World countries, where, despite immense pressures of overpopulation, parks and reserves can contribute both to tourism and to ecological stability.

In recent years, increasing public demand for more protected areas has resulted in several new national parks: Bruce Peninsula, Ellesmere Island, Grasslands, South Moresby/Gwaii Hanaas. Some provincial park systems have expanded considerably, such as those in Ontario and Saskatchewan. All provinces except Ontario now have specific Ecological Reserves Acts. The public has rallied behind programs such as Carolinian Canada, designed to save remnant southern hardwood forests, and the Wild West Program to save prairie environments, sponsored by the World Wildlife Fund Canada, the Nature Conservancy of Canada, and others.

This upswing in public interest and government action in parks and reserves in Canada comes at the eleventh hour. We have lost virtually all virgin old-growth remnants of the Acadian forests in the Maritime provinces. Few patches remain of northern and southern hardwood forests, oak savannah, tall- and short-grass prairie, Osoyoos and the desert biotic area in south-central British Columbia, or the temperate rain forest on the west coast. We have lost almost all of every Canadian biome except the boreal forest and tundra—a scandalous litany. Add to that what we have done to the great auk, passenger pigeon, plains bison, eastern cougar, black-tailed prairie dog. . . .

While our past conservation failures have had many causes, one reason was, and continues to be, the slow expansion of protected areas. Despite the recent increase in park establishment, we are still far behind. Canada entered into the national parks business early, in 1885, but even today less than 2 per cent of the nation's land area is in national parks. Add to that amount the protection-oriented provincial park holdings, and by the time of the 1985 parks centennial there was still less than 4 per cent (Theberge 1987). International objectives, stated in the Brundtland Commission (1987) are set at 10 to 12 per cent for each nation. Canada ranks a poor 22nd in the world in percent of protected land. We still have a long way to go and, with current population and development pressures, not much time to get there.

PROTECTED AREAS AS PART OF CONSERVATION STRATEGY

Conservation, in its best definition, embodies some optimum balance between four strategies of increasingly intensive land use: preservation, protection, multiple use, and extractive use (Nelson *et al.* 1985). Parks and protected areas are therefore necessary but not sufficient. It is a mistake to equate conservation solely with preservation. Included in the concept, both historically and now, must be the notion of *wise use*, incorporating philosophies such as sustainable yield and conservation tools such as environmental impact assessments.

Achieving an optimum balance among these four land-use strategies is not easy. Attempts to do so took place in the 1970s under the banner of *balanced development*, and in the early 1980s as part of the World Conservation Strategy (1980). Currently, the buzzword is *sustainable development*, a term popularized by the Brundtland report (1987). That report largely restates the international objectives and rationale for protected areas described in the World Conservation Strategy (1980).

To a conservation strategy or to regional (or national) environmental management, protected areas provide a repository for species and their gene pools, together with the natural selective forces that mould them. Justifying the designation of lands for this purpose includes such moral reasons as concern for other species and such practical reasons as their future potential use to humans, their use as benchmarks against which to measure human activities, and our knowledge of our ecological ignorance, which cautions us to not alter everything. If enough areas remain natural, perhaps protected ecosystems will help us prevent a global catastrophe by stabilizing biospheric functions.

At present, approximately one-third of the world's land-mass can be categorized as wilderness, in which relatively natural ecosystems still exist in parcels larger than 4,000 sq. km (Martin 1987). This figure includes the Antarctic continent, which is almost all wilderness. In North America the proportion of wilderness is 35.5 per cent, much of it in the Canadian Arctic. There is no accurate worldwide assessment of the per cent of wilderness formally protected in parks or equivalent reserves, but with few nations contributing more than 10 per cent of their landmasses, it cannot be much.

Conservation Objectives of Protected Area Systems

In reviewing nature reserve systems around the world, the most commonly stated reasons for selecting areas are to protect rare or unique species and to retain maximum biotic diversity (Smith and Theberge 1986). Less common are objectives of obtaining maximum size and of naturalness, representativeness, and protection of fragile areas.

In Canada, most parks are established with the objective of representing the biophysical diversity of whatever political jurisdiction is doing the planning. The Canadian Parks Service, for example, uses *representativeness* as its goal and hopes to have at least one national park in all 39 terrestrial and 29 marine natural regions of Canada (see Chapters 4 and 5 and Figures 5.2 and 5.3). For park planning purposes, Canada is divided up into natural regions on the basis of differences in physiography and vegetation (Parks Canada 1971).

Some provincial parks systems and provincial nature or ecological reserve systems use similar provincial biophysical classifications as the basis of accomplishing representativeness (see Chapters 6 and 7). In Ontario, for example, Hill's classification based on vegetation, landform, soils, and climate provides the basis for provincial park system planning both for wilderness and nature reserve parks. In ecological reserve system planning, added emphasis is placed on the protection of rare species.

National wildlife areas, administered by the Canadian Wildlife Service, are planned more appropriately on the basis of species populations. Wetlands in particular have been emphasized. The system of national wildlife areas in Canada is pitifully small, while the United States' equivalent, the system of national wildlife refuges, incorporates more land than the U.S. national parks. Only one national wildlife area exists in the Canadian Arctic and the prospects for establishing more in the foreseeable future seem remote.

SPECIES ESPECIALLY NEEDING PROTECTED AREAS

Some efforts have been made to classify the biological traits of species that make some species more vulnerable than others to human disturbance and the probability of local or widespread extinction. The species showing these traits are important candidates for protected areas.

1. *K-strategists* win the evolutionary game when environmental conditions are stable by producing few offspring but investing a great deal of parental care in their welfare. They are long lived, exhibit habitat specialization, and have low rates of dispersal. They are vulnerable both because of their low reproductive rate, which limits their ability to replace losses, and because of their habitat specificity, which limits their ability to switch habitat types if one habitat is destroyed (Shaw 1985). Larger mammals and large birds tend to be K-strategists. Many amphibians and reptiles, while fecund, do show habitat specificity, which can be a threat to them.

2. *Summit predators* feed at the top of food chains and hence depend on all the lower links (Terborgh 1974). As well, they may suffer from the concentration of toxins in food chains. Most vertebrate summit predators, for example birds of prey, are K-strategists as well, making them doubly vulnerable.

3. *Species that concentrate* spatially are vulnerable because large numbers or even significant portions of regional populations can be wiped out by (e.g.) an oil spill (Figure 8.1), vandalism, or other local environmental insult. Such species include seabirds, goose and swan flocks, and other congregating waterfowl, as well as musk-oxen and caribou (Smith *et al.* 1986).

4. *Migratory birds* are vulnerable because of destruction of migratory or tropical wintering habitats and accumulation of toxins along migration routes (Terborgh 1974). Frightening evidence is accumulating that populations of the neotropical migrant perching birds that nest across Canada may be declining.

5. *Long-distance migratory mammals* are vulnerable if they cross jurisdictional boundaries and if no co-operative management is in place. For example, the George River caribou herd migrates across northern Labrador and Quebec on land managed by both provinces and by two groups of Native peoples, with no joint management agreement. Big-game species migrating across park boundaries commonly are open to exploitation outside the park.

6. *Large-bodied species* are often vulnerable because of generally low reproductive rates (Vermeij 1986).

Considering habitats rather than biological traits, the species most in need of protected areas in Canada include those that live in old-growth forest, tundra, prairie, and wetlands. Old-growth forest species such as Roosevelt elk, black-tailed deer, many herds of woodland caribou, and some large raptors such as eagles and great grey owls need extensive reserves both to conserve their habitat and to free them from exploitation. Tundra species, while affected less by habitat alteration, need large wilderness preserves to protect their often

Figure 8.1
Bird killed as a result of the 1989 oil spill at Pacific Rim National Park
Reserve. It is estimated that over 46,000 seabirds were killed in total.
Photo: P. Dearden

large traditional areas for calving and rutting (caribou and musk-oxen) and to protect herds from overexploitation (Figure 8.2). Prairie species need large protected areas for much the same reasons as do tundra wildlife, although both the dominant wide-ranging herbivore, the plains bison, and its predator, the prairie subspecies of wolf, have vanished. The recovery of the swift fox and even possibly the black-footed ferret, however, will require extensive areas of habitat protection and freedom from exploitation. Wetland wildlife, living in the greatest pockets of species diversity, need protection from marsh drainage or overenrichment from nutrients, as well as from overhunting.

Protected areas are less significant for urban wildlife (gray squirrel, cottontail, cardinal, and other back yard birds), farm wildlife (groundhog, red fox, coyote), and wildlife of early successional forests (white-tailed deer, moose, beaver), although some species need preserves for critical denning, nesting, and rutting functions and for winter cover, especially in heavily lumbered regions.

APPLYING ECOLOGICAL THEORY TO PRESERVATION

Ecology is a rapidly expanding science, both in theory and in application to environmental management. Like most sciences, as it progresses it has experienced trends and foci of attention. From the description and classification of ecosystems, it has matured to analysing of functional attributes. Most notably in the 1960s and 1970s, population science produced theories as to

Figure 8.2
Firth River, North Yukon National Park. One main reason for the establishment of this park was to protect the migration routes of the Porcupine caribou herd.   *Photo: P. Dearden*

how and why population is limited at a particular level or around one particular mean. More recently, research has centred on community behaviour (community being the aggregate of populations of different species in a given area) and is expanding into the newly emerging field of landscape ecology, examining whole regions. Driving this interest in theory is our realization that our understanding of biotic evolution is too reductionist. We have studied life *downward*, from species to DNA structure, but not *upward*. Eldredge (1985) postulates in his book *Unfinished Synthesis* that whole new dimensions of evolutionary understanding await discovery if we study upward as well as downward, exploring the origins, behaviours, and unique attributes of communities and regional landscapes.

We also have new tools to describe and classify ecosystems and regional landscapes: satellite images and geographic information systems. Satellite imagery allows us to see protected areas in their regional setting and is a powerful tool for both park system planning and regional planning. Geographic information systems (GIS) allow us to overlay resource maps such as those showing physiography, soils, hydrology, vegetation, wildlife, and land use, a flexibility that enhances the possibilities of discovering functional relationships. GIS analysis is especially useful for ecological land classifications such as those used in national parks or for resource survey methods for environmentally significant areas.

Advances in both theory and technology have turned the establishment and management of protected areas into an increasingly science-based activity.

Just as importantly, the advances have warned us of the potential failure of protected areas actually to *protect*. Gradually we are seeing protected areas as a vital but merely initial step in protecting the flora and fauna of a region. Increasingly, we learn that regional conservation strategies need to be built around them.

In six topics, ecological theory is being advanced to determine how much protected area is needed overall, how big a specific area ought to be, and where it ought to be located. These are: minimum viable population size, island biogeography, patch dynamics, fragmentation, stress ecology, and catastrophe theory.

Minimum Viable Population Size

Minimum viable population size involves attempts to calculate the smallest size of a park or reserve needed to support the minimum number of individuals for a viable and self-sustainable population. Often it is calculated for the most space-demanding species in an environment, with the hope that the space requirements of other species will be met within that area. Hence calculations often focus on large carnivores such as the grey wolf (Theberge 1983, Shields 1983, Hummel 1990) or the tiger (Tilson and Seal 1987). As well, analyses have focused on the critical or *keystone species* in an ecosystem such as the major herbivore (Soule 1987).

Two conceptual bases exist for calculating minimum viable population sizes: genetics and population demography. The genetics basis is founded upon the 1-per-cent rule: a population should not show more than 1 per cent inbreeding per generation. Inbreeding reduces genetic adaptability and the potential for responding to environmental change. This topic is explored in depth by Franklin (1980) and Soule (1980). From mathematical formulations comes the conclusion that at least 50 free-breeding adults are necessary to prevent more than 1 per cent inbreeding per generation, a population size which must be adjusted upwards for non-breeding animals such as juveniles or those excluded from breeding by social behaviour. Minimum population size and space requirements per individual then determine the minimum size of a park or reserve.

Unfortunately, for large carnivores these calculations show a need for very large reserves. Hummel (1990), based on calculations by A. Bath and H. Dueck at the University of Calgary, roughly estimated a minimum population size for wolves of about 150. With an approximate average density of 100 sq. km per wolf in western parts of the species' range (based on a survey made by Theberge of provincial and territorial wildlife management agencies in 1990), this results in a need for 15,000 sq. km. Few parks in Canada are that large. Even that calculation represents a *minimal* short-term value. For long-term genetic viability the minimum population size may be at least 10 times larger. Given no immigration, Franklin and Soule (1981) calculated that large carnivores (10–100 kg) can be expected to survive the next century in only 0–22 per cent of the world's parks and in none after 1,000 years.

The second basis for calculating minimum viable population size is through demography. Mathematical formulations and computer programs (e.g., Belovsky 1987) have been used to determine the probability of extinction over specified periods through varying such population parameters as birthrate, mortality, and reproductive age and output. These parameters are adjusted by environmental variables such as periodicity of catastrophe, amount of environmental variation, and patchiness of habitat (Goodman 1987).

Unlike the genetics-based calculation of minimum viable population size, these demographic calculations do not result in one single number. Rather, they are expressed in probabilities of extinction, and are both species- and environment-specific (Gilpin and Soule 1986). The minimum areas calculated with reasonable probabilities over even decades tend, unfortunately, to be even larger than those calculated through genetics. Especially at risk of extinction through demographic processes are large-bodied, long-lived species with a low rate of turnover, such as elephants and redwood trees, compared with small-bodied, short-lived species such as shrews and annual plants. For example, elephants require a minimum area of 10,000 sq. km for a 99 per cent probability of persistence for 1,000 years, whereas shrews require 1,000 sq. km (Belovsky 1987).

The lesson from these calculations of minimum viable population sizes is important. The long-term persistence of larger species, and hence of intact ecosystems in parks and reserves, depends on the survival of nearby populations from which periodic immigration may occur.

Island Biogeography

The possibilities of periodic immigration to a park or reserve have been explored through concepts of island biogeography. These concepts arose in the 1960s and contribute to current definitions of landscape ecology by incorporating broad regional environments. The concepts apply to ecological islands, surrounded either by water or by urban or agriculture lands, although these situations may not be completely equivalent.

Several classic studies have shown that small islands are unable to support as many species as large islands of similar habitat (Diamond 1975, Simberloff 1974). As a rough guide, a tenfold increase in area results in a near doubling in the number of species (MacArthur and Wilson 1967).

The number of species surviving on an island is not, however, merely a function of the island's size. It represents an equilibrium between species immigration and extinction, which depend not only on island size but on its distance from a colonizing source (MacArthur and Wilson 1967). In theory, the number of species on an island will be greater if the island is large and sources of immigration are close. For example the same number of species might persist on two islands, one large and far from sources of immigrants, one small but close to sources of immigrants.

These variables of size and distance have led to an interest in the optimum pattern for a system of reserves: the so-called SLOSS debate (Single Large or Several Small). Diamond (1975) proposed that one large reserve was better than a number of small ones; that a number of reserves close together was better than the same number spread out; that three reserves in a triangular pattern is better than three reserves strung out linearly; and that a circular reserve is better than one with an oval shape (having less edge). Soule (1983) proposed that three small reserves are better than one large one, and four reserves spaced out are better than four tightly grouped. Benefits obviously vary with the dispersal abilities, mobility, and habitat requirements of species.

Patch Dynamics

Refining the ideas of island biogeography, and contributing further to the field of landscape ecology, is the study of patch dynamics. All landscapes are composed of patches, corridors, and a matrix (Forman and Godron 1986). Landscapes are heterogeneous and differ structurally in the distribution of species, energy, and materials among these patches, corridors, and matrices. If we consider parks and reserves outside the concept of landscape, we fail to see the flow of species, energy, and materials that may confer long-term viability and persistence on protected areas.

Within-patch dynamics is largely the subject of traditional community ecology. Forman and Godron (1986) argue that ecology has not focused sufficiently on between-patch dynamics, except on species migration in island biogeography. Relationships that involve the exchange of energy and materials as well as species among patches will depend on a whole range of factors: patch shape, isolation, pattern of dispersion across a landscape, ratio of edge to interior, species diversity, patch persistence, and (of course) the existence of corridors between patches. Corridors themselves have been classified by origin and structure (Forman and Godron 1986). Corridors maintain higher species diversity in refuges by allowing reciprocal immigration (Simberloff and Cox 1987). However, corridors have disadvantages, too; they can contribute to the spread of disease, disrupt local genetic adaptation by facilitating outbreeding, increase susceptibility to fire, and make poaching easier (Noss 1987).

The subject of the relationships of patches to their matrix, or surrounding area, has provided a primary focus for the study of the effects of disturbance on patch dynamics. Pickett and White (1985) developed a theory of vulnerability to disturbance that relates to a number of system structures: proportional biomass above and below ground; the availability of nutrients and other resources; growth rates and resource demands of species; competition among species; landscape characteristics such as the composition and configuration of patches; and natural disturbance regimes (fire, flood, etc.). Once again, the message that comes from patch dynamics is that species within parks may not be able to persist if the parks exist as ecological islands (Figure 8.3).

Figure 8.3
Logging near the West Coast Trail Unit of Pacific Rim National Park
Reserve. According to some sources, all old-growth forest surrounding the
park will be logged by the year 2001. Other sources give the forest until the
year 2034. In either case, the park will sooner or later become an isolated
island of old-growth forest.   *Photo: P. Dearden*

Fragmentation

The flip side of patch dynamics is fragmentation, the break-up of a natural
matrix. Fragmentation is seen as critical: 'Habitat fragmentation is the most
serious threat to biological diversity and is the primary cause of the present
extinction crisis' (Wilcox and Murphy 1985); and 'habitat fragmentation
looms on the horizon as one of the most important issues that will affect the
numbers and distribution of wildlife' (Temple 1986). Some generalizations
can be made about habitat fragmentation. For example Wilcove *et al.* (1986)
concluded that the effects of fragmentation are greater in tropical than in
temperate regions. Temperate species occur in higher densities and have
wider distributions and greater dispersal powers than do tropical species.

Species that are especially susceptible to the effects of fragmentation
include deep-forest species and long-distance migrants (Whitcomb 1981).
Other vulnerable species are those with large territories, specialized habitats,
colonial habits, and low productivity. The latter two characteristics make
species vulnerable to overhunting or poaching when fragmentation is caused
by roads.

Much traditional literature on wildlife management, going right back to Leopold's classic *Game Management* (1933), emphasizes the importance of edge
habitat to high species diversity. Habitat manipulations were, and still are,

designed to fragment large blocks of uniform habitat by creating more openings and to improve conditions for the considerable number of edge species. However, conservation concern increasingly is shifting from obtaining maximum species diversity *per se* to providing for deep-forest species that may be jeopardized by fragmentation (Yahner 1988). Soule (1986) coined the term *sedge* for the ratio of edge to size, and observed that 'edge and sedge effects feed upon themselves autocatalytically. The result is a creeping edge that can eventually reach the core of even a relatively large reserve.'

Stress ecology

Both patch dynamics and fragmentation address the impact of external factors on natural areas. So does stress ecology. Closely related to stress ecology is the concept of *ecosystem health*; that is, the identification of fully functional ecosystems with natural rates of energy capture and flow and nutrient uptake and cycling, and with intact food webs and undisturbed mechanisms of population regulation.

Stresses from outside or within play an integral and ongoing role in the organization, evolution, and functions of ecosystems. Many natural stresses exist, differing in intensity, duration, and frequency of occurrence. They may act to influence ecosystems additively, in multiple ways, or by synergistic effects (Turner and Bratton 1987). Lugo (1978) observed that 'without a periodic disruption, ecosystem growth processes stagnate as resources are immobilized by their structure. Bursts of growth and high net productivity usually follow disturbances, and rejuvenated systems replace senescent systems.'

Widespread agreement exists that ecosystems exhibit common patterns of response when stressed by either natural or human causes (Freedman 1989, Woodwell 1983). Indeed, natural stresses such as climate variation, succession, fire, disease, and changes in population sizes of predators may preadapt ecosystems to human-caused stresses. Among characteristics exhibited by stressed ecosystems, extracted from a list of 18 characteristics by Odum (1985) and by Rapport et al. (1985), are the following:

1. Changes in nutrient cycles, including increased *leakiness.*
2. Changes (normally an increase) in net primary productivity.
3. Changes in species composition, including loss of late successional stage species and a greater proportion of small-bodied, rapidly reproducing, hardy species.

Feedback allows ecosystems to cope with the effects of stress. For example, some ecosystems react to stress by replacing their more sensitive species with functionally similar but more resistant species. But just as in human systems, stress can go too far. Lovelock (1988) contends that 'from physiology, we know that the perturbations of a system that is close to instability can lead to oscillations, chaotic change, or failure.' For example, Rapport et *al.* (1985) observed that northern forested areas treated with herbicide stayed under shrubs even after the spraying program was stopped.

Protected areas are subjected to constant human-caused stress from both outside and within. From the exploration of stress ecology and ecosystem health a basis for ecosystem monitoring is emerging (Woodley and Theberge, in press). At present, few parks or reserves in Canada are being monitored, but this situation will undoubtedly change in the next few years. Monitoring for ecosystem stress can not only aid park management but also contribute to regional environmental management; it is a particular and immediate challenge for park managers to seize this opportunity. The task is to translate the theory into practical field procedures based upon indicator organisms and sampling strategies.

Catastrophe Theory

Catastrophe theory, even more than stress ecology, has altered significantly earlier concepts of stability in ecosystems. It has placed a greater premium on resilience in ecosystems; that is, on their capacity to bounce back (Holling 1973). Catastrophe—sudden change such as a population crash or eruption or a wholesale change in the ecosystem through fire or flood—is natural in most ecosystems. It only carries a pejorative connotation if resource management demands a steady state. A steady system is not the objective in most protected areas, where natural ecological forces are supposed to be allowed.

Population models before, during, and after a catastrophe were advanced by Jones (1975). Most frequently cited examples of catastrophe are fire (Bormann and Likens 1979, Holling 1973) and spruce budworm (Holling 1973, May 1977). Olson (1987) used the models to explain the recurrence of the plague-carrying rat in Madagascar. In all the examples, predisposing environmental factors increase in intensity until a catastrophe becomes inevitable.

If we allow for catastrophes with some predictable periodicity (based upon probabilities) in models of minimum viable population sizes, the results again argue for very large reserves. They argue, too, for the protection of more than one example of ecosystems, and for multiple reserves to protect rare and endangered species.

CONCLUSIONS

As exciting as the advances in conservation biology and landscape ecology may be, they have provided few magic answers to the critical questions— how many? how big? and where?—about protected areas. Even without precise answers to these questions, these theories have provided a scientific support for one vitally important thesis: our protected areas everywhere in Canada are too small and too few to withstand external and internal assaults indefinitely or to protect minimum viable population sizes, especially of the functionally dominant large predators and migratory species, over the long term. As a consequence, parks and reserves must be seen for what they are: only parts of any regional conservation strategy. Because parks and reserves are not ecologically self-sufficient entities, regional environmental management is an absolutely necessary component of managing protected areas. No longer can parks agencies justify confining their programs and policies to within park boundaries. The success of protected areas in protecting ecosystems depends entirely upon the response of park management agencies to the challenge, obligation, and opportunity to broaden their scope. More than the parks are at stake.

Ecology is complex. There is a point where our understanding, and hence the strict application of science, ends. That is where philosophy must take over. Why should we be concerning ourselves with *minimum* viable population sizes, *smallest* possible reserves, *fewest* protected areas? Do those of us who care about things wild and free have to invoke scientific justification for saving even small remnants of the natural world around us? Is ecology in the service of establishing protected areas, or even in other forms of environmental management, only another example of our extreme anthropocentric attitude towards nature?

If we must define 'how much? how big? and where?' on the basis of science, even as the new concepts discussed here continue to unfold, we will quite possibly—perhaps inevitably—make mistakes. Consider Canada's losses, summarized in the introduction to this chapter. The world rate of species extinction right now is catastrophic.

One antidote, proposed for the Arctic by Livingston (1981), is to consider the whole environment as a park and to allow, on a case-by-case basis, only enclaves of disturbed areas within it. Indeed, it may take that magnitude of rethinking to save the biosphere. In the meantime, the only hope for the persistence of species in parks and reserves is to view nature as having extrinsic worth everywhere. At the top of the environmental agenda must be the establishment of many more large parks and reserves and the forging of broad and strongly protective regional conservation strategies to buttress them. With all the environmentally destructive forces controlling resource and land management in Canada, there is little chance that we will ever protect too much.

ACKNOWLEDGEMENTS

This essay benefited from a thought-provoking graduate seminar course in applied ecology in the winter term of 1990. I acknowledge the insights of Cameron Douglas, Graham Forbes, Lyle Friesen, Deborah Ramsay, Donna Taylor, and Steve Woodley.

REFERENCES

Belovsky, G.E.
  1987 'Extinction Models and Mammalian Persistence', in *Viable Populations for Conservation*, ed. M.E. Soule, Cambridge University Press, Cambridge, 3–57.
Bormann, F., H. Likens, and G.E. Likens
  1979 'Catastrophic Disturbance and the Steady State in Northern Hardwood Forests', *American Scientist* 67: 66–9.
Diamond, J.M.
  1975 'The Island Dilemma: Lessons of Modern Biogeographic Studies for the Design of Nature Reserves', *Biological Conservation* 7: 129–46.
Eldredge, N.
  1985 *Unfinished Synthesis: Biological Hierarchies and Modern Evolutionary Thought*, Oxford University Press, Oxford.
Forman, R.T.T., and M. Godron
  1986 *Landscape Ecology*, John Wiley and Sons, New York.
Franklin, I.R.
  1980 'Evolutionary Change in Small Populations', in *Conservation Biology: An Evolutionary-Ecological Perspective*, eds M.E. Soule and B.A. Wilcox, Sinauer Associates, Sunderland, Mass., 135–49.
Franklin, O.H., and M.E. Soule
  1981 *Conservation and Evolution*, Cambridge University Press, Cambridge.
Freedman, W.
  1989 *Environmental Ecology: The Impacts of Pollution and Other Stresses on Ecosystem Structures and Functions*, Academic Press, San Francisco.
Gilpin, M.E., and M.E. Soule
  1986 'Minimum Viable Populations: Processes of Species Extinction', in *Conservation Biology: The Science of Scarcity and Diversity*, ed. M.E. Soule, Sinauer Associates, Sunderland, Mass., 19–34.
Goodman, D.
  1987 'The Demography of Chance Extinction', in *Viable Populations for Conservation*, ed. M.E. Soule, Cambridge University Press, 11–34.
Holling, C.S.
  1973 'Resilience and Stability of Ecological Systems', *Annual Review of Ecological Systems* 4: 1–23.
Hummel, M.
  1990 *Conservation Strategy for Large Carnivores in Canada*, World Wildlife Fund Canada, Toronto.
Jones, D.D.
  1975 'The Application of Catastrophe Theory to Ecological Systems', in *New Directions in the Analysis of Ecological Systems*, ed. G.S. Innis, Simulation Councils Proceedings Series, vol. 5, 133–48.
Leopold, A.
  1933 *Game Management*, Scribner, New York.

Livingston, J.A.

1981   *Arctic Oil, the Destruction of the North?* Canadian Broadcasting Corporation, Toronto.

Lovelock, J.

1988   *The Ages of Gaia.* W.W. Norton & Company, New York.

Lugo, A.E.

1978   'Stress in Ecosystems', in *Energy and the Environment*, Stress in Aquatic Ecosystems, United States Department of Energy Symposium, series 78, eds J.H. Thorpe and J.W. Gibbons, National Technical Information Service, Springfield Ill., 61–101.

MacArthur, R.H., and E.O. Wilson

1967   *The Theory of Island Biogeography*, Princeton University Press, Princeton, N.J.

Martin, V.

1987   *Protected African Wilderness Areas: A Preview to a World Wilderness Inventory*, International Wilderness Leadership Foundation, Fort Collins, Colo.

May, R.M.

1977   'Thresholds and Breakpoints in Ecosystems with a Multiplicity of Stable States', *Nature* 269: 471–8.

Nelson, J.G., P.G.R. Smith, and J.B. Theberge

1985   'Environmentally Significant Areas (ESA) in the Northwest Territories, Canada: Their Role, Identification, Designation and Implementation', *Environments* 17: 93–109.

Noss, R.F.

1987   'Corridors in Real Landscapes: A Reply to Simberloff and Cox', *Conservation Biology* 1: 159–64.

Odum, E.P.

1985   'Trends Expected in Stressed Ecosystems', *Bioscience* 35: 419–22.

Olson, S.

1987   'Red Destinies: The Landscape of Environmental Risk in Madagaskar', *Human Ecology* 15: 67–89.

Parks Canada

1971   *National Parks System Planning Manual*, National and Historic Parks Branch, Department of Indian Affairs and Northern Development, Ottawa.

Pickett, S.T.A., and P.S. White

1985   'Patch Dynamics: A Synthesis', in *The Ecology of Natural Disturbance and Patch Dynamics*, eds S.T.A. Pickett and P.S. White, Academic Press, San Diego, 371–84.

Pim, S.L., H.L. Jones, and J. Diamond

1988   'On the Risk of Extinction', *American Naturalist* 132: 757–85.

Rapport, D.J., H.A. Reiger, and T.C. Hutchinson

1985   'Ecosystem Behaviour Under Stress', *American Naturalist* 125: 617–40.

Shaw, J.H.

1985   *Introduction to Wildlife Management*, McGraw-Hill, New York.

Shields, W.M.
  1983   'Genetic Considerations in the Management of the Wolf and Other Large
          Vertebrates: An Alternative View', in *Wolves in Canada and Alaska*, ed.
          L.N. Carbyn, Canadian Wildlife Service Report Series, Number 45, Ottawa,
          90–2.
Simberloff, D.S.
  1974   'Equilibrium Theory of Island Biogeography and Ecology', *Annual Review
          of Ecology and Systematics* 1974/5: 161–82.
Simberloff, D.S., and J. Cox
  1987   'Consequences and Costs of Conservation Corridors', *Conservation Biology*
          1: 63–9.
Smith, P.G.R., and J.B. Theberge
  1986   'A Review of Criteria for Evaluating Natural Areas', *Environmental Man-
          agement*, 10: 715–34.
Smith, P.G.R., J.G. Nelson, and J.B. Theberge
  1986   *Environmentally Significant Areas, Conservation and Land Use Manage-
          ment in the Northwest Territories*, Technical Paper Number 1, Heritage
          Resources Center, University of Waterloo, Waterloo, Ont.
Soule, M.E.
  1980   'Thresholds for Survival: Maintaining Fitness and Evolutionary Potential',
          in *Conservation Biology: An Evolutionary-Ecological Perspective*, eds M.E.
          Soule and B.A. Wilcox, Sinauer Associates, Sunderland, Mass.,
          151–69.
Soule, M.E.
  1983   'Application of Genetics and Population Biology: The What, Where and
          How of Nature Reserves', in *Conservation, Science and Society*, UNESCO-
          UNEP, 252–64.
Soule, M.E.
  1986   'Conservation Biology and the Real World', in *Conservation Biology: The
          Science of Scarcity and Diversity*, ed. M.E. Soule, Sinauer Associates, Sun-
          derland, Mass., 1–12.
Soule, M.E.
  1987   *Viable Populations for Conservation*, Cambridge University Press,
          Cambridge.
Temple, S.A.
  1986   'Book Review of *The Fragmented Forest: Island Biogeography and the
          Preservation of Biotic Diversity*', *Journal of Wildlife Management* 50: 176.
Terborgh, J.
  1974   'Preservation of Natural Diversity: The Problem of Extinction Prone Spe-
          cies', *Bioscience* 24: 715–22.
Theberge, J.B.
  1983   'Considerations in Wolf Management Related to Genetic Variability and
          Adaptive Change', in *Wolves in Canada and Alaska*, ed. L.N. Carbyn, Cana-
          dian Wildlife Service Report Series, Number 45, Ottawa, 86–9.
Theberge, J.B.
  1987   *Our Parks—Vision for the 21st Century*, Environment Canada Parks,
          Ottawa, and the Heritage Resources Center, University of Waterloo, Water-
          loo, Ont.

Tilson, R.L., and U.S. Seal, eds
  1987   *Tigers of the World: The Biology, Biopolitics, Management, and Conservation of an Endangered Species*, Noyes Publications, Park Ridge, N.J.
Turner, M., and S.P. Bratton
  1987   'Fire, Grazing, and the Landscape Heterogeneity of a Georgia Barrier Island', in *Landscape Heterogeneity and Disturbance*, ed. M. Turner, Springer-Verlag, New York, 85–101.
Vermeij, G.J.
  1986   'The Biology of Human-caused Extinction', in *The Preservation of Species: The Value of Biological Diversity*, ed. B.G. Norton, Princeton University Press, Princeton, 28–49.
Whitcomb, R.F., C.S. Robbins, J.F. Lynch, B.L. Whitcomb, M.K. Klimkiewicz, and D. Bystrack
  1981   'Effects of Forest Fragmentation on Avifauna of the Eastern Deciduous Forest', in *Forest Island Dynamics in Man-Dominated Landscapes*, eds R.L. Burgess and D.M. Sharpe, Springer-Verlag, New York, 125–205.
Wilcove, D.S., C.H. McLellan, and A.P. Dobson
  1986   'Habitat Fragmentation in the Temperate Zone', in *Conservation Biology: The Science of Scarcity and Diversity*, ed. M.E. Soule, Sinauer Associates, Sunderland, Mass. 237–56.
Wilcox, B.A., and D.D. Murphy
  1985   'Conservation Strategy: The Effects of Fragmentation on Extinction', *American Naturalist* 125: 879–87.
Woodley, S., and J.B. Theberge
  1992   'Monitoring for Ecosystem Integrity in Canadian National Parks', in *Science and the Management of Protected Areas*, eds. J.H.M. Willison *et al.*, Elsevier, New York.
Woodwell, G.M.
  1983   'The Blue Planet: Of Wholes and Parts and Man', in *Disturbance and Ecosystems*, eds H.A. Mooney and M. Gordon, Springer-Verlag, Berlin, 2–10.
World Commission on Environment and Development
  1987   *Our Common Future*, Oxford University Press, New York and Oxford.
World Conservation Strategy
  1980   IUCN-UNEP-WWF, Gland, Switzerland.
Yahner, R.H.
  1988   'Changes in Wildlife Communities Near Edges', *Conservation Biology* 2: 333–9.

CHAPTER 9

Environmental Management in Parks

—

PAUL F.J. EAGLES

INTRODUCTION

Managing the environment is an essential aspect of park administration. Parks are often, but not always, established because of a natural resource that attracted attention. For example, the creation of a provincial park in 1970 in Ontario's Hudson Bay Lowlands was for the protection of significant low-arctic tundra ecosystems (Ontario Ministry of Natural Resources 1977). The presence of an impressive population of polar bears gave the park its name. However, some significant natural ecosystems have been protected in parks almost by accident. The land for Kootenay National Park was given by the province of British Columbia to Canada in return for the building of a highway, resulting in the park's corridor shape, five miles each side of the highway (Boissonneault, pers. comm.). Only long after its establishment did the importance of the park's forest and grassland ecosystems become known.

It is important to recognize that the phrase 'natural resource management' is value laden. If a resource is something that people value, then, a natural resource is a part of nature that people value. For example, trees are usually considered to be a natural resource because of their valuable byproducts, wood and fibre. Conversely, parts of nature that people do not see to be of immediate use are not considered natural resources. Is the squirrel that lives in the tree a natural resource? Not usually, unless someone wants to hunt it, or eat it, or look at it. The concept of a natural resource, then, is inherently anthropocentric. Something achieves this status when people decide that it is of use and therefore of value.

In recent decades, the term 'natural resources' management has been broadened as our changing philosophy of nature starts to include more concern for the processes and elements of the environment, whether or not they are of immediate use to humans. Most parks give value to all living and non-living features because all elements of nature are seen as being part of the biosphere and therefore part of functioning ecosystems. Since all people depend upon the biosphere for survival, the essential parts of the biosphere are valuable. The phrase 'environmental management' is now being used to indicate a broader emphasis on all aspects of the environment, not just on those seen as natural resources.

Dorney (1989) points out that this change in emphasis is due to a change from a *market* point of view, based upon growth and progress, to an *ecological* point of view, based upon the maintenance of an equilibrium between humans and nature. From this latter view comes the notion that all nature is of value because it exists. It does not have to be of use to humankind, or even to be known about. It simply has to be.

The concept of management is also value laden. To manage is to guide or to control. Typically, management involves setting goals, marshalling resources, and taking action to fulfil those goals. It is inherently manipulative. Some managers feel that they must interfere, must change the environment, or they are not properly fulfilling their management role. They also argue that, given the global forces which negatively affect the world's environment, 'too many ecosystems need help to survive, or get back into a healthy, functioning, self-sustaining balance. This will require increasingly active management' (Watson, pers. comm.).

ENVIRONMENTAL MANAGEMENT

Consider typical natural resource management outside parks. A forester managing a woodlot sees the trees as the primary focus of attention. Those trees that produce the most valuable market commodity are ranked highest, and the goal of management is to produce as many of those trees in as short a time as possible. The entire ecosystem is manipulated towards that goal. Management sees species that interfere with the 'right' tree as a nuisance, and so tree herbivores are killed and competing plants, called weeds, are removed if possible. Abiotic (non-living) elements of the environment are also manipulated to produce maximum growth; management adds fertilizers and perhaps water. Imperfect individuals of the important species are culled, so that only the best remain.

This type of management regime is inherently simple. The goals are clear and unambiguous—to produce the maximum of a particular species as quickly as possible. This is a typical approach to resource management.

What are the implications of such an approach? The value of the elements of the ecosystem is determined by the marketplace and those with the highest monetary value are given elevated status. But this concept is ecologically illiterate. The value of each element to the functioning of the natural environment is not taken into account in assessing what is important.

The spotted owl controversy is an example of the clash of values between traditional resource management and the environmental approach. The rain forests of western North America extend from northern California along the Pacific coast through Oregon, Washington, British Columbia, and Alaska. This area of rich soils, abundant moisture, and temperate climate encourages the growth of magnificent forests of very old, very large Douglas fir, giant sequoia and Western red cedar. The trees have become a much-sought natural resource. They have been cut since the last century at a prodigious rate and the amount of old-growth forest remaining is shrinking rapidly.

The spotted owl lives in these forests, as far north as southwestern British Columbia (Godfrey 1986). The owl has a territory of several hundred hectares and depends on old-growth trees. As the forests go, so goes the bird. The bird has no commercial value. Therefore, the marketplace sees it as being an externality, an irrelevance.

The question now asked in the United States and Canada is 'How many spotted owls should be allowed to live in the world?' Every spotted owl pair that survives takes valuable timber out of the natural resource economy. The timber industry views the idea of preserving millions of dollars worth of trees for a few owls as being at the very least silly and more often as sheer heresy.

Naturalists see the issue differently. One line of reasoning says that the owl has a role to play in the ecosystem and it thus achieves value. Another view is that the owl exists and therefore is of value; it achieves its right to exist by being. Humans have no right to destroy this species. Yet another argument is that the owl is an indicator of a mature ecosystem that should be preserved because of the age and stability of that system.

The debate is now at the highest level of officialdom in the United States and Canada. Recent discussions in the U.S. resulted in the bird being listed as an endangered species under national legislation. A hard-fought debate between short-term economics and long-term species preservation is underway. In Canada, the issues are similar. However, Canada does not have national endangered species legislation, so this option is not available for the discussion of the species' future in this country.

Throughout the world, debates similar to this are raging around the allocation of the few remaining natural areas. The protection of some of these areas as parks is one option; so are agriculture, forestry, and urbanization (Eagles 1984).

Understanding the ecosystem, and the value placed on this knowledge, are inherent parts of management. The values put on the ecosystem and its parts underlie all resource allocation decisions.

ECOLOGICAL FUNCTIONS OF PARKS

Parks fulfil many significant ecological functions. It is important that park visitors and park administrators both understand the associated concepts. Any management policy must take such functions into account.

Preservation of Genetic Diversity

Parks play a critical role in preserving representative samples of plant and animal populations. One long-term goal of Canada's park system is to preserve examples of every major ecosystem type in the country. Parks also protect different copies of similar ecosystems in various areas—perhaps, for example, a slightly different ecotype of a species. Species' genetic composition varies throughout the species' range due to varying environmental influences. For example, peregrine falcons have different subspecies in the western mountains, the Arctic, and the eastern forests of Canada (Weir 1987). Conserving this diversity is important both for its own sake and because genetically depauperate species are highly vulnerable. Therefore, protected areas need to be established throughout the country for the breeding sites of each subspecies of this falcon.

Parks play a very special role when they help conserve the last few members of an endangered species and their habitat. In recent years, it has become clear that by themselves parks are too few and too small to fulfil the role of genetic preservation. Other categories of land must also serve the same function. Forest reserves, cottage country, and farmlands contribute to regional ecological diversity. They must be managed in the future to continue this contribution.

Benchmark Protection

The impact of humans on an environment can only be fully understood if there are relatively unchanged areas for comparative purposes. Such an area is a *benchmark*, a term derived from the starting point used by land surveyors when laying out property lines. Parks that have had minimum human impact serve vital roles as ecological benchmarks for measuring ecological change both within the parks and in nearby areas.

A classic example of this is Killarney Provincial Park in Ontario. Dr Harvey of the University of Toronto, conducting research on the fish populations of the park in the 1960s, noticed that fish were becoming scarce in certain lakes. Furthermore, the pH concentration of the water in these lakes was decreasing. He postulated that the chemical fallout from the nearby Sudbury refineries might be a cause.

It has been subsequently discovered that Harvey was essentially correct in his hypothesis; wind-born acid-forming gases deposited in the lakes caused the loss of the fish. However, the source of the acid was industrial activity throughout central North America, not just Sudbury. Harvey's work was one of the first discoveries of that well-known phenomenon, acid rain. Killarney Park had inadvertently served as a very important water quality benchmark.

Conservation of Critical Ecological Processes

Parks often play important roles in conserving ecological processes, for example, for the cleaning of water and air by natural ecological processes. Parks also allow for the natural functioning of nutrient cycles and energy flows. Products of these cycles, such as a portion of a wildlife population, also go outside the park.

Ecological processes may be heavily altered by human activities outside parks. It is virtually impossible to study natural ecological relationships within an ecosystem that is under constant stress from human activities. For example, some of the most significant long-term population studies of timber wolf populations have been in parks; Algonquin Provincial Park in Ontario is a prime example. In this park, the wolf and its prey, beaver, deer and moose, have not been hunted for many decades until very recently. But logging in Algonquin, which has a large impact on the natural ecological processes, may affect the wolf populations in ways that are not well understood. Similar long-term timber wolf population studies have been carried out in Isle Royale National Park on the U.S. side of Lake Superior. This park has no logging and therefore is probably a better example than Algonquin of naturally functioning ecological processes (Watson, pers. comm.).

Park Products

Most parks have a role in creating products that people want, from ducks hunted in a wildlife preserve and eaten to deer watched appreciatively in a provincial park.

Such products can also be the clean air and clean water that flow out of the park. One justification for the establishment of Algonquin Provincial Park in 1893 was the retention of forest in the headwater areas of rivers that were of critical importance as transportation corridors; water flow needed to be retained for this purpose. In essence the park 'produces' water throughout the year for downstream users.

Parks also act as conservatories for as yet undiscovered products. For example, many common antibiotics are simply fungal antibacterial agents, which we appropriate for our own benefit. We have no notion what the soils, fungi, plants, and animals contain that could be of use in the future.

Sustainable Utilization

We have not learned how to live within our environmental means in a long-term sustainable way. We continue to squander our natural capital. The production processes in parks can be of use as models for developing sustainable utilization strategies outside parks. For example, the natural flow of energy through an ecosystem is the result of millennia of evolutionary experimentation. The study of such processes can provide vital insight into how nature has solved the problem of the sustainable utilization of resources (World Conservation Union et al. 1991).

Protecting Unique Features

Parks are often established to protect extraordinary natural features such as the Nahanni National Park gorges in the Northwest Territories, Niagara Falls, the extraordinary fossils of the Burgess Shales in Yoho National Park in British Columbia, migrating birds at Point Pelee National Park, or the very old trees in the Cathedral Grove Provincial Park in British Columbia. Sometimes these features were discovered or recognized only after the park was created (Boissonneault, pers. comm.).

ENVIRONMENTAL MANAGEMENT IN PARKS

In parks an environmental resource is any feature or element of nature, from a forest to a fossil. Assigning value to each element in a park is vital to all management and will determine later environmental protection policy and management choices, such as the types of activities permitted.

Assessing Value in a Park

Setting value to any environmental resource relies on a variety of means. One must assess its ecological value and its role in the ecosystem, as well as its scarcity or abundance. Its aesthetic value is often important; we see grizzly bears as more appealing than the black widow spider. Commercial value is usually not the first priority, but it is nevertheless important. However, the market for parks is different. Nature is neither removed nor altered, merely observed—and there is a market for nature observation. Some people do want to see really big trees and the spotted owls and other creatures that live among them, and are willing to travel, to buy books or videos, or to watch television shows. Some people merely want to know that the trees and the owls exist, even if they never see them in person. Some will join study groups; others will join politically active organizations. All these desires create a market for what a park has to offer—observation, learning, reflection, and conservation.

Assigning value to a park element is important but difficult. Examining some of the factors used in determining such value may be helpful.

One strain of thought states that *all aspects of a park are of value* simply because they exist. All species, all landscapes, and all ecological processes have inherent value. This concept has recently been recognized as being part of the environmental management activities in Canadian national parks.

According to this concept, the processes of the ecosystem determine the value of each element. We know little of how ecosystems function; the most prudent course of action is to study the ebb and flow of nature as it exists. Man should watch, not interfere; management should be hands-off as much as possible. Environmental management means the study of nature to understand these processes and the management of the park *visitor*, so that visitors do not interfere with the natural processes.

A second strain of thought states that *all aspects of a park are of value, but not of equal value.* An endangered species is of higher value than a common species. A species at the edge of its range is of higher value than a species in the centre of its range. A species, landscape, or natural phenomenon that is aesthetically pleasing or attractive to visitors is of higher value.

Examples of this approach are legion. Building a road to a point of interest in a park is typical. Labelling one area of a park as a point of interest is a value determination. One place in nature is given more value; other points become less valuable. The road destroys some other, less valued feature of the park. Parks are not isolated islands in a sea of tranquillity. They are part of the world's biosphere, which is under assault by humans and their activities. Therefore we cannot leave nature to its own devices in a park because the influences coming from outside the park are too big and too important. *Active management and intervention in nature is inevitable.*

An example of the differing philosophies involved in management is the issue of beach management in Point Pelee National Park. This park is a long sand funnel sticking south into Lake Erie. The entire length of the peninsula is beach, while its northern edge abuts land that was once extensive marsh but has been drained for vegetable and fruit farming. In recent years the lake level has fluctuated widely. In the late 1980s, the water hit record high levels. During periods of storm, the wave damage was extensive as the waters swept into the dryland forests at the tip of the park (see Figure 9.1) and eroded areas of marshlands that had been previously protected behind barrier beaches.

Some people felt that the water level changes were an act of nature and that remedial action was inappropriate. Others pointed out that Point Pelee was composed entirely of sand that has been deposited by lake currents. The source of this sand is eroded cliffs elsewhere along the shore, but anti-erosion measures had been taken, depriving the park of this supply. Part of the beach erosion in the park was therefore the result of interference in a natural system outside the park. Therefore, remedial action was an alternative, as the changes were not entirely natural. A third line of argument stated that no matter what the reasons for the changes were, the entire system was too poorly known for accurate predictions to be made.

Here we have a classic example of the questions that must be faced. What is causing the change? Is the change natural or caused by humans? If intervention must be considered, what alternatives are available? What is the probability of failure or of unanticipated consequences of any management action?

At Pelee, the managers stuck to the non-interference philosophy as much as they could, but some action was taken to reduce erosion, including rock rip-rap, offshore pilings, and concrete structures embedded offshore, to trap moving sand and encourage shoreline deposition. Unfortunately, the shoreline erosion increased and necessitated the removal of several damaged structures and their replacement by buildings in areas out of harm's way, at the expense of other parkland.

During the same period, the U.S. Corps of Engineers were taking a very active intervention approach towards reducing the impact of high lake level at Presque Isle State Park in Pennsylvania on the south shore of Lake Erie. This park is also a forested sand spit projecting out into the lake and was

Figure 9.1
Winter storm damage on East Beach, Point Pelee National Park, 3 May
1986. The high water levels in Lake Erie, combined with winter storms,
resulted in severe forest damage to the sand-based forests of Point Pelee.

Credit: P. Eagles

also suffering erosion. The Corps dumped millions of tons of sand onto the
exposed beaches and let the currents move the deposit along the sand spit.
This new sand buffered the action of the lake waves, and this park suffered
little from beach erosion. On the other hand, the high lake level raised the
ground-water level in the forests, flooding the roots of the trees and killing
many (Eagles 1988a).

In 1988 the lake levels started to drop dramatically, thereby slowing the erosion. If the lake level had stayed high, would the park managers at Pelee have allowed the forests to be destroyed? Even if the managers decided to interfere, would they have been able to find the money to do so on a large scale? The Pelee and Presque Isle examples show that many managers feel that, given the vagaries of nature and the omnipresent actions of human society, active intervention in parks is inevitable.

A third strain of thought holds that it is our duty to manage nature. This philosophy holds that humans were given domination over the earth and have the right, and indeed the obligation, to manage nature. This approach is very widely held by many resource extraction businesses and professionals, especially by their older members (Bos *et al.* 1977; Eagles 1980). For example Rondeau Provincial Park, on the north shore of Lake Erie half-way between Windsor and Niagara Falls, contains 2,500 ha of mature southern forest of a type found in Canada only in southwestern Ontario (Allen *et al.*, 1990). Outside the park, these forests virtually vanished due to clearing for agriculture. During the 1930s, crews were sent into the parks on makework projects. They set about 'cleaning up' the parks, removing dead trees and brush. They also removed massive but imperfect trees, cutting a tulip tree that was 3 m in diameter because it was hollow (North, pers. comm.). Such interference within a natural ecosystem can have serious consequences.

This active interference, based upon the idea of cleaning up, civilizing, or beautifying nature, is still practised in some parks. It is frequent in municipal parks, especially those with an emphasis on horticulture.

Who Determines Value?

Determining the value of a park resource, and therefore its management, is a central issue. Which groups should have a stake in this process? A number of interested parties have claims to be involved in parks decision making.

First, park agencies have staff, often highly trained and with long experience, who are familiar with the agency's policies and with the park system itself. These people often have strong emotional and professional ties to the park in question and an in-depth knowledge and appreciation of its features that cannot be ignored.

Second, Canada has a large pool of outside expertise, in universities, government, and industry, with considerable knowledge of topics like botany, zoology, ecology, and geology. It would be foolish to exclude their insight and information from the decision making process.

Third, parks are political, in that park agencies have political masters, although many board or commission members are appointed, not elected. Politicians presumably represent the will of the people, and ours is a democratic society. Moreover, governments usually foot the bill for the consequences of decisions made by parks agencies, and financial and policy constraints cannot be ignored. Should park policy be the same across Ontario?

across Canada? What is this political constituency? And since our parks may include features of worldwide significance, like the Burgess Shales, should the international community not have a say in the process as well?

Fourth, whatever decision the park managers make, local communities are likely to feel the after-effects. Restricting logging, for example, may dramatically increase unemployment among local people, whereas encouraging tourism will bring in additional income. These people often have an in-depth knowledge of their own landscape and what it contains. Their stake in the park cannot be ignored.

Fifth, park visitors, simply by coming to the park, have invested their time and money in it; sometimes they do so year after year and take an almost proprietorial interest in the park. Decisions made by park managers will affect them directly. An increase in fees may make it difficult or impossible for them to camp, for example; or restricting certain activities may debar them from their favourite sports. Perhaps facilities they need—wheelchair access, for example—are not available. Perhaps they want better access to wilderness areas, or fewer crowds, or a more informal approach. Their ideas, too, should not be neglected.

In practice, park management is influenced by all these constituencies and any decision making process must take into account the views of all interested parties. No one group should dominate. What is crucial to the decision making process is public knowledge and appreciation of ecological issues, since without this awareness, the political will to support and implement these decisions will not exist.

We need a procedure for consulting all groups with an interest in park decision making. Our current conservation of nature is largely the product of accident, but now the survival of the world's genetic diversity is at stake. This consultation should ideally be international; we have a stake in what happens in Brazil's rain forests, and Norway has a stake in what we do in our Arctic. Practically, the impediments to international consultation should be obvious, and until *all* political systems recognize the value of parks to the biosphere, we can expect environmental management to be decided within individual states.

EXAMPLES OF ENVIRONMENTAL MANAGEMENT IN CANADIAN PARKS

The best way to understand environmental management in parks is to study practical examples. Certain areas of environmental management have a body of literature and a wealth of practical experience. Several of these have been chosen for a fuller discussion of individual issues, with an example from a Canadian park. These areas of management are: fire, endangered species, vegetation, fish and wildlife, and paleontological resources. Each topic is discussed with a similar format; first an outline of the issue, then a range of possible management actions, some relevant examples and finally a few conclusions.

Fire Management in Parks

The Issue   Those who value forest products see fire as destructive; therefore, fire suppression was common for decades. More recently, ecologists have started to recognize that fire is a natural component of most terrestrial ecosystems. Some species depend on fire; for example the cone of the jack pine will not release seeds until heated. Such an adaptation is advantageous to a species frequently exposed to fire. We now see that the boreal forest, of which jack pine is an important part in Canada, is a fire-adapted ecosystem. These forests burn at frequent intervals and have done so for millennia.

Fire suppression can have unanticipated results. Without burning, a deep layer of leaves, branches, and other organic litter develops on the forest floor. When a fire does occur it may be far more extensive and hotter, with serious results for the ecosystem. The massive fires in Yellowstone National Park in the summer of 1989 are an example. Almost one-half of the park's forest burned in one short period of intense fire (Jeffery 1989). This fire occurred during a drought and fed on fuel created by decades of fire prevention. Many parks are now developing new policies that recognize fire as part of the ecosystem (Canadian Parks Service 1986; Day *et al.* 1990).

Possible Management Actions   Modern fire management policy in parks tries to mimic the natural fire regime. However, since fire has been suppressed for decades, the natural regime may not be known. The fuel load is often large and the forests are ready for a heavy, intensive burn. Before any management action is taken, an assessment of the frequency and role of fire must be made. How often do fires normally occur? How do they burn? Are they small local fires? Are they large intensive burns? What kind of impact is anticipated? Once the research has been done and the questions answered, managers can develop a fire management regime (Hawkes 1990).

Many managers now face the difficult proposition of reintroducing fire into the ecosystem. This has to be done under carefully controlled conditions. Often buildings, trails, and other facilities are too valuable to burn. The fire might burn out of control or spread outside the park to forests that are valuable for timber. Public safety is also a major concern. An important consideration for the introduction of fire into an area is the fire control capability of park management. It is possible to alter the ecosystem by physical manipulation instead of allowing fire, for example, by clearing fuel from around sensitive features such as buildings or prize trees.

The Banff National Park Case Study   Banff National Park started planning for the use of fire in 1979 and was followed by the other national parks in the system. The 1989 fire policy provided a national direction for management (Canadian Parks Service 1989). In Banff, early planning concentrated on the lower Bow River Valley. Fire planning here had to deal with a complicated and challenging situation. The forests in this area are prone to fire, surround the town of Banff, and constitute one of the most heavily used portions of any Canadian national park. Fire had been suppressed for a long time.

One of the first jobs was to try to discover the past cycle of forest fires. This was done by looking at fire scars on old trees and related information to estimate the size and intensity of past fires. Out of this came a simulation of past forest fire behaviour (Lopoukhine and White 1985).

The planners then developed a vegetation plan. This outlined what kind of vegetation communities the Bow Valley should have. The valley vegetation was mapped into vegetation ignition units (Figure 9.2), and a time for the burning of each unit was chosen randomly. Plans are in place to burn the various units at different times up to the year 2035 (Lopoukhine and White 1985; REMS Research Ltd. 1988; see Table 9.1).

Concluding Remarks   Fire management is now well accepted by most ecologists. However, the anti-fire campaign of the U.S. Forest Service and similar efforts in Canada have made their impact on public opinion across North America. Many of the public are against burning forests for any purpose. This can be a stumbling block to the intentional use of fire. Many managers are finding that they can overcome this resistance with a carefully conceived public education program before any fire introduction program starts.

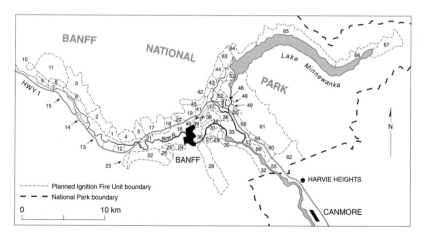

Figure 9.2 The lower Bow River Valley showing planned ignition fire units. Numbers keyed to Table 9.1.

Table 9.1 Examples of the Lower Bow River Valley Planned Ignition Burn
Units 1 to 15, with a Simulated Random Burning Schedule

Map	Area (ha)	Last Fire Year	Fire Cycle	Simulated Burn Years (1986-2035)
1	112	1891	40	1987
2	362	1904	40	2008
3	900	1801	40	
4	375	1891	40	2035
5	281	1903	40	1991, 1992, 1993
6	69	1930	20	2011
7	82	1861	40	2035
8	84	1801	40	1998, 2032
9	56	1881	40	1998, 2032
10	81	1881	40	
11	937	1881	40	
12	125	1881	60	1996
13	80	1891	60	
14	62	1891	40	2019, 2026
15	100	1925	40	2030

Source: Lapoukine and White 1985.

Endangered Species Management in Parks

The Issue A species is endangered when its numbers are so low there is a
real possibility of extinction in the immediate future. Typically, such species
have reached this level due to loss of both habitat and population, usually
through human intervention.

There are many examples in Canada. The passenger pigeon was extirpated
by overkill and the loss of its forest habitat in eastern North American. The
great auk, a flightless, fish-eating bird, was the North Atlantic ecological
equivalent of the penguin of the South Atlantic. This bird nested on islands
and was routinely killed by sailors. The species was wiped out by 1844
(Burnett *et al.* 1989). The gravel chub was eliminated when its habitat, the
Thames River in southern Ontario, was polluted by the silt from agricultural
operations. Canada lost many species of plant and animals due to the destruction of forests, prairies, and wetlands across the country.

Endangerment is increasing. As natural lands throughout the world are
modified, many species are becoming rare. King (1981) lists 437 species of
birds as endangered, or 4.7 per cent of 9,250 known species. A similar situation holds for most other groups of animals and plants. The Global Diversity Strategy (World Resources Institute *et al.*, 1992) estimates that over the

next three decades as many as 60,000 plant species, or 25 per cent of the world's total, may become extinct if the present rate of deforestation continues.

Possible Management Actions   Many parks in Canada play a critical role in protecting endangered species and the habitat on which they depend (see Chapter 8). In recent years, protecting critical ecosystems for rare species has been a major reason for establishing new parks and reserves. The Committee on the Status of Endangered Wildlife in Canada has the job of assessing the rarity of Canada's flora and fauna. Before a species' status is determined, sufficient information must be collected on its past and present geographical distribution. The current range is then compared to the historical range to obtain an idea of the extent of change. The *Breeding Bird Atlas of Ontario* assesses the geographical distribution of every bird that currently breeds in Ontario (Cadman *et al.* 1985). Similar compilations are underway in other provinces. This type of data shows the existing range and is very useful as a benchmark for the determination of future changes.

The Nature Conservancy of the United States and the Nature Conservancy of Canada have taken on the mammoth task of evaluating and ranking every species in North America. They work within each province and state and provide a rarity ranking for each species within the province and the country and globally (Hoose and Crispin 1990). The Nature Conservancies use this information to determinate which lands are the most critical sites for acquisition. They then raise the money, purchase the land, and either manage the land themselves or give it to a park agency.

Ontario's Endangered Species Act stipulates that no endangered species or its habitat may be harmed. It applies across the province and to all landowners. It does not apply to Indian reserves, as they are under federal jurisdiction (Woodliffe, pers. comm.) Each endangered species is designated under the powers of the Act by regulation. The Ontario Act is limited by a restrictive designation of endangered species and by spotty enforcement. However, the Act is powerful and is potentially very useful for protecting endangered species.

To get a fuller understanding of the ability of a species to survive, we need a wide range of information. Its general habitat characteristics must be assessed, using data on such things as its preferred climate regime, its interrelationships with other species, its preferred food, and its breeding characteristics. The existing threats to survival must be understood, as well as possible impacts of conservation actions and outdoor recreation activities (Woodliffe, pers. comm.).

Many provinces in Canada have established ecological reserves for the specific purpose of protecting important examples of ecosystems. Taschereau (1985) documents this effort in his excellent summary of the status of ecological reserves in Canada. Ecological or nature reserves have special roles to play in the protection of endangered species. Other parks are also important in this regard, as illustrated by the following examples.

The large white whooping crane has been badly affected by overhunting and habitat loss. Wood Buffalo National Park, in northern Alberta and the southern Northwest Territories (Figure 2.1), contains the only nesting area in the world for this endangered species. The park places very high emphasis on keeping disturbance to the nesting areas to a minimum. After nesting, the adults and the young migrate to Aransas National Wildlife Refuge, on the gulf coast of Texas, for the winter (Godfrey 1986). Both critical breeding and wintering habitats are therefore protected in parks.

Protecting endangered plant populations is often the focus of efforts to establish parks. For example, there are only three populations of the large whorled pogonia in Canada (Burnett *et al.* 1990). The largest of these is protected in the Backus Woods Conservation Area, near Simcoe, Ont., administered by the Long Point Conservation Authority. All three populations in Canada of the endangered spotted wintergreen are on protected lands. One is in Wasaga Beach Provincial Park and two are in reserves on the St Williams Provincial Forestry Station. One of the latter areas was bought from a private landowner in 1989 for the specific purpose of protecting several endangered butterfly, wildflower, and tree species.

Often the forces causing population reduction are very difficult to stop or deflect. The populations are so low that extreme caution is necessary. All of this is usually complicated by a paucity of biological information.

The Ojibway Prairie Nature Reserve Case Study   Prairie is an open landscape dominated by herbaceous plants, and with few trees. This community type is rare is Ontario, but a few significant remnants have survived agricultural clearance in southwestern Ontario (see Figure 9.3). One of these occurs within Windsor. When the rarity of the vegetation in this area became recognized, suggestions were made for the establishment of a park. In 1957 Windsor acquired 44 ha of oak woods and oak savannah, later named Ojibway Park. Facilities such as a picnic area, two parking lots, a nature interpretation centre and many trails were constructed. In 1989 the city purchased an additional 52 ha of an area known as the Black Oak Woods. As more information was collected on the prairie communities in the area, the Ministry of Natural Resources became involved. Starting in 1971 the ministry started an active land purchase program that has continued until the present time, with some funding from the Nature Conservancy of Canada. As of 1990, 81 ha have been bought for the Ojibway Prairie Provincial Nature Reserve and an additional 25 ha were under active negotiation (Woodliffe, pers. comm.). In total, the city and the ministry have 187 ha of the prairie preserved as parkland.

This type of prairie once covered an estimated 1,000,000 sq km of North America. As only 0.16 per cent of the original area is now officially pro-

Figure 9.3
Long-grass prairie in the Ojibway Prairie Provincial Park (Nature Reserve Class). All of this is within the city limits of Windsor, Ontario.

Photo: P. Eagles

tected, there are vigorous efforts to protect prairie remnants throughout the U.S. midwest (Woodliffe, pers. comm.). Hence, the Ojibway Prairie is of national and international significance. These two small parks in Windsor contain half of all the prairie plants known to occur in Ontario—533 species, or approximately 13 per cent of the flora of Canada (Pratt 1979), including at least 103 species that are considered rare in Canada or Ontario (Woodliffe, pers. comm).

Managing such a unique and interesting area is a considerable challenge. The Ministry of Natural Resources, with the co-operation of the Parks and Recreation Department of the city of Windsor, undertook a detailed investigation of the site. This included: tracing the history of prairie development in Ontario; mapping vegetation communities on-site; and making detailed inventories of plants, birds, mammals, reptiles, and amphibians. Once the state of the environment had been determined, policy development could begin. Detailed recommendations were made for the long-term maintenance and restoration of the prairie (Pratt 1979). This was followed by a resource management plan (Ontario Ministry of Natural Resources 1991b) which included directives on land acquisition, recreation use, archaeological and ecological research, derelict site restoration, exotic plant removal, groundwater monitoring, reintroduction of extirpated species, pet control, trail management, environmental education, vegetation management, and biological inventories. The goal of the resource management plan is 'to ensure the protection and perpetuation of an outstanding example of tall-grass prairie, oak savannah and prairie ecotone communities within Ojibway Prairie provincial nature reserve through various maintenance, rehabilitation, and restoration management techniques' (Ontario Ministry of Natural Resources 1991*b*).

The vegetation management section of the plan points out that the maintenance of prairie communities requires active management to keep in check undesirable woody and herbaceous plants. The possibilities for vegetation control include natural fire, woody stem cutting, artificial fuel burns, herbicides, and mowing. Prairies are typically fire succession communities. Without fire, woody plants invade and subsequently shade out the low-growing plants, a continual problem at Ojibway Prairie. But controlled burns are difficult because the prairie is now an urban park; local homeowners are not enthusiastic about fire nearby. The policy suggests using very small burns under rigorous control, with ample fire control at hand (Pratt 1979). Since 1982, the Ministry of Natural Resources has been able to carry out successful prescribed burns in five seasons over approximately 80 per cent of the reserve. Public opposition appears to be decreasing as local residents see the results and the professional manner in which burning is conducted. Mowing and herbicides have not been used, but herbicides are being considered for controlling persistent foreign species such as black locust. Some cutting has been done in areas where the woody thickets are too thick to be burned off (Woodliffe, pers. comm.).

Concluding Remarks The Ojibway Prairie complex is a good example of the role of parklands in protecting endangered species and their habitats. The site also shows municipal and provincial park agencies' co-operation in joint conservation and environmental education. The environmental education program is noteworthy for fostering a community appreciation for this prairie ecosystem. Detailed and thorough research in the development of management policy has been evident in this case.

Vegetation Management in Parks

The Issue The management of trees, shrubs, grasses, and wildflowers is one of the critical issues in resource management. All wildlife ultimately depends upon the structure, form, distribution, and quantity of plants, which also contribute to the beauty of the landscape.

Possible Management Actions There are three levels of intervention in vegetation management. One is the hands-off approach. The forces of nature determine the vegetation structure and the manager should try to have as little impact as possible. A second is to see some minor management as necessary.

For example, dangerous trees pose a safety hazard and are removed. Fertilizers may be needed in areas of heavy visitor use. Some plants must be removed when facilities are constructed. The third is to believe major intervention is necessary. This approach argues that there may be good reasons for changing the vegetation. It might be desirable to reintroduce an extirpated plant species. A rapidly invading foreign plant may need aggressive control. It may be desirable to change the habitat to create ideal conditions for an endangered wildlife species.

How, and how much, to manage plant communities are questions under constant debate. Canadian national parks and many provincial parks often attempt to follow the first of these approaches—as little intervention as possible. However, as the fire management policies in Banff show, active intervention through the introduction of burning may be needed to correct past interventions. Wilderness parks, nature reserves, natural environment parks, and ecological reserves usually take a hands-off approach.

Many provincial parks follow the second of these approaches—moderate intervention. Parks with many visitors and intensive facilities will inevitably affect the vegetation. Heavy-use areas may require turf management. Trail and roads drastically change the vegetation in their immediate vicinity, but when visitors use them, traffic pressure on nearby areas will likely be reduced. The restoration of derelict sites such as old farms may be encouraged.

Some provincial parks, many wildlife areas, and most municipal parks follow the last approaches—major intervention. Two Ontario provincial parks, Algonquin and Lake Superior, are logged and require extensive road construction for logging access. Active recreation sites, such as the golf course in Turkey Point Provincial Park on Lake Erie, cause extensive ecosystem change. In Pinery Provincial Park on Lake Huron a forest burning program is necessary to remove thousands of white pine trees that were planted mistakenly during the 1950s and 1960s.

Wildlife area managers may actively and aggressively change the vegetation to enhance wildlife habitat. In the Long Point National Wildlife Area on Lake Erie, the lakeshore marshes were extensively diked to manipulate water levels to create ideal conditions for the maximum production of game waterfowl. In Luther Marsh Conservation Area north of Arthur, Ont., the extensive damming of creeks has resulted in the creation of large, rich wetland communities on the site of former farmlands. These wetlands are valued for the ducks that breed and stop here during migration. In Killarney Provincial Park along the shore of Georgian Bay, the forests in the park were extensively cut to produce shrubby conditions for the winter browse of white-tailed deer populations for hunting. This type of intervention to encourage a particular species is quite common among managers who look after the needs of the hunting community.

All vegetation management should be based upon a thorough knowledge of the plants that occur in the park and their distribution and basic life cycles, as well as their community dynamics. Any active intervention without this information may have unanticipated and possibly disastrous consequences.

The Long Point Wildlife Area Case Study   Long Point is a peninsula in the eastern reaches of Lake Erie. On the northeastern leeward side of the point, extensive marshes have developed that have been known to hunters and fishers for centuries. In the last century, a private company, the Long Point Company, started operating the majority of the point as a private hunting preserve.

In 1973 the Big Creek National Wildlife Area was established at the base of the peninsula. In 1979 a large portion of the Long Point Peninsula was donated to the Canadian Wildlife Service by the Long Point Company and the Nature Conservancy of the United States. This became the Long Point National Wildlife Area. These two areas are now part of a system of over 40 Canadian national wildlife areas (McKeating 1982)

The management plan for the Big Creek National Wildlife Area states several goals. The third speaks directly about management of the site for waterfowl: 'To create, maintain or enhance a high quality habitat complex for waterfowl and other marsh-dependent wildlife species with emphasis on the provision of staging habitat during the spring and autumn waterfowl migrations' (McKeating and Dewey 1984).

This goal was the basis for a proposal to manipulate the marsh vegetation in the wetlands. The 1982 management plan stated that:

> Management of the National Wildlife Area will be undertaken to provide optimum habitat diversity for the benefit of all wetland dependant wildlife. An ideal marsh environment is one that approximates a 50/50 ratio of open water and vegetation.

The Canadian Wildlife Service has concluded that the marsh will be greatly enhanced for wildlife purposes if it actively intervened in the natural processes of the marsh (McKeating and Dewey 1984).

Management actions have included building large water-control dikes, mechanically removing stands of emergent vegetation, manipulating water levels, creating open water areas and channels, dredging ponds and channels, and stabilizing the barrier beach along Lake Erie.

But conditions that suit one species will not suit all species. A rare species, the prothonotary warbler, breeds in the woodlands near the marshes (Eagles and McCauley 1982; Eagles 1988b; McColeman and Eagles 1990). Will flooding kill off the trees it nests in? If so, its breeding habitat will cease to exist and so will the warbler. Will the dikes affect the ability of the northern pike to move from the lake to the marshes to breed each spring? These effects on non-target species are often controversial spinoffs from any single-species management program.

Concluding Remarks   The development of vegetation management policy is fraught with challenge. The basic policy of the park will determine the range of options to be considered. Past landscape management actions may have created a canvas upon which new patterns must be painted. An understanding of the existing vegetation conditions and their history must precede any change, and any active intervention may have unanticipated outcomes. All actions must be carefully monitored to measure their effects.

Fish and Wildlife Management in Parks

The Issue   Animals are an essential component of natural ecosystems and visitors enjoy watching wildlife. As well, all parks play a role of global importance in maintaining fish and wildlife populations, and some parks play critical roles for rare species. A few of these roles are worthy of discussion.

Large or predatory animals typically require extensive habitats. The grizzly, wolverine, and timber wolf are upper-level predators that need large territories. Some Canadian parks are large enough to allow these species to live out their life cycles without leaving the parks or remote enough to allow them to range in nearby areas.

In recent decades parks have become the only safe refuge for many large animals. For example, in the U.S., the grizzly bear and timber wolf are almost gone from the lower 48 states. The bear is only found in Yellowstone and Glacier national parks. The wolf is largely gone except in Minnesota, Wisconsin, upper Michigan, Glacier National Park, and the Flathead National Forest in Idaho (Savage 1988). The few remaining animals are under constant hunting attack (*National Geographic* 1990).

Fortunately, the four contiguous Canadian National Parks in the Rocky Mountains (Banff, Jasper, Kootenay, and Yoho) have populations of all the big predators native to the area, including the mountain lion, grizzly bear, black bear, and timber wolf. No parks in the United States south of Alaska still have all of these species. This fact gives these parks a role of considerable international significance.

Land use around the park is often critical to the survival of wildlife in the park. Most animals move in and out of the park during the year. When a park becomes a green island in a sea of hostile habitat, as in cities, some species cannot cope.

Parks that forbid hunting are particularly important, as virtually all other public lands do not. Only here can research be done on populations subject to relatively natural ecological forces. Banning hunters is especially important to observation, as the animals do not fear people. On the other hand, these species may be exposed to hunting and other influences during parts of their life cycles that take them out of the parks.

On the other hand, if hunting is forbidden and natural predation declines, herbivore populations can build to very high levels. For example, the three sandspit parks on the Canadian side of Lake Erie, Long Point National Wildlife Area, Rondeau Provincial Park, and Point Pelee National Park, all saw population explosions of white-tailed deer in the 1980s, with major damage to forest vegetation. Some tree species stopped reproducing as all seedlings were devoured, and very rare herbaceous plants suffered from the deer browsing. The park wardens allowed a recreational hunt at Long Point and culled the Point Pelee herd, but they took no action at Rondeau as a result of conflicting public pressures.

Possible Management Actions   Any management of fish and animals must start with a knowledge of the numbers and range of the species in question. All parks should have extensive information on their own flora and fauna, from the informal recording of observations by staff and visitors to highly sophisticated research programs using computer database management and geographical information systems. Fish and wildlife management policy must be based on knowledge of the resource, on the legal mandate of the park system, and on park policy. Administration of that policy, proper policing, and monitoring the policy's effectiveness and impact are also necessary.

The Fundy National Park Case Study   Pacific, Atlantic, and Arctic salmon migrate into fresh water for spawning. Fundy National Park is located on the New Brunswick shore of the Bay of Fundy (Figure 2.1). The park's streams attract spawning Atlantic salmon, which spend three years of their life in the streams and then go to sea for one or two years, returning to the streams to spawn when they reach breeding age.

Fundy National Park policies recognize the significance of the park's streams to the salmon, controlling water quality and carrying out research into the number of spawning salmon and the survival rates of the young. Recently the numbers of spawning salmon have declined. The park's response was a catch-and-release program, in which sport fishermen are not allowed to keep any fish they catch.

In 1986, Atlantic salmon returned to the Point Wolf River for the first time in over 100 years. A logging dam that prevented salmon from entering the river was removed after three years of stocking the river with juvenile salmon obtained from nearby rivers. The juveniles were able to go downstream over the dam. After one year in salt water, the first grilse salmon returned to spawn in the river (Woodley, pers. comm.).

This reintroduction program was successful, but the rate of return was much lower than anticipated (Woodley, pers. comm.), as it is in all local rivers. Overfishing while the salmon are at sea or other unknown factors may be responsible. Atlantic salmon prove the connection between parks and their surroundings. The critical spawning habitat Fundy provides is not sufficient to protect the salmon populations from the consequences of heavy exploitation at sea.

Algonquin Provincial Park Case Study   Black bear are common in forests of central Canada, and Algonquin Provincial Park in Ontario has a thriving population, much appreciated by visitors. Black bears are hunted everywhere in Canada, except in most parks. As a result, most are wary of people. In a park as large as Algonquin, however, most bears live out their lives free from being hunted and have little fear of humans.

Black bears are large and potentially dangerous. They are omnivorous, eating large amounts of berries and seeds, but are quite willing to eat meat if given the opportunity. Algonquin has many canoers each year. Bears have learned that campers carry food that is usually easy to get. As a result a bear 'problem' has developed as the animals steal food and often damage equipment.

Typically, the bears do not bother people directly, as long as the people stay out of the bears' way. Herrero (1985) has documented the 26 deaths caused by black bears in North America from 1900 to 1983. On 13 May 1978, three teenaged boys on a fishing trip in Algonquin were killed; one boy survived and provided details. A 276-pound male bear was later shot and linked to the boys' deaths. Herrero (1985) concluded that this bear killed the boys as food. There was no evidence that the bear was old or diseased, two factors often thought to drive bears to attack people. It was a healthy male that decided to stalk human prey.

The management of the interactions between park visitors and dangerous animals is a special and important concern. The park has several options.

First, bears that develop dangerous habits are often killed. This approach has become less acceptable in recent years as the concept that the animal has a right to exist became prevalent. The practice now is only to kill specific animals that pose a serious threat—for example, over-aggressive, injured, or diseased animals. Animals that actually injure or kill people are usually slaughtered. Second, interpretation programs may inform the public of the danger of bears, encouraging appropriate camping procedures to lessen the potential of attracting bears to a campsite. Educating visitors about the danger and means of minimizing it has become widespread. Third, the restriction of visitor activities is becoming common and accepted (Figure 9.4). In some parks, visitors are not allowed to enter certain areas when grizzly sows with cubs are present. In others, visitors must be accompanied by guards when they visit areas with dangerous animals. When visitors travel by road, they are not allowed to leave their vehicles.

In parks the visitors have to learn to accept nature as it is. They must learn to adapt to its ways, not to have nature changed for their needs. Not all visitors agree that they should take the environment as they find it. Some feel that all dangerous animals should be removed, while others feel that the

Figure 9.4
Sign warning of bear activity. *Photo: P. Eagles.*

park management has a duty to protect the visitor from any harm from such animals. The Canadian Park Service has been sued by a park visitor who was injured by a bear in a mountain national park.

Concluding Remarks In both the Fundy and Algonquin examples, fish and wildlife management problems are actually human management problems. The salmon do not need management; people need to stop overfishing them. Bears do not need management; people need to respect their territory and habits.

Paleontological Resource Management in Parks

The Issue Parks often have significant abiotic resources. Mountains, rivers, geological formations, and fossils are all examples of resources that require special consideration. Canada has important fossil deposits such as the Burgess Shales in Yoho National Park, a World Heritage Site, with some of the most significant early Cambrian fossils in the world. Their analysis has fundamentally altered our understanding of the earliest evolution of soft-bodied animals (Gould 1990).

Not only are fossils important to paleontology, but private collectors are often quite willing to pay large sums for prize specimens. Who can collect fossils, and under what conditions, is a vital aspect of management, since some methods can be highly destructive. Some early collection practices at the Burgess shales verged on the catastrophic, both to the fossils and to the surrounding landscape.

Possible Management Actions Canada has established several parks for the specific purpose of conserving and interpreting fossil deposits, but both specimen collection and vandalism are constant problems. The park administration can provide a degree of protection. Interpreting the significance of the fossils to the public is one important facet of park operation (see Chapter 11). Providing a site for long-term scientific research and collection is a second option.

The Dinosaur Provincial Park Case Study The badlands of southern Alberta are a spectacular series of valleys and hills, used by Native people for millennia. Rivers have carved deep into the dry soil, exposing ancient fossil strata and allowing easy access to buried specimens (see Figure 9.5). The badlands contain one of the world's most important fossil deposits, including well-preserved dinosaur specimens from the upper Cretaceous period.

Dinosaur Provincial Park in Alberta was established specifically to protect these deposits, as well as a large tract of badlands and the rare semi-desert species native to them. Staff monitor all activities and ensure that no unlicensed fossil collection occurs. Important deposits are protected from the weather until they can be studied or removed for conservation. More than 300 complete or near-complete dinosaur skeletons have been taken from the area in the last 80 years and are now in museums around the world. Prospecting continues; in an active summer, researchers discover an average of six skeletons. Roughly 30 per cent of the specimens are in good condition. Thirty-five species have been identified thus far, and hadrosaurs are particularly abundant (Alberta Provincial Parks Service n.d.)

The park also plays an important educational role. It is the best place in Canada for the public to see fossils *in situ* and to watch excavations. In addition, interpreters with special paleontological training provide educational enrichment.

Park managers operate under two pieces of provincial legislation. The Provincial Parks Act prohibits the collection, removal, or damaging of any geological specimen. The Historical Resources Act states that all archaeological and paleontological resources within Alberta are owned by the province. This Act also forbids the excavation of Alberta's historic resources without a permit (Thesen 1990). In 1987 one person was prosecuted for the unauthorized collection of fossils in the park (Alberta Provincial Parks Service n.d.).

To control access to the most important fossil areas, one-third of the park has been designated a natural preserve. Access is only allowed for specialized activities such as scientific research and collection, guided interpretive tours, and approved photographic work. Enforcing the restrictions in the natural preserve is, however, not as complete as the Parks Service would like. Illegal collection may be occurring because staff are too few to patrol the more remote areas of the park (Alberta Provincial Parks Service n.d.).

Figure 9.5
Dinosaur Provincial Park, Alberta. The constant erosion exposes new
dinosaur skeletons each year.   *Photo: P. Eagles.*

Concluding Remarks   Dinosaur Provincial Park is an example of specialized environmental management, providing for resource protection, scientific
research, and public education. Similar functions occur in all parks. What is
unique is the park's paleontological value, recognized when UNESCO placed
the park on the World Heritage List in 1979. A World Heritage Site is of
such importance that it is considered of value to all of mankind.

NATIVE RIGHTS AND LAND CLAIMS

Recent years have seen the establishment of parks in which Native people continue their hunting and fishing activities. The Supreme Court recently affirmed the exercise of Treaty and Aboriginal rights in national parks, subject to conservation requirements (Bartlett 1990). For example, Algonquin Park must now allow Native people access to hunting and fishing. What are the implications for parks management?

The primary questions are 'how much?' and 'where?' Some parks may have to allow considerable hunting and fishing, something with enormous implications for their ecosystems. Moreover, these activities may interfere with other park users' animal-watching activities. Certainly, management will have to take Native issues into consideration in decision making.

This issue is evolving very rapidly, and we can expect considerable debate and change in the years to come. The question of Native rights and park issues will be dealt with more fully later in this text (see Chapters 4 and 12).

INFORMATION FOR MANAGEMENT

All management requires information. In any decision making process, there are several critical steps where the data are essential.

First, we need baseline information on the characteristics of the environment. Before any resource can be assessed, we must answer the following questions:

1. How much is there?
2. Where is it?
3. How has it changed over time?
4. How does it relate to other aspects of the environment?
5. What types of information should be collected?
6. How much information is necessary to solve the problem at hand?

Eagles (1987) studied the use of natural resource information in planning and management in the national parks of Canada. The research found that the Canadian Parks Service's information base is adequate for the demands placed upon it and is well used. This information has been transferred to computer database storage and linked to the impressive manipulation and display capabilities of geographical information systems. This technological advance allows for computerized analysis and presentation of mapped information and has become very useful for the manager who wants to translate raw field data into useful information on trends.

Thorsell (1990) has suggested that a manager needs accurate biophysical information on five different topics before management decisions can be made: basic inventory; species needs; ecological relationships; monitoring and the dynamics of change; and predictive manipulation of ecosystems.

The basic inventory provides estimates of the most important natural features of a park—the plants, animals, soils, and geological phenomenon. The inventory should estimate both total numbers and spatial density. Any threats to the natural environment should be identified. So should the needs of those species of significance, including rare species and those of particular cultural significance. We must also collect information on the ecological relationships of key species. This includes key predators, species of high visibility, endangered species, and species with particular importance in the food chain.

Possibly the ecosystem is in flux; if so, we must monitor the change. New species may be invading. Erosion may be under way. Water levels may be changing. Such changes might have profound effect on the ecosystem and must be tracked with care.

Where these changes run counter to the objectives of management, then we may need to take steps to control them. This in turn requires the prediction of the environmental impact of our activities.

Once we have enough information to be confident that we can answer our six questions we can state the problem, whatever it is, and begin to look at solutions. Environmental assessment policies or legislation, where these exist, require managers to look at alternative solutions, which must be assessed and compared to determine which is most environmentally suitable.

Once a course of action is decided upon, it can take place. Again, monitoring the effect of the intervention is critical and should be long-term.

SUMMARY

Managing the natural resources of a park is a critically important aspect of park administration. Whether the resources are living creatures, landscape features or resources, or fossils, management has several critical components.

First, the resource must be known and understood. Research is vital to the early stages of all resource management policy making.

Second, the value put on the resource must be known and understood. These values will determine what options will be available for management.

Third, the methods used to elicit input in the decision making process will largely determine what types of policies will result.

Fourth, we must realize that the vast majority of environmental management is really people management; this is the largest issue to be tackled.

Fifth, we must also understand that management is undertaken with less than complete knowledge, and outcomes are rarely predictable.

Park management must also consider what occurs outside their bailiwicks. Outside land or sea practices may have serious consequences for species that depend on a larger area.

Parks play a major role in the long-term protection of the world's genetic diversity and in providing outdoor recreation for many people. Parks are under constant pressure from influences that degrade environmental quality. The preservation of environmental quality within parks is globally important.

REFERENCES

Alberta Provincial Parks Service
  n.d.   *Dinosaur Provincial Park Resource Management Plan*, Alberta Recreation and Parks, Edmonton, Alta.
Allen, G.J., P.F.J. Eagles, and S.D. Price
  1990   *Conserving Carolinian Canada*, University of Waterloo Press, Waterloo, Ont.
Bartlett, R.
  1990   'Indian Summer in the Supreme Court: The Sparrow Quartet', *Resources: The Newsletter of the Canadian Institute of Resources Law* 32: 6.
Boissonneault, J.
        Chief Park Warden, St Lawrence Islands National Park, personal communication.
Bos, W., L. Brisson, and P. Eagles
  1977   *A Study of Attitudinal Orientations of Central Canadian Cultures Towards Wildlife*, Canadian Wildlife Service, Environment Canada, Ottawa.
Burnett, J.A., C.T. Dauphine, S.H. McCrindle, and T. Mosquin
  1989   *On the Brink—Endangered Species in Canada*, Western Producer Prairie Books, Saskatoon.
Cadman, M.D., P.F.J. Eagles, and F.M. Helleiner
  1987   *Atlas of the Breeding Birds of Ontario*, University of Waterloo Press, Waterloo, Ont.
Canadian Parks Service
  1986   *Fire Management*, Management Directive 2.4.4, Natural Resources Branch, Parks Canada, Ottawa.
Canadian Parks Service
  1989   *Keepers of the Flame: Implementing Fire Management in the Canadian Parks Service*, Natural Resources Branch, Canadian Parks Service, Ottawa.
Day, D.L., C.A. White, and N. Lopoukhine
  1990   'Keeping the Flame: Fire Management in the Canadian Parks Service', in *Proceedings, Interior West Fire Council Annual Meeting*, Kananaskis, 1–18.
Dorney, R.S.
  1989   *The Professional Practice of Environmental Management*, Springer-Verlag, New York.
Eagles, P.F.J.
  1980   *Wildlife Issues in Newspapers in Central Canada*, Social Studies Division, Canadian Wildlife Service, Ottawa.
Eagles, P.F.J.
  1984   *The Planning and Management of Environmentally Sensitive Areas*, Longman, Harlow, U.K.

Eagles, P.F.J.
1987   *The Use of Biophysical Inventories in Park Planning and Management in National Parks in Canada*, Occasional Paper Number 9, Department of Recreation and Leisure Studies, University of Waterloo, Waterloo, Ont.

Eagles, P.F.J.
1988a   *Criteria for the Designation of Environmentally Sensitive Areas Within a Park: The Presque Isle Case Study*, Bureau of State Parks, Department of Environmental Resources, Commonwealth of Pennsylvania, Harrisburg, Pa.

Eagles, P.F.J.
1988b   *Frequency of Breeding Bird Species in Ontario: Summary of Atlas Data*, Occasional Paper No. 13, Department of Recreation and Leisure Studies, University of Waterloo, Waterloo, Ont.

Eagles, P.F.J., and J.D. McCauley
1982   *The Rare Breeding Birds of Ontario*, Biology Series No. 24, Department of Biology, University of Waterloo, Waterloo, Ont.

Godfrey, W.E.
1986   *The Birds of Canada*, National Museum of Natural Sciences, Ottawa.

Gould, S.J.
1990   *Wonderful Life: The Burgess Shale and the Nature of History*, Norton, New York.

Hawkes, B.C.
1990   *Wilderness Fire Management in Canada: Some New Approaches to Natural Areas*, Western Wildlands, University of Montana School of Forestry.

Herrero, S.
1985   *Bear Attacks—Their Causes and Avoidance*, Lyons and Burford, New York.

Hoose, P. and S. Crispin (eds)
1990   'The Status of Natural Heritage Data Centres in Canada', in *Conserving Carolinian Canada*, eds G.M. Allen, P.F.J. Eagles, and S.D. Price, University of Waterloo Press, Waterloo, Ont, 327–31.

Jeffery, D.
1989   'Yellowstone—The Great Fires of 1988', *National Geographic*, 175: 255–73.

King, W.B.
1981   *Endangered Birds of the World*, Smithsonian Institution Press, Washington, D.C.

Lopoukhine, N., and C. White
1985   'Fire Management Options in Canada's National Parks', in *Proceedings of the Intermountain Fire Council 1983 Fire Management Workshop*, ed. D.E. Dube, Information Report NOR-X-271, Northern Forest Research Centre, Canadian Forestry Service, 59–68.

McColeman, K.L., and P.F.J. Eagles
1990   'An Assessment of the Protection of Selected Rare Bird Breeding Sites in the Carolinian Forest Region of Ontario', in *Conserving Carolinian Canada*, eds G.M. Allen, P.F.J. Eagles, and S.D. Price, University of Waterloo Press, Waterloo, Ont. 163–9

McKeating, G.
1982   *Preliminary Management Plan: Long Point National Wildlife Area*, Canadian Wildlife Service, Environment Canada, London, Ont.

McKeating, G., and K. Dewey

1984 *Management Plan: Big Creek National Wildlife Areas*, Canadian Wildlife Service, Environment Canada, London, Ont.

National Geographic

1990 'Wolves in Study Shot, Killed in Minnesota', *National Geographic* 178: iii.

North, G.

Hamilton Naturalists Club, Hamilton, Ont., personal communication.

Ontario Ministry of Natural Resources

1977 *Polar Bear Provincial Park Background Information*, Queen's Park, Toronto, Ont.

Ontario Ministry of Natural Resources

1991a *Rondeau Provincial Park Management Plan*, Chatham, Ont.

Ontario Ministry of Natural Resources

1991b *Draft Resource Management Plan for Ojibway Prairie Provincial Nature Reserve 1991–1996*, Chatham District Office, Chatham, Ont.

Pratt, P.D.

1979 *A Preliminary Life Science Inventory of The Ojibway Prairie Complex and Surrounding Area*, City of Windsor and Ontario Ministry of Natural Resources, Windsor, Ont.

REMS Research Ltd.

1988 *Fire Management in the Canadian Parks Service: Evaluation and Recommendations*, Canadian Parks Service, Environment Canada, Ottawa.

Savage, C.

1988 *Wolves*, Douglas and McIntyre, Vancouver.

Taschereau, P.M.

1985 *The Status of Ecological Reserves in Canada*, Canadian Council on Ecological Areas and the Institute for Resource and Environmental Studies, Dalhousie University, Halifax.

Thesen, C.

1990 Acting District Manager, Badlands District, Provincial Parks Service, Alberta Recreation and Parks, Patricia, Alta., letter dated 12 October 1990.

Thorsell, J.W.

1990 Research in Tropical Protected Areas: Some Guidelines for Managers, *Environmental Conservation* 17: 14–18.

Watson, M.

Chief Planner, Ontario Region, Canadian Parks Service, personal communication.

Weir, R.D.

1987 'Peregrine Falcon', in *Atlas of the Breeding Birds of Ontario*, eds M.D. Cadman, P.F.J. Eagles, and F.M. Helleiner, University of Waterloo Press, Waterloo, Ont., 130–1.

Woodley, S.

Park Ecologist, Fundy National Park, Canadian Parks Service, personal communication.

Woodliffe, A.

District Ecologist, Chatham District, Ontario Ministry of Natural Resources, personal communication.

World Conservation Union, United Nations Environment Program
1991   *Caring for the Earth: A Strategy for Sustainable Living*, Gland, Switzerland.
World Resources Institute, World Conservation Union, United Nations Environment Program
1992   *Global Biodiversity Strategy*, Washington, D.C.

CHAPTER 10

Visitor Planning and Management in Parks and Protected Areas

R.J. PAYNE AND R. GRAHAM

INTRODUCTION

The management of parks and protected areas has traditionally been based on natural science and conducted by natural scientists. This tradition takes it as a given that the natural environment requires management. If natural environments are the focus of management, then it follows that managers ought to be able to understand and to use natural science knowledge and techniques. This train of thought confirmed that people with natural science training ought to be preferred for management and planning positions in agencies responsible for parks and protected areas.

While this view of management in parks and protected areas may have been adequate until 1945, the post-war explosion in recreational activity worldwide has substantially changed the nature of park and protected area management. Managers themselves have identified new problems associated with more visitor use (Machlis and Tichnell 1985). These new management problems take three forms.

The first sort is produced by the sheer popularity of some parks and protected areas, in which increasing numbers of visitors have produced management problems. The continuing presence of large numbers of people causes long-term damage to valued natural environments. Regulating such visitors, although an effective response for control and enforcement purposes, does not deal with the legitimate desires of people to appreciate and enjoy the park or protected area. Nor does regulation by itself build support for park and protected area programs among members of the public.

In a second problem, chance encounters between animals and people who are relatively unfamiliar with nature can produce unpleasant results for both sides. Again, a regulatory response can be only one component of effective management.

A third type of problem occurs entirely among visitors or between groups of visitors. People with different interests and motivations for their park visits may find that they do not appreciate each other's company. Research has shown that one group may so disrupt the experiences and activities of another that the latter will be moved to leave the area, perhaps never to return.

These kinds of management problems require skills and knowledge that are not traditional in natural science. Not that natural science is irrelevant to parks and protected areas management; merely, it is not broad enough to manage the sorts of problems and issues occurring in parks and protected areas today. Social sciences such as sociology, psychology, anthropology, (human) geography, political science, and recreation and leisure studies must be drawn on to deal with the visitors for whom parks and protected areas, at least to some degree, are intended, and from whom many management issues originate.

We will examine in detail four visitor planning and management frameworks[1] that have been developed and implemented by agencies in Canada and the United States. Each of these frameworks or 'preformed decision structures' (Kauffman 1960) is intended to complement existing management processes, most of which depend on natural science techniques and knowledge.

First, we will describe the visitor planning and management frameworks and their origins, with special attention to their historical contexts, which account for some of the significant differences among the frameworks.

Second, we will present a critical assessment of each of the four to determine their relative merits. A number of analytical factors, selected for their significance in the broader park planning and management process, form the basis of this examination.

Finally, we examine the similarities and differences among the frameworks and identify and discuss, for each framework, issues requiring resolution in the future.

VISITOR PLANNING AND MANAGEMENT FRAMEWORKS

The four frameworks discussed in this section provide decision making and decision building support for the agencies employing them. All four, to varying degrees, are integrated with management frameworks designed to manage the natural environment. The four frameworks analysed are:

1. Recreation Opportunity Spectrum, U.S. Forest Service;
2. Limits of Acceptable Change, U.S. Forest Service;

---

[1] In February 1989, a visitor management workshop at the University of Waterloo brought together Canadian and American agencies in the parks and protected areas field to share their experiences with these four frameworks. The proceedings of that workshop (Graham and Lawrence 1990) are a rich source of information for visitor management. In May 1992, a second visitor management workshop was held at the University of Wisconsin. Proceedings from that meeting, under the editorship of Donald Field and William Burch, Jr, are in press at this writing.

3. Visitor Impact Management, U.S. National Park Service; and
4. Visitor Activity Management Process, Canadian Parks Service.

Recreation Opportunity Spectrum

The Recreation Opportunity Spectrum (ROS) was developed by the U.S. Forest Service to support efforts to meet the agency's mandate for outdoor recreation management and integrated resource management in American national forests. Various writers (e.g. Wilkinson and Anderson 1987; Clark and Stankey 1990) have pointed out that the Forest Service is mandated by the National Forest Management Act (1976) to produce an optimum range of social and economic benefits from the national forests under its management. Complicating the planning and management tasks for the Forest Service is the fact that a large proportion (approximately 75 per cent) of American wilderness areas, designated under the Wilderness Act (1964), are found in national forests. For an agency which had paid lip service to an integrated resource management (multiple use) approach to land and resource management and functioned primarily as a timber management agency, the requirement to manage natural resources in an integrated fashion was difficult to accept. However, the Forest Service has acknowledged that recreation delivers such a wide array of social and economic benefits that, in several national forests in Colorado, timber activities have ceased (Driver 1990a pers. comm.). ROS is the tool that has enabled the Forest Service to respond to the requirement to optimize national forest resource use and benefits.

Clark and Stankey, in an early publication of the framework (1979) indicate that some of the concepts underlying ROS can be traced back to the Outdoor Recreation Resources Review Commission in the early 1960s. Reports from that commission suggested that a broad range of outdoor recreation opportunities, from developed to undeveloped, ought to be available to the American public. In its focus on 'recreation diversity' (Driver 1990b, 163), ROS has the capability to identify just such a range of opportunities.

In its most common form, the framework distinguishes among six recreation opportunity classes: urban, rural, roaded natural, semi-primitive motorized, semi-primitive non-motorized, and primitive (Driver 1990b 166). These opportunity classes, covering the spectrum from developed to undeveloped settings, vary systematically according to the logic of the ROS framework. Thus, an urban opportunity setting features man-made recreation facilities, easy access by several modes of transportation, high numbers and densities of users, and an obvious and significant management presence. In contrast, a primitive setting is characterized by little or no human modification of the natural environment, remoteness, very few users, and little or no overt management.

Human modification, access, user interaction, and management regime lie at the heart of ROS. Variation among these factors determines the nature of the setting in which recreation activities occur. By *describing* areas in terms of these factors, ROS maps out opportunity classes as the basis for zoning decisions. By *manipulating* these factors—for example, by providing road access to an area previously without road—settings may be managed to produce the desired results (Figure 10.1).

The ROS framework focuses on settings within which recreation activities may occur. These are *opportunity settings*, allowing the nature and sensitivity of each park or protected area, its use, and management direction to interact in a way that is unique. Management efforts are geared to the *experiences* that each setting will support, and ultimately to the social and economic benefits[2] that will be generated (Driver 1990c). Rather than merely focusing on recreation activities or the natural environment within which human activity takes place, ROS is based on the idea that people participate in recreational activities in specific settings to achieve desired experiences and benefits. By changing the setting—for example, by closing the only road into an area— we may alter user densities and promote a series of experiences more natural than social. Similarly, by prohibiting motor boating on an inland lake, we change both the activity and the kinds of experiences available to visitors.

Implicit in this view of recreational engagements in parks and protected areas is the idea that it is not sufficient to look only at activities or at natural settings. Activities are multi-dimensional in the ROS framework. Take cross-country skiing, for example. One group of people, a family, may cross-country ski on a municipal golf course for the fun of skiing, to experience and learn about nature, and to take part in a family-oriented activity. Another group, young members of a ski club, may train for competitive racing on a trail that has been groomed and supplied with lights for night skiing. For these skiers, fitness and competition provide the motivation. Still another group, this time of friends, cross-country skis in the backcountry where they set their own trails and depend on their own wilderness skills. All these groups are doing the same thing, but each variation in its particular setting yields its particular group of experiences.

Although ROS was developed by an agency with an integrated resource management perspective, the framework has been used by organizations that do not include resource extraction of any kind. Park systems in Australia, New Zealand, and Scandinavia have adopted the ROS framework. In Canada, ROS has been used in national parks to a limited extent. In the planning process for the four mountain parks (Banff, Yoho, Kootenay, and Jasper), for example, ROS was used to identify opportunity settings (Canadian Parks Service 1986). In Pukaskwa National Park in Ontario (Jones 1988, pers.

---

[2]Driver and his associates continue to develop the ROS. Whereas the original focus was on *experience-based* planning and management, Driver is now working to establish connections among experiences, activities, and benefits, thus moving toward *benefit-based* planning and management (see Driver 1990c).

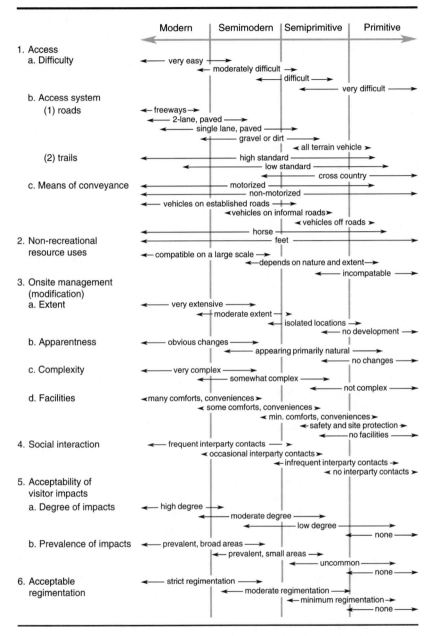

Figure 10.1 The Recreation Opportunity Spectrum (ROS) showing the relationships between the range of opportunity setting classes and management factors.

Source: R.N. Clark and G.H. Stankey (1979). *The Recreation Opportunity Spectrum: A Framework for Planning, Management, and Research.* General Technical Report PN-98, Range Experiment Station, U.S. Department of Agriculture, Seattle.

comm.), ROS guided planning efforts for the backcountry or wilderness components of the park. In British Columbia, an adaptation of the ROS framework is being used by the provincial Forest Service to manage recreation on forested Crown land (British Columbia Ministry of Forests 1989; Rollins 1991, pers. comm.).

Limits of Acceptable Change

The Limits of Acceptable Change (LAC) framework was also developed by the U.S. Forest Service and a group of researchers for use in planning and managing designated and undesignated wilderness areas under the agency's jurisdiction. It seems fair to consider the LAC framework as an extension and elaboration of ROS (McCool 1990a 187). Like ROS, LAC is concerned with identifying opportunities for recreation activities. In wilderness areas, most issues revolve around the intensity of recreational use. Questions concerning appropriate levels of use by individuals by commercial outfitters using back country areas are common. So too, are those issues which stem from the traditional dilemma of protection versus *any* use. Recent applications of LAC (e.g., Idaho's Snake River Plan) have developed management objectives, indicators, and standards to define limits of change for a wide range of possible resource uses.

The LAC framework consists of four basic components (Stankey, McCool, and Stokes 1990; Stankey et al. 1985):

1. Identifying acceptable and achievable social and resource standards;
2. Documenting gaps between desired and existing circumstances;
3. Identifying management actions to close these gaps; and
4. Monitoring and evaluating management effectiveness.

Figure 10.2 details the nine steps through which the framework is implemented.

The LAC framework was initially developed and implemented to aid in setting standards for remote areas. Such standards may focus on social or ecological conditions. For example, encountering more than one commercial horseback riding party per day might constitute an unacceptable level of social interaction for most users of semi-primitive back country areas, while one such party per day might be acceptable. The definition of ecological standards focuses more on what we perceive as naturalness of an area. Standards respond to those perceptions and to ecological determinations of environmental quality.

Two important aspects of the LAC framework spring from this discussion of standards. McCool (1990a 185–6) points out that LAC arose out of dissatisfaction with the concept of 'recreational carrying capacity'[3] and disillusion with its implementation in forest management plans. Determinations of

---

[3]The notion of recreational carrying capacity is explored and criticized fully in Graefe et al. 1984 and in Manning 1986.

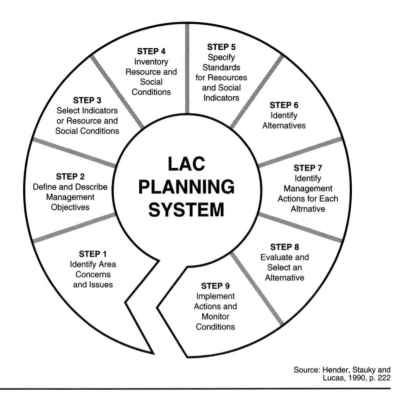

STEP 4
Inventory
Resource and
Social
Conditions

STEP 5
Specify
Standards
for Resources
and Social
Indicators

STEP 3
Select Indicators
or Resource and
Social Conditions

STEP 6
Identify
Alternatives

LAC
PLANNING
SYSTEM

STEP 2
Define and Describe
Management
Objectives

STEP 7
Identify
Management
Actions for Each
Altrnative

STEP 1
Identify Area
Concerns
and Issues

STEP 8
Evaluate and
Select an
Alternative

STEP 9
Implement
Actions and
Monitor
Conditions

Source: Hender, Stauky and
Lucas, 1990, p. 222

Figure 10.2 The Limits of Acceptable Change (LAC) planning system.

Source: J.C. Hendee, G.H. Stankey, and R.C. Lucas (1990). *Wilderness Management*, North American Press, Golden, Colo.

carrying capacity were simply not objective. Elsewhere, Stankey, McCool, and Stokes (1990, 218) elaborate: 'such a conception [of carrying capacity] obscured the important distinction between carrying capacity as the product of a technical assessment as opposed to its establishment through value judgements that weighed resource and social impacts, along with human needs and values.' The realization that value judgements are implicit in determinations concerning recreational carrying capacity requires a different approach to planning. Just *whose* value judgements are considered in such determinations becomes a significant question that can only be answered by involving visitors or users in a decision building process (Stankey, McCool, and Stokes 1990). The LAC framework represents an attempt to go beyond recreational carrying capacity by developing realistic standards based on people's use, understanding, and valuation of natural areas.

The second significant aspect in LAC is the origin of potential standards. They do not come only from technical and recreational staff, but from discussion among all *stakeholders*—that is, those individuals and organizations with clearly defined economic, recreational, or ecological interests in a wilderness area (Shands 1992). Once standards within a plan are developed and reviewed through an environmental impact assessment, the agency, stakeholders, and members of the public are responsible for monitoring and reporting on an annual basis on how well the standards have been met. This participative or co-operative management function enables those involved to modify standards or visitor use in response to actual ecological and social impacts.

Although the LAC framework is based on the same sort of experience-based setting management concepts as ROS, it differs dramatically in its non-technical and consensual approach to decision making. In the LAC framework, decisions are not made but built (Graham 1990).

Perhaps because the application of the LAC framework requires a good deal of risk-taking on the part of any agency, examples of implementation are rare compared to ROS. However, in one of the most notable wilderness areas in the U.S. National Wilderness Preservation System, the Bob Marshall Wilderness Area in Montana, LAC was used effectively to develop a management plan to deal with a widely diverse public and private recreational pressures (Stankey, McCool, and Stokes 1990). In Canada, the LAC framework is being employed in developing a management strategy for back country areas of Yoho National Park (Krys and Anderson 1992).

Visitor Impact Management

The Visitor Impact Management (VIM) framework was developed in collaboration among the National Parks and Conservation Association, an American non-governmental parks organization, and academic researchers led primarily by Alan Graefe (see Graefe *et al.* 1984, 1990*a*, 1990*b*). It arose from a review of the literature on recreational carrying capacity, with a view toward providing managers of parks and protected areas with the tools necessary to manage visitor impacts. It also considered environmental issues and visitors' experiences in national parks (Graefe 1990).

The VIM process consists of eight steps, involving a combination of legislation/policy review, scientific problem identification (both social and natural), and analysis and professional judgement (Figure 10.3). In its constituent steps, the VIM framework is quite similar to LAC. However, their differences owe much to their origins, their operating requirements, and the scales at which they operate.

The first two steps in the VIM framework (Graefe 1990) include a review of legislative, policy and database situations for the sites or areas under scrutiny and a review and identification of specific management objectives for

BASIC APPROACH:
   Systematic process for identification of impact problems, their causes, and effective management strategies for reduction of visitor impacts.
CONDITIONS FOR USE:
   Integrated with other planning frameworks or as management tool for localized impact problems.

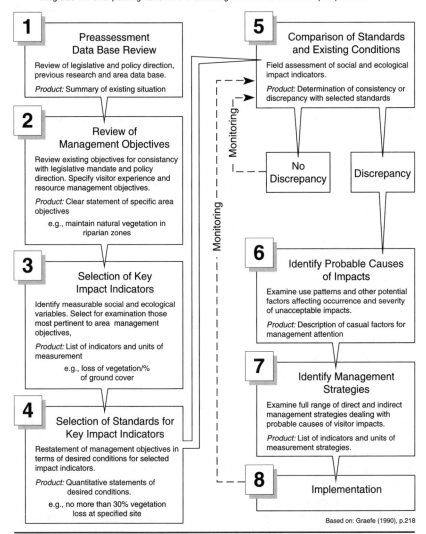

Figure 10.3 Visitor Impact Management (VIM) process.

Source: A.R. Graefe (1990). 'Visitor Impact Management', in *Towards Serving Our Visitors and Managing Our Resources*, eds R. Graham and R. Lawrence, Proceedings of the First Canada/U.S. Workshop on Visitor Management in Parks and Protected Areas, Waterloo, Ont., Tourism Research and Education Centre, University of Waterloo, and Canadian Parks Service, Environment Canada, 213-34.

visitor and resource management. Of particular interest here is the involvement of legislation, policy, or both at such an early stage in the process.
Notable, too, is the fact that the process considers the effects on both visitors
and natural systems. The next steps bring social and natural scientific knowledge into play in the selection of important indicators, the choice of standards
for these indicators, and the comparison of standards and current conditions.
If discrepancies exist between standards and actual conditions on a site or in
an area, then problems exist.

The next two steps seek to identify the causes of the problems and to
develop appropriate and effective management responses or solutions. Finally,
the preferred solution is implemented, with monitoring to ensure that the gap
between actual conditions and defined standards is closing for the area in
question.

Although carrying capacity remains at the heart of the VIM framework, it
is precisely defined in relation both to the problem and to the relevant ecological or social standards. VIM requires social and natural scientific research
in order to establish relationships between people and impacts, between uses
and impacts, and between impacts and site conditions. This application of
social science in a parks and protected areas agency has been greatly facilitated by Co-operative Park Service Units, joint efforts of the National Parks
Service and several American universities.

This scientific orientation, however, is firmly guided by the legislation,
policies, procedures, and administrative culture of the National Parks Service.
Science, social or natural, is a tool in problem-solving within this context.
Finally, the professional judgement of managers is also brought into play.

Graefe (1990) offers several examples which illustrate the use of the VIM
framework in parks and protected areas. In Great Smoky Mountains National
Park, human waste and trash and consequent pests were a problem at trail
shelters. Potential solutions included installation of pit toilets, education programs on minimum-impact camping and hiking, reducing capacity, and providing more maintenance patrols. In a mountain pass in Glacier National Park
(U.S.), new standards for visitor use, to deal with human impact on wildlife,
species diversity, and trail degradation, were established to deal with a number of problems caused by the popularity of the alpine site and its sensitivity
to visitor use.

The VIM framework offers a problem-solving approach to visitor management, predicated on reacting to undesirable changes in the natural or social
environments caused by inappropriate or excessive visitor use.

Visitor Activity Management Process

The Visitor Activity Management Process (VAMP) was developed by the
Canadian Park Service (CPS) and a group of academic researchers. Concerns
existed within the agency throughout the 1970s about the effectiveness of
interpretation and visitor services. In the early 1980s, external criticisms,

notably from the Auditor General, brought those concerns into sharper focus. Throughout these years, other Canadian federal government departments continued to promote national parks, especially Banff National Park, as international tourism destinations.

Internal and external criticisms convinced CPS staff that interpretation and visitor services would have to be conducted in a more professional manner. The continuing tourism focus on national parks convinced senior management that, like it or not, CPS was in the tourism business (Payne, Graham, and Nilsen 1987; Graham, Nilsen, and Payne 1988; Graham 1990).

The VAMP framework is meant to act in concert with another long-established agency process, natural resource management (see Figure 10.4). Together, the two feed information into two decision making structures. One structure is systems planning, in which candidate national parks are evaluated. The other is park management planning, in which management plans are

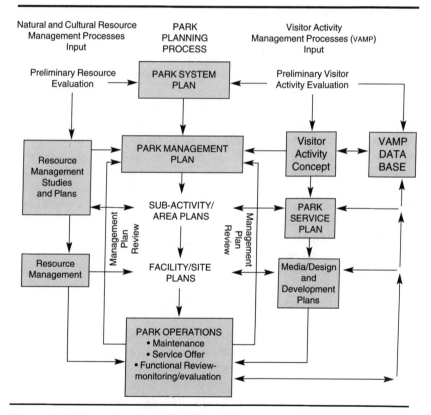

Figure 10.4 The national park planning process, showing the role of the Visitor Activity Management Process (VAMP).

Source: Canadian Parks Service (1986). *Getting Started: A Guide to Service Planning*, Environment Canada, Ottawa.

developed to implement national park policy in established national parks (see Chapter 5).

The VAMP framework revolves around visitor activity profiles. This focus is unique. It avoids the difficulties common to market research of inferring or predicting behaviour from geographic, demographic, and psychographic characteristics of visitors, by dealing with *actual* activity.

A visitor activity profile connects a particular activity (for example, cross-country skiing) with the social and demographic characteristics of participants, with the activity's setting requirements, and with trends affecting the activity. For cross-country skiing, the visitor activity profile used by the CPS is composed of four subactivities: recreation/day-use skiing, fitness skiing, competitive skiing, and back-country skiing. Differences among participants' sociodemographic characteristics, equipment, and motivations, as well as their setting needs, make each of these subactivities—all involving cross-country skiing—quite distinct. More importantly for planning and management, these distinct variations require differing levels of service and have differing environmental effects. Competitive skiing, for instance, requires creating courses that meet standards set by cross-country skiing associations. On the other hand back-country (telemark) skiing requires no changes to the landscape, since the natural setting is such a large part of what these skiers want.

Two significant aspects of VAMP framework are highlighted by this discussion on visitor activity profiles. First, the VAMP framework, and, specifically the visitor activity profile, allow us to assess an activity or subactivity in terms of its relationship to the four policy objectives for national parks: protection, understanding, appreciation, and enjoyment. Given this policy, competitive skiing (for instance) may not be an appropriate activity in national parks, because it imposes demands for dramatic modifications of the natural environment and participants are not likely better to understand or appreciate the national park as a result of the activity. Back-country skiing, however, imposes no such demands on the natural environment, nor is it so popular that sheer numbers of skiers pose environmental threats. It does give people opportunities to understand and appreciate the natural heritage of the national park. As a result, back-country skiing may be an appropriate activity in national parks.

The second significant aspect to be noted about the visitor activity profile is the insight it brings to the question of services for visitors. How involved should national park management be in providing recreational activity? This is a question that the visitor activity profile helps to answer. Activities depend upon specific settings, facilities, programs, services, or all of these. The extent to which park managers can meet demands for visitor services is an issue in most parks. Other agencies, public or private, may be able to provide the required services. Facilities, programs, and services may require scarce capital and operating funds. While an activity such as recreational or day-use skiing may not be particularly damaging to the environment in parks, it does require that trails be groomed and parking lots be cleared of snow. There may also be demands for instruction and equipment rentals. *Service planning* for interpretation, safety, and general visitor services connects the requirements of recreation with park operations. By itself, service planning becomes a unique product of the VAMP framework (Canadian Parks Service 1988).

VAMP is now being used in national parks, in national historic parks, and in heritage canals (e.g., the Rideau Canal in Ontario). In Pukaskwa National Park, for example, park managers using the VAMP framework identified two main groups of visitors: campers and back-country hikers. These groups differed in obvious ways: in their choices of settings, their activities, the equipment they used in those activities, and their motivations. Further research revealed that campers could be subdivided into three groups: destination campers, en-route campers, and local campers. These three groups obviously must be managed somewhat differently. For example, interpretation services for first-time or en-route visitors would not be appropriate for local or repeat visitors.

These four decision structures share more than a basic concern with managing visitors to parks and protected areas. As similar as they are, there exist marked differences among them which can be accounted for by the characteristics of the administrative cultures in which they have developed. In the section which follows, these visitor planning and management frameworks will be compared and assessed.

COMPARING AND ASSESSING THE FRAMEWORKS

Using analytical techniques from established approaches to park and protected area policy analysis (Nelson 1977, 1991; Payne 1990), each framework can be evaluated to determine how well it contributes to the task for which it was devised—namely, the integration of visitor issues with the more traditional environmental issues in planning and managing of parks and protected areas.

We must look at three issues in our analysis: theory, process, and how well the framework relates to society. *Theory* deals with the relationship of the frameworks to established theories of planning. *Process* is concerned with the ways in which the frameworks operate. Finally, *external relations* are concerned with the relationship between the framework and relevant aspects of the environment outside the agency in question. How and where do the various stakeholders with whom the agencies must deal become involved in the processes? Included as well is the factor of regional integration, which puts the park or protected area into its regional context with respect to social, economic and environmental issues.

Theory

Each of these frameworks aims to assist the management planning process. Planning no longer consists merely of professionals setting goals and objectives, identifying alternative means of achieving them, selecting the best alternative, and then monitoring goal achievement. Although this 'rational' theory of planning is still in wide use, its dominance is challenged by theories (e.g., transactive planning) in which professionals play a less technocratic role and in which the 'affected publics' are given many more opportunities to participate and to be involved at more stages in the planning process. Rational theory was really only an ideal. In reality, especially in public sector bureaucracies, planning has always been constrained by policies, procedures, and administrative cultures. A broad-minded consideration of alternatives, including unusual alternatives, is extremely difficult under such constraints. Rationality may still figure prominently, but it is a form of rationality which is bounded (Simon 1957) by organizational policies, procedures, and culture. Nonetheless, the four frameworks differ substantially in relation to planning theory.

The Recreation Opportunity Spectrum is the most rational of the four. It allows a wide-ranging consideration of options and apparently avoids becoming a mere check-list. Several writers on the framework (e.g., Clark and Stankey 1990) in fact explicitly exhort users not to treat ROS as a cookbook approach but rather to adapt it to regional conditions. On the other hand, control of the framework rests with the social and natural scientists in the U.S. Forest Service. While various groups are affected by decisions made using the ROS framework, opportunities for their public involvement can be limited, often depending upon management style (Shannon 1987).

Although the Limits of Acceptable Change framework depends upon ROS for the identification of opportunity classes, its theoretical basis departs from ROS quite radically. The LAC framework is the only one of the four which could be characterized as being based on transactive planning theory (Friedmann 1987). In its extensive opportunities for involvement by the public and representatives of interest groups, LAC allows these interested parties to participate in decisions concerning wilderness management. Stakeholders play important roles in decision building and monitoring, because they have knowledge and a legitimate claim to be involved. The LAC framework involves consensus rather than selecting the 'best' alternative course of action in light of agency goals. Sharing power, knowledge, information, and rewards in decision building for wilderness areas relies on those American traditions of accountability and involvement in public policy-making.[4]

---

[4]It is important to note that no such traditions currently exist in Canada. For elaboration, see Payne and Graham 1987, 1988; and Payne 1990*b*.

The Visitor Impact Management framework typifies a rational approach to planning, but a rationality clearly bounded by the organizational context and the problem at hand. The approach is one of fine-tuning existing actions, the better to achieve existing goals and objectives in national parks. Visitors or others are acted *upon* in the VIM framework to achieve *agency* goals. In this, VIM differs significantly from the LAC framework, in which stakeholders are acted *with* to achieve *mutual* goals. Professional expertise is the basis for setting standards for measuring management performance.

Like VIM, the Visitor Activity Management Process is based on a rational approach to planning. Unlike VIM, however, VAMP exhibits a much less bounded sort of rationality. The information required for visitor activity profiles must be valid scientific data. In its intent, VAMP is much closer to the approach to planning as seen in ROS than to the more restricted rationality of VIM. Through its ability to include informal traditional or customary knowledge (Graham and Payne 1990), VAMP may come to incorporate a transactive dimension as well. VAMP shares a limited role for the public with the ROS and VIM frameworks. However, there is an important difference between VAMP and these two at the level of service, where VAMP is beginning to consider the roles of stakeholders in planning its services.

In terms of planning theories, the frameworks are noticeably and significantly different. The ROS is rational; LAC is transactive; VIM can be described as rational but tightly constrained by the problem's context; VAMP is also rational, but less constrained, with the potential to rival ROS in its holistic approach.

Process

The theoretical bases of the frameworks have profound implications for how they operate and for what they produce. Beliefs about how parks and protected areas ought to be managed have been 'designed into' each approach. Each constitutes a technology, a way of getting something done, a tool. As with any tool, the tool's purpose and how it functions will determine what it produces.

One important aspect of how the frameworks function revolves around information: What kind of information is needed? How important is it? And how is it used in decision-making? There are two basic types of information: informal (the customary and traditional knowledge held by non-professionals); and formal (the natural and social scientific information and expertise held by park and protected area professionals). Different approaches give different weights to these two classes of information. Finally, these different forms of information make possible different decision making methods. Technical (i.e., model-based) methods need scientific (formal) information; bureaucratic methods may use both formal and informal information; and consensus-based methods depend heavily upon informal information.

The Recreation Opportunity Spectrum requires formal information on technical models. For this reason, ROS has been labelled 'data-driven' by some (see e.g., Graham 1990).

Adopting the Limits of Acceptable Change approach commits an agency to using informal information. Since LAC is transactive, formal information is necessary but not sufficient for the framework to function as intended. Informal knowledge, obtained from stakeholders and presented in consensus-building sessions, is also essential.

In the Visitor Impact Management framework, formal natural and social scientific information is used in a problem solving context. Moreover, it is this context that dictates the kind and amount of information needed. Although VIM looks much like the LAC framework, both the way information is acquired and the nature of the information set VIM apart.

In the Visitor Activity Management Process, formal social science information is blended with informal information from park staff and others. Although there is no particular barrier in theory to the use of informal knowledge, such a barrier does exist in the Canadian Parks Service, which historically has been more comfortable with natural science information.

How these frameworks operate also depends on how each one relates to relevant legislation and policy and to other functional units in the respective agencies.

It is clear that ROS is a direct response to the major piece of legislation under which the U.S. Forest Service operates, the National Forest Management Act. That legislation requires the Forest Service to manage national forests for the optimum range of economic and social benefits. This relationship dominates all others and underlies ROS operations. The relationship between ROS and other Forest Service functions reflects the diversity of those functions. ROS must accommodate non-recreational uses such as logging as well as usual and back-country recreation. Managing visitors is firmly integrated with other management activities in the Forest Service.

The LAC framework has neither the scope nor the central role of ROS. The National Forest Management Act provides the basic legislative context for LAC; however, the Wilderness Act provides the primary legislative direction. Policy is of little importance as a source of direction for the LAC framework. The LAC framework depends upon ROS and utilizes the same underlying conceptual approach. However, the LAC framework is guided by the Wilderness Act, a piece of legislation which is overtly oriented to the preservation of wildlands. The concerns addressed by LAC are, therefore, quite narrow, encompassing types and levels of recreational use, facilities, and services, as well as levels of protection. In its applications to date, the LAC framework represents an extension of ROS, applicable in specific circumstances where American legislation so demands.

The Visitor Impact Management framework is a partial reflection of each of the pieces of legislation that establish and manage national parks in the

United States. Both recreational use and protection of natural values are mentioned in these acts. Policy statements are on a case-by-case basis, not at a system-wide level, in the U.S. National Parks Service. The VIM framework reflects the prevailing administrative culture within the National Parks Service in its emphasis of the protection and maintenance of natural or desired conditions.[5]

With its problem-solving orientation, VIM potentially connects to a wide variety of other management processes, but the nature of the problem dictates which of those other processes is included in the VIM solution. A problem for which visitor education is seen as the best management action will necessarily involve interpretation services; a problem caused by the circulation of visitors through an area is likely to be addressed in the national park management plan.

The Visitor Activity Management Process, operating in Canadian national parks, is a logical outgrowth of the National Parks Act, a generic piece of legislation that states that national parks are to protect natural heritage and to promote its appreciation, understanding, and enjoyment. National parks policy, established in 1979 (see Chapters 4 and 5), assigns priorities to these aims in this order: protection, understanding, appreciation, and enjoyment. The VAMP framework explicitly focuses upon understanding, appreciation, and enjoyment. This direct connection to policy provides crucial guidance in determining which recreational activities are appropriate in national parks, as we saw in the discussion of cross-country skiing. Its closer link to policy distinguishes VAMP from the other frameworks.

The VAMP framework is also meant to operate in parallel to the natural resource management process in national parks to produce a park management plan. Its connections to interpretation, visitor services, and safety in parks planning also serve to distinguish it from the other three frameworks. At this 'service planning' stage, which ideally occurs following the completion of the park management plan, strategies for interpreting the themes of the park, for supporting visitor activities, and for ensuring visitor safety during all phases of a visitor's trip are developed for each visitor activity group identified in the management planning process.

Another aspect of importance is the tangible result or product of each framework. Applying ROS yields a regional, mapped identification of settings for recreation. This 'map' represents the various recreational opportunities that could be provided. Combining this assessment of supply with information about demand allows managers to determine the type and extent of recreation to be offered or allowed in individual areas.

---

[5]It remains to be seen whether the LAC framework is changed when it is applied in other jurisdictions, in semi-wilderness settings. The application of LAC in Canada's Yoho National Park may offer insight into such applications.

Using the LAC framework, in a much narrower set of circumstances, produces a plan for a wilderness area based on social and ecological standards. While this is both tangible and important in itself, the less measurable benefit of consensus must also be considered. Because of this co-operation, the plan is more than a plan by an agency; it is an acceptable plan to a constituency.

The VIM framework has effects quite unlike those produced by the others. The formal identification of a problem and its cause(s), the determination of a relevant standard to be maintained, and the management response to eliminate the problem all constitute products in one sense of the term. However, unlike the other three frameworks, VIM does not produce strategies to allocate settings for recreation. It produces action plans which provide site-specific solutions and means to monitor the maintenance of standards.

Finally, using VAMP yields different products at different stages in the park management planning process. In assessments of candidate national parks, VAMP contributes a preliminary assessment of visitor activity. In park management planning, VAMP generates visitor activity profiles, a visitor activity concept, and a plan to acquire needed data on visitors. In service delivery, it produces plans for interpretation, visitor services, and safety.

While all four frameworks are generally concerned with the planning for and management of visitors to parks and protected areas, each approaches these tasks in ways which reflect the nature and traditions of the agencies involved.

External Relations

Two factors comprise this category: public involvement and regional integration. Of the two, public involvement has received much more general attention, especially in academic literature and in the planning and management process. Regional integration has been pursued formally by only one of the agencies involved, the U.S. Forest Service.

As the primary planning tool for national forests, ROS incorporates the legislative direction that these areas produce the best possible array of social and economic benefits for Americans. That accountability is reinforced by the requirement to assess the social and environmental impacts of national forest plans. However, ROS allows relatively limited involvement of the public or interest groups. ROS's technical nature makes it complex and not hospitable to more informal information from broad public participation.

The LAC framework, on the other hand, depends on public involvement, and quite intensive public involvement at that. Stakeholders and other members of the public work with agency personnel to develop decisions for wilderness areas in which all parties have an interest. While LAC also yields standards much like VIM does, it does so by building acceptance for, and agreement about, those standards through discussions. The extent of public involvement in LAC framework sets it apart. People involved are generally stakeholders with quite specific and often radically opposed interests: for examples, an outfitter whose livelihood depends on the wilderness area, and staff from the Sierra Club. The information they bring to the planning situation from their various points of view is valued and incorporated into the plan.

Of the four frameworks, VIM is perhaps the least concerned with public involvement. Professional expertise is crucial to problem identification and solution.

Public involvement in the establishment of Canadian national parks has become more common (Payne *et al.* 1992). However, it does not occur at every stage, from park establishment to management planning to service planning. At the early stages—new park establishment and management planning—VAMP does not generally include the public. In service planning, where decisions are made about levels of service and roles of stakeholders in providing services, the involvement of specific sectors of the public plays a significant role.

Regional integration refers to the possible roles of the four frameworks in assessing economic, social, or environmental benefits to the surrounding (non-park) regions. Three of the frameworks deserve attention from this point of view. The VIM framework, because it operates at the site rather than at the regional level, is not considered here.

Both ROS and LAC bear the marks of the U.S. Forest Service's continuing role in supporting economic, social, and community stability, especially in those areas with few economic alternatives to resource extradition. Both frameworks make considerable efforts to identify the range of economic and social benefits that might arise from alternative resource allocations. Their similarity in this is a direct reflection of the role of national forests, and, indeed, of the U.S. Forest Service, as generators of economic and social well-being.

A regional development role is of much more recent origin in the Canadian Parks Service, dating from the formal introduction of VAMP as a management process in 1985. The agency has no traditional roots as an agent of social and economic stability or change. While other levels of government have seen national parks as tourist attractions, only the introduction of VAMP formalized that view in the Canadian Parks Service itself.

The VAMP framework gives strong support for assessing the regional social and economic impacts of national parks (e.g. see Graham, Nilsen, and Payne 1987). At the new park establishment stage, VAMP, through a preliminary assessment of visitor activities, provides estimates of numbers of visitors and of types of recreational activities that could be expected in a new park. At the management and service planning stages, VAMP provides more detailed assessments and guidance for decisions about facilities, programs, and services.

ISSUES AND CONCLUSIONS

Issues

Each of these four structures for visitor planning and management decision is confronted by particular issues that require solution if the framework is to be used to its full potential.

While it is the most established of the four, ROS faces two large obstacles: it is quite complex, and it is perceived as being data-driven. These issues account for the continuing difficulty the Forest Service has experienced in encouraging managers to implement ROS in National Forests. Training sessions, instructional films, and visits from Forest Service personnel with experience using the framework are helping to overcome these difficulties. ROS also currently lacks an appropriate environmental planning process with a more holistic view of the natural environment than it now has. A landscape ecology approach, emphasizing ecological processes and biodiversity, will be needed if ROS is to be a truly integrative planning and management framework.

LAC may offer stakeholders and other members of the public much more control of wilderness and other protected area planning than was possible earlier. But this also means that power will have to be shared. Rarely does an organization want to reduce its own power in decision making. Internal resistance may be the biggest problem facing the LAC framework.

The VIM framework, unlike the other three, functions primarily at a site level. This fact circumscribes its usefulness to a considerable extent. It is also a very 'inward-looking' framework, in that it depends upon professional judgement from staff and on scientific information. VIM's problem-solving orientation also prevents it from managing shifts in visitor program or service provision. It seeks to regulate visitors, not to manage them.

The VAMP framework is only now coming into wide use in the Canadian Parks Service. It has faced, and to some degree, still faces, internal resistance because it represents a radically new way of managing national parks. That resistance may well evaporate as Canadian Parks Service personnel come to understand that VAMP is not meant merely to open the park gates to more people.

There are some difficult issues to be overcome if VAMP is to rival ROS as a visitor planning and management framework. First, the issue of opportunity assessment, so well handled by ROS, is unresolved in Canadian national parks. This issue requires a technical solution; such technical manipulations are beyond VAMP at present. A related issue is the fact that VAMP does not contribute to decisions about park zoning. Clearly, the solution to this issue will require a solution to the opportunity assessment issue. It will also require considerable tact, since decisions concerning national park zoning are now made in the natural resource management process, VAMP's elder companion process, by personnel trained in natural science approaches to park planning and management. VAMP has the potential to encourage the development of a co-operative style of management involving customary users, stakeholders, and other neighbours. However, at present, limited VAMP implementation during systems planning or park establishment and the continued use of advisory committees during management and service planning are barriers to the effectiveness of this decision structure.

Conclusions

We set out to describe and analyse four frameworks for visitor planning and management that are in use in North America. While all four share a concern with visitors to parks and protected areas, the theoretical approaches to these concerns, the processes themselves, their effects, and how the processes relate to matters outside the park or protected area all differ significantly.

All, to varying degrees, demand social science information; only the LAC framework departs radically to include informal information. Much the same pattern is evident in relation to public involvement. The frameworks show clear differences in relation to planning theory. ROS holds the position closest to rational, holistic planning; VAMP and VIM are rational planning frameworks, constrained somewhat by policies and procedures; and LAC is clearly a trans-active approach.

As contributions to visitor planning and management, the four can be ranked in the following manner. ROS and VAMP are in a tight race for the designation of the best of the four. They are different, but they both do many of the things necessary to manage visitors well. Their respective deficiencies—the lack of an ecological planning structure to support ROS, and the inability of VAMP to affect park zoning decisions—are flaws that may be overcome by their strengths. The LAC framework sits by itself in third place, offering a degree of public involvement unmatched in any of the other frameworks. It is quite narrow in its range of applications, and such openness to public involvement may limit its acceptance by organizations with pronounced bureaucratic tendencies. Finally, the VIM framework offers considerably less for visitor planning and management than the other three. In its technical focus on standards, it excludes informal information. In its problem-solving orientation, it treats people as the source of problems and seeks to regulate rather than manage visitors.

Visitor planning and management frameworks do, of course, add further complications to the park and protected area management process. On the other hand, if these areas are to continue to allow people to find both rec-reation *and* natural heritage protection, management will have to reflect these competing uses. To varying degrees, all four of the visitor management frameworks reviewed here contribute to this broader form of park management.

REFERENCES

British Columbia Ministry of Forests
  1989   *Managing Wilderness in Provincial Forests: A Policy Framework*, Recreation Section, Integrated Resources Branch, Ministry of Forests, Victoria, B.C.
Canadian Parks Service
  1988   *Getting Started: A Guide to Service Planning*, Environment Canada, Ottawa.
Canadian Parks Service
  1986   *In Trust for Tomorrow: A Management Framework for Four Mountain Parks*, Supply and Services Canada, Ottawa.
Canadian Parks Service
  1979   *Parks Canada Policy*, Environment Canada, Ottawa.
Clark, R.N., and G.H. Stankey
  1990   'The Recreation Opportunity Spectrum: A Framework for Planning, Management and Research', in *Towards Serving Our Visitors and Managing Our Resources*, eds R. Graham and R. Lawrence, Proceedings of the First Canada/U.S. Workshop on Visitor Management in Parks and Protected Areas, Waterloo, Ont., Tourism Research and Education Centre, University of Waterloo, and Canadian Parks Service, Environment Canada, 127–58.
Clark, R.N., and G.H. Stankey
  1979   *The Recreation Opportunity Spectrum: A Framework for Planning, Management and Research*, General Technical Report PNW-98, Pacific Northwest Forest and Range Experiment Station, U.S. Department of Agriculture, Seattle.
Driver, B.L.
  1990a   U.S. Forest Service Research Scientist, Fort Collins, Colorado, personal communication (May).
Driver, B.L.
  1990b   'Recreation Opportunity Spectrum: Basic Concepts and Use in Land Management Planning', in *Towards Serving Our Visitors and Managing Our Resources*, eds R. Graham and R. Lawrence, Proceedings of the First Canada/U.S. Workshop on Visitor Management in Parks and Protected Areas, Waterloo, Ont., Tourism Research and Education Centre, University of Waterloo, and Canadian Parks Service, Environment Canada, 159–83.
Driver, B.L.
  1990c   'The North American Experience in Measuring the Benefits of Leisure', in *Proceedings of a Workshop on Measurement of Recreation Benefits*, ed. E. Hamilton-Smith, Phillips Institute of Technology, Bundora, Victoria.
Driver, B.L., and P.J. Brown
  1983   'Contributions of Behavioral Scientists to Recreation Resource Management', in *Behavior and the Natural Environment*, eds I. Altman and J.F. Wohlwill, Plenum Press, New York, 307–39.
Friedmann, J.
  1987   *Planning in the Public Domain: From Knowledge to Action*, Princeton University Press, Princeton, N.J.

Graefe, A.R.
  1990   'Visitor Impact Management', in *Towards Serving Our Visitors and Managing Our Resources*, eds R. Graham and R. Lawrence, Proceedings of the First Canada/U.S. Workshop on Visitor Management in Parks and Protected Areas, Waterloo, Ontario, Tourism Research and Education Centre, University of Waterloo, and Canadian Parks Service, Environment Canada, 213–34.

Graefe, A.R., F.R. Kuss, and J.J. Vaske
  1990a   *Visitor Impact Management: A Review of Research*, vol. 1, National Parks and Conservation Association, Washington, D.C.

Graefe, A.R., F.R. Kuss, and J.J. Vaske
  1990b   *Visitor Impact Management: The Planning Framework*, vol. 2, National Parks and Conservation Association, Washington, D.C.

Graefe, A.R., J.J. Vaske, and F.R. Kuss
  1984   'Social Carrying Capacity: An Integration and Synthesis of Twenty Years of Research', *Leisure Sciences* 6: 395–431.

Graham, R.
  1990   'Visitor Management and Canada's National Parks', in *Towards Serving Our Visitors and Managing Our Resources*, eds R. Graham and R. Lawrence, Proceedings of the First Canada/U.S. Workshop on Visitor Management in Parks and Protected Areas, Waterloo, Ont., Tourism Research and Education Centre, University of Waterloo, and Canadian Parks Service, Environment Canada, 271–96.

Graham, R., P. Nilsen, and R.J. Payne
  1988   'Visitor Management in Canadian National Parks', *Tourism Management* 9: 44–62.

Graham, R., P. Nilsen, and R.J. Payne
  1987   'Visitor Activity Planning and Management in Canadian National Parks: Marketing Within a Context of Integration', in *Social Science in Natural Resource Management Systems*, eds M.L. Miller, R.P. Gale, and P.J. Brown, Westview Press, Boulder, Colo., 149–66.

Graham, R., and R.J. Payne
  1990   'Customary and Traditional Knowledge in Canadian National Park Planning and Management: A Process View', in *Social Science and Natural Resource Recreation Management*, ed. J. Vining, Westview Press, Boulder, Colo., 125–50.

Hendee, J.C., G.H. Stankey, and R.C. Lucas
  1990   *Wilderness Management*, North American Press, Golden, Colo.

Jones, M.
  1989   Ontario Ministry of Natural Resources Recreation Planner, Thunder Bay, Ont., personal communication (February).

Kauffman, H.
  1960   *The Forest Ranger: A Study in Administrative Behavior*, Johns Hopkins University Press, Baltimore.

Knopf, R.C.
  1990   'The Limits of Acceptable Change (LAC) Planning Process: Potentials and Limitations', In *Towards Serving Our Visitors and Managing Our Resources*, eds R. Graham and R. Lawrence, Proceedings of the First

Canada/U.S. Workshop on Visitor Management in Parks and Protected Areas, Waterloo, Ont., Tourism and Recreation Education Centre University of Waterloo and Canadian Parks Service, Environment Canada, 201–11.

Krys, S., and J. Anderson
1992   'Yoho National Park Demonstration Project', presented at poster session, applications forum, Second Canada/U.S. Workshop on Visitor Management in Parks, Forests and Protected Areas, University of Wisconsin, Madison.

Machlis, G.E., and D.L. Tichnell
1985   *The State of the World's Parks*, Westview Press, Boulder, Colo.

Manning, R.E.
1986   *Studies in Outdoor Recreation: A Review and Synthesis of the Social Science Literature in Outdoor Recreation*, Oregon State University Press, Corvallis, Ore.

McCool, S.F.
1990a   'Limits of Acceptable Change: Evolution and Future', in *Towards Serving Our Visitors and Managing Our Resources*, eds R. Graham and R. Lawrence, Proceedings of the First Canada/U.S. Workshop on Visitor Management in Parks and Protected Areas, Waterloo, Ont., Tourism and Recreation Education Centre, University of Waterloo, and Canadian Parks Service, Environment Canada, 185–93.

McCool, S.F.
1990b   'Limits of Acceptable Change: Some Principles', in *Towards Serving Our Visitors and Managing Our Resources*, eds R. Graham and R. Lawrence, Proceedings of the First Canada/U.S. Workshop on Visitor Management in Parks and Protected Areas, Waterloo, Ont., Tourism and Recreation Education Centre, University of Waterloo, and Canadian Parks Service, Environment Canada, 195–200.

McCool, S.F.
1989   'The Challenge of Managing Wilderness in an Era of Change', in *Outdoor Recreation Benchmark 1988: Proceedings of the National Outdoor Recreation Forum*, ed. A.H. Watson, General Technical Publication SE-52, Southeastern Forest Experiment Station, U.S. Forest Service, Department of Agriculture, Asheville, N.C., 385–98.

McCool, S.F., and G.H. Stankey
1992   'Managing for the Sustainable Use of Protected Wildlands: The Limits of Acceptable Change Framework', paper presented at the fourth World National Parks Congress, Caracas, Venezuela.

Nelson, J.G.
1991   'Research in Human Ecology and Planning: An Interactive, Adaptive Approach', *Canadian Geographer* 35: 114–27.

Nelson, J.G.
1977   'Canadian National Parks and Related Reserves: Research Needs and Management', in *Managing Canada's Renewable Resources*, eds R.R. Krueger and B. Mitchell, Methuen, Toronto, 173–93.

Payne, R.J.
1990a   'Issues in Visitor Management Strategies', in *Towards Serving Our Visitors and Managing Our Resources*, eds R. Graham and R. Lawrence, Proceedings of the First Canada/U.S. Workshop on Visitor Management in Parks

and Protected Areas, Waterloo, Ont., Tourism Research and Education Centre, University of Waterloo, and Canadian Parks Service, Environment Canada, 59–66.

Payne, R.J.
1990*b* 'A Canadian Perspective on Visitor Management', in *Towards Serving Our Visitors and Managing Our Resources*, eds R. Graham and R. Lawrence, Proceedings of the First Canada/U.S. Workshop on Visitor Management in Parks and Protected Areas, Waterloo, Ont., Tourism Research and Education Centre, University of Waterloo, and Canadian Parks Service, Environment Canada, 481–9.

Payne, R.J., R. Rollins, S. Tamm, and C. Nelson
1992 'Managing Social Impacts of Parks and Protected Areas in Canada', in *Science and the Management of Protected Areas*, eds J.H.M. Willison, S. Bondrup-Neisen, C. Drysdale, T. Herman, N. Munro, and T. Pollock, Elsevier, New York, 513–18.

Payne, R.J., and R. Graham
1988 'Implementing Citizen Participation in Canada: Single and Multiple Actor Cases', in *Environmental Dispute Resolution in the Great Lakes Region: A Critical Appraisal*, eds L.S. Bankert and R.W. Flint, Great Lakes Program, Monograph No. 1, State University of New York, Buffalo, N.Y., 67–76.

Payne, R.J., and R. Graham
1987 'An Assessment of Northern Land Use Planning in Canada', *Journal of Canadian Studies* 22: 35–49.

Payne, R.J., R. Graham, and P. Nilsen
1986 'Preliminary Assessment of the Visitor Activity Management Process (VAMP)', on file, Interpretation and Visitor Services, National Parks Branch, Environment Canada, Ottawa.

Rollins, R.
1991 Tourism Coordinator, Malaspina College, Nanaimo, B.C. personal communication (January).

Shands. W.
1992 'Leadership in a Community of Interests', paper presented at the Second Canada/U.S. Workshop on Visitor Management in Parks, Forests, and Protected Areas, University of Wisconsin, Madison.

Shannon, M.
1987 'Forest Planning: Learning With People', in *Social Science in Natural Resource Management Systems*, eds M.L. Miller, R.P. Gale, and P.J. Brown, Westview Press, Boulder, Colo., 233–52.

Simon, H.A.
1957 *Models of Man: Rational and Social*, Free Press, New York.

Stankey, G.H., D.N. Cole, R.C. Lucas, M.E. Petersen, and S.S. Frissell
1985 'The Limits of Acceptable Change (LAC) System for Wilderness Planning', Forest Service, Intermountain Forest and Range Experiment Station, U.S. General Technical Report INT-176, Department of Agriculture, Ogden, Utah.

Stankey, G.H., S.F. McCool, and G.L. Stokes
1990 'Managing for Appropriate Wilderness Conditions: The Carrying Capacity Issue', in *Wilderness Management*, 2nd ed., eds J.C. Hendee, G.H. Stankey, and R.C. Lucas, Fulcrum Press, Golden, Colo., 215–39.

Stankey, G.H., S.F. McCool, and G.L. Stokes
  1984   'Limits of Acceptable Change: A New Framework for Managing the Bob
          Marshall Wilderness', *Western Wildlands* 10: 33–7.
Wilkinson, C.F., and H.M. Anderson
  1987   *Land and Resource Planning in the National Forests*, Island Press, Wash-
          ington, D.C.

CHAPTER 11

Interpretation as a Management Tool

—

JAMES R. BUTLER

ORIGINS

'To Get Near the Heart of the World'

A recognition of the role of interpretation and visitor education has been fundamental to the concept of national parks and wilderness protection from the beginning. The first appeal for a 'Nation's Park' in 1833 by American artist George Catlin, who called for an area 'preserved for its freshness of nature's beauty', included the assumption that the area would have to be *understood* to be *appreciated*. This implication was reaffirmed by Nathaniel P. Langford, co-leader of the Yellowstone expedition, which in 1870 led to the establishment of Yellowstone National Park. As Langford wrote, 'while you see and wonder, you seem to need an additional sense, fully to comprehend and believe.'

During this same period, a then little-known sawmill operator in the Yosemite Valley by the name of John Muir was diversifying his income by leading early park tourists on nature hikes. Apparently he was quite good at it, for one of his followers wrote, 'Never was there a naturalist who could hold his hearers so well, and none had so much to tell.' Influenced by the wilderness of Yosemite, Muir would find his niche as a spokesperson for the concept of wilderness preservation. While working in the Yosemite Valley, Muir would hone his interpretive skills and his understanding of the ecology and dynamics of wildland ecosystems. He wrote during this time, 'I'll interpret the rocks, learn the language of flood, storm and avalanche. I'll acquaint myself with the glaciers and wild gardens, and get as near the heart of the world as I can.' As far as we know this was the first use of the word *interpret* in a park context.

James Harkin, the first Director of Canada's Dominion Parks Branch, was an admirer of Muir and used his words in Canada's first national parks policy documents and annual reports, to clarify the value of wilderness and the philosophy and purpose of what national parks are about.

The fundamental role for interpretation in national parks was reaffirmed when the U.S. National Parks Service was established as a distinct bureau, five years after the Dominion Parks Branch, to supervise and formalize policies for America's first national parks. The report on the establishment of this agency and its first uniform policies in 1916 (written by R.B. Marshall) stated that national parks were not designed solely for the purpose of recreation. Fostering recreation as such is more properly the function of city, county, and state parks, and there should be a sharp distinction between the character of such parks and national parks. *National Parks possess an educational value that cannot be estimated.* In his initial annual report, the U.S. Park Service's new Director, Stephen T. Mather, further emphasized this final point. 'One of the chief functions of the national parks and monuments is to serve educational purposes.'

Returning east by railroad in 1919, Mather stopped over at the Fallen Leaf Lodge at Lake Tahoe. Filled with the frustrations of managing the challenges and threats to the fragile Yosemite environment, his attention was drawn to the popularity of an interpretive presentation at the lodge. The lodge owner, who held a biology degree from Stanford, had imported the idea from Norway, where nature guiding and evening nature talks were popular at some resorts.

Mather saw this as an opportunity to win public support for the natural values of Yosemite—to use education as a way to protect the park's environment. During the following summer, the first park naturalists employed by a government agency, working in Yosemite and Yellowstone, would begin a tradition that would, in spite of wavering commitments and administrative cutbacks, continue within American and Canadian national parks to the present time.

Shifts in Emphasis Over Time

Since the 1920s interpretation in parks has become considerably more sophisticated in planning and technological applications, and eventually in systems planning and interagency co-operation and co-ordination (Table 11.1). Important shifts in interpretative focus over this period may be divided into three phases. In phase one, park interpretation was concerned with acquainting visitors with *features* in the park, often those most dramatic, majestic, and exceptional by nature. The emphasis was in providing explanations for these phenomenon, often as examples of the wonders of God's creation.

In phase two, interpretation expanded to stress inter-relationships, ecology, and the landscape in general, even when these were less dramatic than hot springs or waterfalls. Management issues received greater attention, at last. Communication was, however, concerned only to what existed within the park boundary.

Phase three, the present period, includes increasing interest in expanding park interpretation to foster a broader environmental consciousness among park visitors. This shift from internal to external perspectives relies on five principles:

Table 11.1 Historical Chronology of Natural Park Interpretation in North America

1784	First natural history museum to utilize interpretive techniques opens in Philadelphia, with Charles Wilson Peale exhibiting wildlife collections from the American west.
1869	First park interpretive publication: *The Yosemite Guidebook*, by California State Geologist J.D. Whitney.
1870s	John Muir leads groups on interpretive hikes into Yosemite backcountry.
1887	Scottish caretaker and guide David D. Galletly conducts visitors through the lower Hot Spring cave, Banff: first formal interpretive walks conducted by an interpreter in a Canadian national park.
1889	Enos Mills, called the father of nature guiding and influenced by Muir, formalizes and teaches principles of nature guiding in Rocky Mountain National Park, Colo.
1895	First park interpretive museum, and first museum in any national park, is established at Banff.
1904	First park interpretive trail is established at Yosemite; Lt Pipes of the Army Medical Corps establishes a trail with labelled trees and other plants.
1905	C.H. Deutschman, who discovered Nakimu Caves in Glacier National Park, B.C., begins to conduct visitors through the cave system.
1911	Evening campfire programs and tours of park features well established in several Canadian and U.S. national parks, but all are conducted by concessions.
1914	First Canadian national park interpretive publications appear in Banff.
1915	Esther Burnell Estes becomes first licensed woman interpreter.
1918	U.S. establishes its first park museum in Mesa Verde, with exhibits and lectures given; next museum opens in 1921, in Yosemite.
1919	Nature guiding has become popular in Rocky Mountain resorts in U.S.; concept had been imported from Norway. Steven Mather, Director of U.S. Parks Service, observes the popularity of an interpretive talk at a Lake Tahoe resort and gets the idea to institutionalize it in the U.S. national parks system.
1920	First U.S. Park Service interpretive programs begin with government-employed interpreters in Yosemite and Yellowstone.
1929	First seasonal interpretive programs begin in the Rocky Mountain national parks of Canada, with the appointment of J. Hamilton Laing.
1931	Grey Owl employed as interpreter by Parks Service at Riding Mountain; later transferred to Prince Albert.

Table 11.1 Continued

1944	Early interpretive events conducted in Banff; wildlife warden Hubert Green feeds aspen cuttings to beavers of Vermillion Lakes before 25–30 tourists nightly while discussing beaver life history.
1954	Interpretive programs begin in provincial parks of Ontario.
1958	First co-ordinated interpretive service established in Ottawa for Canada's national park system.
1964	First permanent naturalists located in Canadian Rocky Mountain national parks.
1969	First Canadian wildlife interpretation centre opens at Wye Marsh, near Midland, Ont.

---

1. National parks cannot in themselves survive independent of the surrounding landscapes.
2. We need a federal vehicle to demonstrate and communicate models and fundamentals to support a national environmental strategy.
3. National parks offer benchmarks of natural processes, to compare and contrast with landscapes where renewable resource activities such as logging are undertaken.
4. National park visitors generally represent a more highly educated segment of the population, with greater receptivity to environmental education and a disproportionately higher influence on decision making.
5. Untouched national park environments represent one possible basis for building a new philosophy and ethics, turning away from post-industrial values and changing land ethics for the nation as a whole. Such a re-orientation, although a long-term goal, will be critical to the protection of the ecological integrity of national parks and the environment as a whole in the future.

DEFINITION AND PURPOSE OF PARK INTERPRETATION

A well-rounded interpretation program can go a long way toward the goal of better public use of a park. Interpretation's specific purposes are to provide essential facts about the area, its program, and its facilities, and to help the visitor understand, appreciate, and enjoy not only nature but the area as a whole. Interpretation serves to awaken public awareness of park purposes and policies and strives to develop not only a concern for preservation but a different approach to life.

The assumption underlying interpretation is that awareness leads to knowledge and knowledge leads to understanding. Once people begin to understand the environment, their appreciation deepens, and they begin to respect and even love the environment. Action follows. Interpretation is not the mere transfer of information to others, nor is it only a catalogue of things to see and do. Interpretation should fill visitors with a greater sense of wonder and curiosity (Figure 11.1). It should leave the visitor both better informed and with a desire to know more. The degree to which a visitor enjoys and values his or her experience in a park depends largely upon the individual's perception of that area's resources. For this reason, interpretive strategy should be designed to enhance the visitor's perception of these resources and ultimately to be a positive influence on the interactions between visitor and resources.

The quality of interpretation improves if the visitor is brought into direct contact with the area's resources and if these resources are described as, or revealed to be, relevant to the visitor's own experience. Proper presentation of natural and cultural features can add greatly to visitors' enjoyment and understanding of what they see.

Interpretation has been defined as 'a communications process designed to reveal meanings and relationships of our cultural and natural heritage to the public through first-hand involvement with an object, artifact, landscape, or site' (Interpretation Canada 1976). It is the opportunity of 'first-hand experience' with the environment that distinguishes park interpretation from other

Figure 11.1
'Interpretation should fill visitors with a greater sense of wonder and curiosity.' Visitor scanning for wildlife, Firth River, North Yukon National Park.
Photo: P. Dearden

forms. An interpretive centre in a park will introduce, clarify, and direct the visitor to the outdoors, unlike (for example) a museum or an historic site, where interpretation focuses on other matters. *Interpretation* in parks differs from *information* in that it deals with meanings and relationships as well as with hard facts, although informational publications and signs are, of course, important components of visitor services in parks.

Interpretation in national parks is both a science and an art. As a science it relies on proven learning principles and current understanding in psychology, sociology, communications, and education; it requires familiarity with the area's people and visitor motivations. But it must also communicate to the public such areas as geology, paleontology, anthropology, geography, zoology, and botany. This combination of natural and social sciences is applied in a park setting.

Art enters the picture during the stage of interacting with the audience. The process, procedures, and rationale for selecting (for example) a given concept may be based in the sciences, but the effective communication and presentation of that concept requires art. Elements such as dramatics, visual design, and music improve visual and verbal communications. Complex relationships are often introduced in an entertaining fashion, to arouse the visitor's interest; more refined treatments of specific concepts may then follow. Because interpretation involves meanings and relationships, it strives for a holistic approach rather than merely presenting isolated facts. Since audiences are seldom homogeneous, interpretation must appeal to visitors of all ages and backgrounds, experiences and personalities. This may require a variety of interpretive programming strategies to reach audiences on a variety of levels.

There are seven distinct components in the definition of an interpretive service.

1. It is *on-site*, emphasizing *first-hand experience* with the resource.
2. It is an *informal* form of education.
3. It deals with a *voluntary, non-captive audience* who participate by their own free choice during their leisure time.
4. Participants normally have an *expectation of gratification*.
5. It is *inspirational* and *motivational* in nature, not just the presentation of factual information.
6. *Shifts in attitude, expansions of knowledge*, and *alterations in behaviour* are its goals.
7. It is an *extrinsic* activity, which is based upon *intrinsic* values and is intended to facilitate an appreciation, understanding, and eventually the protection of those intrinsic values.

Principal Objectives of Park Interpretation:

1. To provide an orientation and information service to visitors in such a way as to minimize uncertainty and to maximize opportunity for a

diverse range of users of varying levels of age, interest, physical capabilities, and previous cultural exposure.

2. To enhance visitor awareness, appreciation, understanding, and enjoyment.

3. To help minimize negative effects on the local community and natural environment, to enhance visitor safety, to minimize recreational conflicts, and generally to improve the method of visitor dispersal.

4. To develop a good environmental education experience for schoolchildren, designed to develop an appreciation of the dynamics of natural environments and a sense of pride in and urgency about the preservation of their heritage.

5. To assist park management by developing programs and facilities that will aid in minimizing destructive behaviour and enforcement problems, while guiding visitors towards designated and selected locations.

6. To provide training in interpretation skills for employees, community residents, and volunteers.

7. To demonstrate by example the agency's and nation's philosophy and beliefs about conservation, wildlife protection, environmental preservation, and the innate value of its natural and cultural heritage.

8. To inform, co-operate with, and contribute to local and regional events and media as a way of promoting improved understanding of the value of natural areas.

Interpretation and Conservation in Resource Protection: Writing-On-Stone Provincial Park

Despite the assumption, widely held by interpreters, that visitors are motivated to protect resources after being exposed to interpretation, there has been little specific research to support it. One situation example, however, seems to prove a direct relationship.

Recognized as a significant international cultural resource, Writing-On-Stone Provincial Park, Alta., contains several hundred petroglyphs (rock carvings) and numerous pictographs (rock paintings) created by Native peoples at least 300 years ago. Many of these carvings have been damaged by the public. Increasing vandalism aroused the concern of park managers and government officials. Interpretation subsequently received increased attention in the park and the interpretive program put more emphasis on resource protection, with a follow-up study to determine if interpretive programming does in fact help motivate people to protect such fragile resources as these ancient carvings.

Groups of park visitors saw an interpretive program, which emphasized the significance of the native petroglyphs and the consequences of vandalism. The next day at the rock art site, a researcher posed as a vandal pretending to carve his initials on the petroglyph wall and recorded his observation of the visitor reaction. Another researcher interviewed the same visitors shortly afterwards to obtain their reactions. The interviewer gave the visitors an opportunity to report the act of vandalism, without prompting them to do so. The reactions of those who had been exposed to the interpretive program were compared to the reactions of those who had not. Those who were exposed to the program demonstrated significantly stronger reactions against the 'vandal' than did those who had not. They accounted for 73 per cent of the 'high level reactions', those which called for confronting the vandal. Of those in the control group who also exhibited a strong reaction against vandalism, a majority also had attended interpretive programs in the park before the experiment. If we count this group with the experimental group, together they accounted for 82 per cent of the strongest levels of reaction against the vandal. This suggests that the influence of the interpretive message may have longer-lasting effects than some researchers believe.

The study also showed that frequency of visiting the park in itself had little if any effect on a visitor's reaction to vandalism. Subjects with higher education levels reacted most positively toward resource protection. Slightly more than half (54 per cent) of the high reactors had completed university or graduate studies. Only 9 per cent of high reactors had less than a high school education. The study also suggested a generalized profile of high reactors and low reactors. A low reactor (a person less likely to intercede or show concern when confronted with a destructive act) is less likely to attend park interpretive programs, possesses a high school education or less, lives in a rural area not far from the park, is aged 13 to 45, is likely to be a student, rural housewife, or farm worker, and is slightly more likely to be male.

A high reactor (a person with a strong tendency to intercede and show strong concern when confronted with a destructive act) is likely to attend park interpretive programs, has a post-secondary education, is employed in a trade or profession, lives in an urban setting, is slightly more likely to be male than female, and is more likely to be between 19 and 30. The study did support the results of previous research that people are reluctant to report vandalism, but most of those who chose to do so had been part of an interpretive attendance.

Given the results of this experiment and the supportive recommendations of other researchers, recreation agencies should use interpretation as one element in resource management. It should be viewed as one of several approaches needed to ensure the preservation of natural or cultural sites and features. Protective facility design, proper legal designation, and a real commitment to enforcement are also essential to ensure against destructive acts.

FORMS OF INFORMATION SERVICE

Personal Services

Interpretation services may be both personal and non-personal in nature. Non-personal services include displays, exhibits, signs, trails, and publications, described below. Personal services involve direct contact between the interpreter and the public (Figure 11.2). These activities fall into two categories; informational duty and presentation duty.

Informational Duties   Information services tell the visitor where specific facilities and opportunities are located and how to make use of them. Informational services staff are not interpreters (although interpreters often perform information service duties), in that they do not present programs,

Figure 11.2
Park interpreter leading hike, Riding Mountain National Park, Manitoba.
Photo: P. Dearden

conduct walks, or otherwise interpret the natural and cultural environment. They are, however, front-line representatives of the park and the agency.

It goes without saying that all information duty staff should have a positive attitude and be approachable and receptive when in contact with the public. They must be kept up to date on information, new procedures, community events, etc., through supplementary training, meetings, memos, or verbal notices from supervisors. This new information should be passed along to the public when appropriate.

Presentation Duties *Scheduled services* are among the most common forms of interpretive events. Examples include guided tours, slide shows, prop talks, evening campfire programs, and any other activity that takes place at a predetermined time and is advertised accordingly.

Guided interpretive tours are one way of managing groups of people while simultaneously providing them with insight into an area. They also permit visitors to venture into areas otherwise restricted to the general public. The nature of guided tours varies with the opportunities and limitations of the natural area, but they can include trail or beach walks, snorkelling or goggling tours, bus tours, bicycle trips, boat tours, and horseback rides. All involve an interpreter leading visitors along a predetermined route, stopping frequently to point out or demonstrate something that will contribute to the group's understanding and appreciation.

Slide shows, films, and other audiovisual aids conducted by staff are extremely useful ways of conveying abstract messages and providing excellent substitute experiences. They can also be used to set moods and show perspective. Prop talks, using objects or artefacts as focal points of a talk, can also provide valuable first-hand involvement. Dramatic presentations generally require more elaborate production but can prove highly effective and entertaining. They are popular for historical topics, and they can create high interest and accommodate large audiences.

Point duty involves stationing an interpreter at a prominent feature or gathering place (i.e., a waterfall attraction, or a concentration of wildlife) during periods of high visitation. *Travelling point duty or roving duty* is similar, except that travelling point duty implies interpreting along the way. The interpreter would walk through the area, informally interpreting sites through casual conversation at points where people naturally choose to pause.

Impromptu events are not formally scheduled but they are planned; they are impromptu only for the spectator. They are far more formalized and better rehearsed than roving duties. The sudden presence of an interpreter on a beach with table, aquarium, net, bioscope, and sample jars will draw quite a crowd as the interpreter allows visitors to look close up at sand particles and aquatic invertebrates.

Living interpretation demonstrates an historical lifestyle or a contemporary culture that is different from the visitors'. Living interpreters in period costumes and in authentic settings carry out day-to-day activities, showing visitors how people actually lived (or still live, in alternative cultures) and demonstrating crafts or skills, often with technical information or authentic products as an additional feature.

Extension programs are presentations of natural and cultural interest, taken into communities or schools or communicated through media such as newspapers, radio, or television, with the intention of expanding the audience for an interpretive message.

Non-personal Services

The presentation of a natural area's features and story also relies on inanimate interpretative aids such as park facilities and publications.

Visitor Centres   The visitor centre is essentially a communication facility. Through a variety of personal and technical media, visitors here are briefed about the area, its regulations, its values, opportunities for the visitor, special features, the area's role in the overall park system, and how visitors can best enjoy and understand the dynamics of the immediate environment. It also serves as a repository for park information for both visitors and staff.

To do all this, the visitor centre requires a wide variety of components. Layout and co-ordination of these components must permit the smooth and logical flow of visitors through the building and allow users easy and comfortable access to its features.

The design of the visitor centre should be compatible with its surroundings and the theme of the area. It should be readily identifiable as a visitor centre, without dominating its surroundings. While the building must be attractive and inviting to the visitor, it must not become the central attraction. The real attraction must remain nature itself; the facility serves only to direct the visitor outside with a new perspective and expanded knowledge.

Exhibits   A variety of exhibits are often used in parks; these may include dioramas, changeable design, artefacts, reconstructions, and models. Exhibits in visitor centres must be versatile, so they can be changed frequently over the years and with the season. Panels with dry-mounted photographs, rear-lighted transparencies, and backlit self-activated projector exhibits are all highly suitable, since they are readily adapted for changing themes.

Throughout the exhibit, objects should be available to touch or handle whenever possible. Audio phone pickups familiarize visitors with natural sounds (birds, frog voices) to prepare them for the multisensory experience of the real world. Other exhibits could focus upon the dynamics of the park food chain, floral and faunal highlights, and the like.

Most formal exhibits would be located in the visitor centre; but kiosks (an outdoor consolidation of several exhibit panels, usually under a roof) are often set at appropriate locations along trails or near features whose explanation is too complex for a normal sign.

Signs   The placement of a sign is the most basic form of an interpretive service. Interpretive signs are self-pacing; that is, readers can go at their own speed and read only what they are interested in. Thus, people in a hurry can check the headlines, subheadings, or illustrations to see if they are interested in reading further. If they decide not to read the text, they have at least received an outline of the message. The self-pacing feature of signs is also helpful to teachers and parents, as they can explain things to their children without disrupting an interpreter's more formal talk.

A number of considerations govern what to say in the sign and why a sign should be there in the first place. Is the message significant and worth telling? Is the message simple and easy to understand? Is the message accurate and brief? Is the style of writing appropriate for the occasion? Does the message evoke a response in the visitor?

Interpretive Trails   Interpretive trails are self-guided, generally using signs or leaflets for information.

> The self-guided trail, in natural and human history interpretation, is a device which places visitors, usually in family-sized groups, in direct contact with the park or forest resources. A self-guided trail, in contrast to a conducted tour, means that the visitors are on their own; there is no one to guide them through the trail experience. The self-guided trail is a meandering footpath along which the visitor's attention is drawn to interesting or unusual features which might otherwise be overlooked or not fully appreciated. (Sharpe 1976)

Publications   Publications can present a topic in greater depth than other methods. They can be taken home as souvenirs and referred to many times. They can make leaders of teachers, parents, or individuals introducing others to the area's natural features. Publications do, however, present the possible adverse effect of litter and are not always cheap or easy to update. For large and important historic sites, monographs may be available for specialists with an interest in the subject.

The writing style of interpretive publications should be appropriate to the intended audience. The style should strike a balance between entertainment and instruction and should relate to existing natural values of the area. Texts should be as succinct as possible, with an emphasis on illustrations or photographs. Style and tone will best vary to suit the type of publication required.

Environmental Education

Environmental education should be seen and carried out as an essential component to the overall interpretive effort. Such programs are developed principally for schools. Personal services include teacher training and conducted events led by volunteers and park staff. Non-personal services include pre- and post-trip resource kits, brochures on self-guided field studies, exhibits developed specifically for children, and slide and tape programs and films to be shown in the classroom before the field trip.

In its broadest perspective, environmental education is aimed at producing people who are knowledgeable about the whole environment and its associated problems, aware of how to help solve these problems and skilled at helping others do the same, and motivated to work toward their solution. The environmental education component of a park cannot by itself do all this. It should concentrate on providing an awareness, appreciation, and understanding of the immediate environment by permitting first-hand observation and personal involvement with the park.

School Field Trips to the Park   The teacher would normally be the principal guide for a field trip to a park, although on some occasions park staff may be available for this purpose. The teacher's responsibility is to make appropriate plans to suit the class and individual students' needs. The park should help in this planning, clarifying the options and alternatives, recommending an appropriate sequence of activities, identifying the interpretive storylines, and perhaps providing staff to help in programming for the student.

One of the primary benefits of a field trip is to enhance classroom activities and broaden students' perspectives. It is, therefore, important to develop park experiences as an extension of the classroom program. Field trip planning guides should be developed and distributed to potential visiting groups to help them plan their trip and ensure a successful experience.

A study kit is a supplement to the planning booklet and can be distributed before the trip. These kits are collections of slides, tapes, objects, photographs, posters, reading materials, and suggested activities that can be presented in class beforehand. Preliminary activities stem from the belief that environmental concepts and principles can be taught in back yards, in vacant lots, or on the school grounds. The field trip is ideally a reinforcement and expansion of the concepts introduced on the school grounds and in the classroom.

The field trip is an opportunity for learning, but is constrained by the availability of time, the degree of inherent interest for children, and the students' willingness to learn and interest, and their preparedness.

Interpreting for children poses a considerable challenge. Programs will have to be appropriate for the age level of the group, which will vary. They will have to be interesting and challenging enough to get the group's attention and keep it, without being either baffling or condescending.

CONCLUSION

Effective interpretation is essential to the successful management and operation of a park or protected area. Natural areas cannot survive as islands. Their survival is closely tied to people's attitudes, beliefs, and way of life. Public support, at both the political and community level, is essential if an area can ever hope to succeed in meeting its conservation and preservation goals.

An important goal of any protected area is to give local residents and visitors both information and chances to increase their awareness and understanding of the area's natural values and to relate these experiences to modern life. Achieving this goal will result in informed and understanding people who can capitalize on the educational and recreational opportunities available to them, have a deeper appreciation for their area's natural and cultural heritage, and transfer these values and experience into their daily lives. Attitudes toward the environment are learned, not inborn.

Protecting parks and wilderness areas is in many ways comparable to a library's acquiring important works to ensure the availability of the literature of the past and present. Acquisition and protection are indeed important, but the books have to be read and understood for their true worth to be realized. While the librarian (or manager) may conserve the volumes, the visitor must also be shown how to read them. Most visitors to parks and wilderness settings today lack the experience adequately to 'read' such places. As Huxley once noted, their visit is comparable to passing through a corridor of fine paintings nine-tenths of which are turned face to the wall. To learn to read and therefore to appreciate such works, is the role of interpretation.

REFERENCE

Sharpe, G.W.
   1976   *Interpreting the Environment*, Wiley, New York.

CHAPTER 12

The Role of Aboriginal Peoples in National Park Designation, Planning, and Management in Canada

LAWRENCE BERG, TERRY FENGE,
AND
PHILIP DEARDEN

ABORIGINAL PEOPLES AND PROTECTED AREAS: A GLOBAL CONTEXT

Numerous authors have acknowledged that the concept of national parks as we know it today, originated in the United States (see e.g. Nash 1970; Dasmann 1976; Harmon 1987). Nash (1970) asserts that the origins of the national park idea can be traced precisely to the year 1832. At that time, he observes, the artist-explorer George Catlin called for the creation of a 'nation's park' to protect the Native peoples and wild animals of the American plains (also see Dasmann 1976; Machlis and Tichnell 1985). The institution proposed by Catlin differs very little from the essential concept of the national park as it exists today. Perhaps ironically, the one significant difference was Catlin's proposal that Native people be part of 'the [life] in the preserve' (Nash 1970, 730). On 1 March 1872, over two million acres (810,000 ha) of northwestern Wyoming were designated as the world's first national park—Yellowstone.

Since the establishment of this first park, more than 2,600 protected areas have been set aside worldwide and are of sufficient status to be included on the *United Nations List of National Parks and Equivalent Reserves* (Harrison *et al.* 1984). Many of these protected areas have been created on lands traditionally used by Aboriginal peoples. Often, they have been established without input from these peoples, who have in many instances been forcibly removed from regions in which protected areas were established (Dasmann 1976, 1984; Harmon 1987).

The policy of establishing protected areas without regard for the needs of Aboriginal people has created problems both for Aboriginal societies and conservation initiatives. Displacement of Aboriginal people, for example, often disrupts traditional social and economic systems and results in catastrophic social problems such as malnutrition and loss of cultural identity (see e.g. Gomm 1974; Dasmann 1976; Mishra 1982, 1984; Machlis and Tichnell 1985; Nowicki 1985). In extreme cases, certain Aboriginal cultures have been pushed to near extinction (see e.g. Calhoun 1972; Turnbull 1972; Pallemaerts 1986). At the very least, this policy reduces popular support among Aboriginal peoples for protected areas. A survey by the African Wildlife Foundation, for example, found that a majority of a sample of Tanzanian school children had negative attitudes towards parks, believing that parks presently take up too much land (Abrahamson 1983). Consequently, the effectiveness of conservation has been compromised by poaching, clandestine exploitation of resources, or other non-compliance with protected area regulations (see e.g. Crush 1980; Lusigi 1981; Marks 1984; White 1986; Brockelman and Dearden 1990).

In reacting to these problems, recent management literature emphasizes the need to involve Aboriginal peoples in protected area planning and management and to allow exploitation of protected area resources for subsistence purposes (e.g. Lusigi 1984; Atmosoedarjo et al., 1984; Nietschmann 1984; Klee 1985; Kermani and Khan 1986; Reti 1986; Task Force on Park Establishment 1987; Hough 1988; Berg 1990). The ninth resolution of the World Congress on National Parks (Bali, Indonesia), entitled 'Protected Areas and Traditional Societies', provides a summary of the sentiments found in the literature:

> Acknowledging that traditional societies which have survived to the present in harmony with their environment ... deserve our respect for their wise stewardship of areas and environments which we now seek to protect ... and provide instructive examples of environmental management strategies worthy of emulation ... [t]he World National Parks Congress, meeting in Bali, Indonesia, October 1982 ... recommends that those responsible at every level of protected area research, planning, management and education *fully investigate and utilise the traditional wisdom of communities* affected by conservation measures. ... [emphasis added]. (World National Parks Congress 1984)

The relationship between Aboriginal people and national parks has become an important area of concern for protected area managers and social scientists worldwide. It is of special interest to those who study and manage Canadian national parks. Aboriginal peoples in northern Canada have played a significant role in national park planning and development (Kovacs 1984). Northern national parks have been established in conjunction with Aboriginal land-claim settlements, while park reserves await settlement of these claims before attaining full park status (Theberge 1978; Gardner and Nelson 1980; Bayly 1985; Sadler 1989; Fenge 1992).

The literature contains a number of case studies of Aboriginal peoples' involvement in national park management in Canada, most focusing on single parks (see Theberge 1978; Griffith 1987; Berg 1990), or reviewing the role of Aboriginal peoples in northern park management (see Gardner and Nelson

1980, 1981; Stix 1982; Bayly 1985; Lawson 1985; Weeks 1986; Sadler 1989). None has provided an overview of the role that Aboriginal people play in national park designation, planning and management throughout Canada. This chapter attempts to provide such an overview.

First, we provide an introduction to Aboriginal people in Canada, briefly defining who they are and their changing social and legal status within Canadian society. This is followed by a discussion of present Canadian Parks Service policy, regulations, and legislation as they relate to Aboriginal peoples. Using case studies from one completed (Inuvialuit) and one pending (Inuit) land-claim settlement in the Canadian north, the next section illustrates Aboriginal peoples' involvement in northern national park management. Two case studies—Pacific Rim National Park Reserve and South Moresby/Gwaii Hanaas National Park Reserve—provide examples of Aboriginal peoples' involvement in national park management in southern Canada. Finally, some conclusions, as well as a discussion of future directions, are presented.

ABORIGINAL PEOPLES IN CANADA: SETTING THE CONTEXT

Definition

At least one million people in Canada can claim Aboriginal ancestry (McMillan 1988). The Constitution Act, 1982 defines three categories of Aboriginal peoples: Indian, Inuit, and Métis. It is, however, important to note that these three categories of Aboriginal people are not homogeneous cultural groups but rather include a wide variety of peoples with differing histories, languages, and cultures. Accordingly, the name 'First Nations' has been adopted by many Aboriginal peoples when referring to themselves, to reflect their perception of their status as separate and sovereign entities.

Much has been written about the history of Aboriginal-white relations in Canada (see e.g. Cardinal 1969; Patterson 1972; Miller 1989). Aboriginal author Harold Cardinal (1969, 1) summarizes that history as 'a shameful chronicle of the white man's disinterest, his deliberate trampling of [Aboriginal] rights and his repeated betrayal of our trust'. The treatment of Aboriginal peoples by the dominant white society has led a number of commentators to characterize Aboriginal people as being members of a Canadian *internal colony* (see e.g. Boldt 1980, 1981; Tennant 1982; Frideres 1988).

Aboriginal Treaties in Canada

A number of 'Peace and Friendship' treaties were signed with Aboriginal people in what are now the Atlantic Provinces. These treaties, made in the 17th and 18th centuries, assured the British of Indian assistance in wars against the French. They do not include extinguishment of title or purchase of land; nor do they promise the Indians reserves or payments (see McMillan

1988). The process of acquiring legal title to Aboriginal land, on the other hand, is a 19th- and 20th-century phenomenon.

Southern Canada, with the exceptions of the Atlantic provinces and most of Quebec and British Columbia, is covered by treaties which lay out certain legal obligations the Crown has to Aboriginal peoples. Between 1780 and 1850, a number of small treaties were negotiated with the Native people of what is now southern Ontario. These treaties usually involved small lump-sum payments in return for extinguishment of Aboriginal title (Cumming and Mickenberg 1972). On rare occasions, fishing and hunting rights were guaranteed and reserves were granted. In 1850, the Crown negotiated the Robinson-Superior and Robinson-Huron Treaties with Native peoples of the upper Great Lakes region. In return for surrender of large areas of land, Aboriginal people received lump-sum cash payments, annual payments to each person, and promises of continued hunting and fishing on unoccupied Crown land (Cumming and Mickenberg 1972).

Robinson's 1850 treaties became the model for the subsequent 'numbered' treaties that cover much of Ontario, all of Manitoba, Saskatchewan, and Alberta, and parts of British Columbia and the Yukon and Northwest Territories. These treaties, numbered 1 to 11, were completed between 1871 and 1929 by federal government representatives (Cumming and Mickenberg 1972; McMillan 1988). The Williams treaties, completed in 1923 by the federal government, purportedly extinguished Aboriginal title to lands in southern Ontario. With some minor differences, treaties negotiated by the federal government are all similar. In return for giving up their title, Aboriginal peoples received reserves, small cash payments, hunting and fishing gear, annual payments to each member of the signatory group, and promises of continued hunting and fishing rights.

About the same time as Robinson completed his treaties, James Douglas, chief factor of the Hudson's Bay Company and later Governor of the Colony of Vancouver Island, began treaty-making with a number of island tribes. Between 1850 and 1854, Douglas completed 14 treaties, extinguishing Aboriginal title to lands around Victoria, Nanaimo, and Fort Rupert (present-day Port Hardy). In return for surrender of their lands, Aboriginal people maintained possession of their village sites and fields and were guaranteed the right 'to hunt on unoccupied lands, and to carry on our fisheries as formerly' (British Columbia 1875, 5–11).

Aboriginal Rights in Canada

Most of the Yukon, Northwest Territories, British Columbia, Quebec, and the Atlantic provinces were never covered by treaties. Aboriginal peoples living in these areas have not ceded their Aboriginal title, nor have they been conquered by overt act of war. Nonetheless, they have been denied their Aboriginal rights and title and they have been colonized and marginalized, some for almost 400 years. In spite of this, Aboriginal peoples in Canada have never stopped pressing government for recognition of their Aboriginal rights (see e.g. Frideres 1988; Miller 1989; Tennant 1990). Until relatively recently, however, such efforts have been largely unsuccessful. This situation is gradually changing following two important legal rulings and amendments to Canada's constitution. These events are discussed below.

The Calder Case   In 1967, the Nisga'a brought a suit before the Supreme Court of British Columbia, asking the court for a declaration that their Aboriginal title had never been extinguished (Sanders 1973; Berger 1982; Raunet 1984). The trial, which came to be known as the Calder case, opened in the Supreme Court of British Columbia. The court ruled against the Nisga'a, asserting that their Aboriginal rights were firmly and totally extinguished by overt acts of the Crown (see *Calder v. Attorney General of British Columbia* 1969). The Nisga'a appealed, but the British Columbia Court of Appeal (*Calder v. Attorney General of British Columbia* 1970) upheld the lower court ruling. The Nisga'a then appealed to the Supreme Court of Canada (*Calder v. Attorney General of British Columbia* 1973) and lost by a decision of four to three. However, closer inspection of the decision revealed that they had in fact won a partial victory.

Justice Judson, speaking for himself and two other judges, ruled that the Nisga'a had Aboriginal title, and further that this title was recognized under English law. However, he went on to state that this title had been extinguished by enactments of the old colony of British Columbia. Chief Justice Hall, speaking for himself and two other judges, ruled in favour of the Nisga'a. He stated that the Nisga'a 'in fact are and were from time immemorial a distinctive cultural entity with concepts of ownership indigenous to their culture and capable of articulation under the common law' (*Calder v. Attorney General of British Columbia* 1983, 190). He went on to say that, although it is within the authority of the Crown to extinguish Aboriginal title, such acts of extinguishment must be *clear and unambiguous* in their intent. According to Hall, then, the Nisga'a continue to have Aboriginal title to their lands. The seventh judge did not rule on the issue of Aboriginal title but instead held against the Nisga'a on a technicality. On the basis of this technicality, the Nisga'a lost by a decision of four to three.

The Calder case had important repercussions for Aboriginal policy and law. For the first time, the Supreme Court of Canada recognized that Aboriginal title existed at the time of colonization as a legal right derived from the Aboriginal peoples' historical occupation and possession of the land, independent of any proclamation, legislative act, or treaty (Berger 1982; Raunet 1984; Elias 1989). Following this judgement, the federal government announced its willingness to negotiate 'comprehensive' land claim settlements in other areas of Canada—that is, in British Columbia, Quebec, and the two northern territories (see Canada 1981; Sanders 1983; Task Force to

Review Comprehensive Claims Policy 1985; Canada 1987). In addition, government confirmed its willingness to negotiate 'specific' claim settlements relating to alleged faulty implementation of treaties.

Constitution Act, 1982   After intense lobbying on the part of Aboriginal groups (Berger 1982; Slattery 1982–3), the Constitution Act, 1982, was enacted. Two of its sections protected Aboriginal rights. Section 25 of the Act is found in Part I, the Canadian Charter of Rights and Freedoms, and protects Aboriginal, treaty, or other rights from infringement by other guarantees in the Charter. Section 35, in Part II of the Act, is entitled 'Rights of the Aboriginal Peoples of Canada', and entrenches Aboriginal rights in the Constitution:

> 35. (1) The existing Aboriginal and treaty rights of the Aboriginal peoples of Canada are hereby recognized and affirmed. (2) In this Act, 'Aboriginal peoples of Canada' includes the Indian, Inuit and Métis peoples of Canada. (3) For greater certainty, in subsection (1) 'treaty rights' includes rights that now exist by way of land claims agreements or may be so acquired. (4) Notwithstanding any other provision of this Act, the Aboriginal and treaty rights referred to in subsection (1) are guaranteed equally to male and female persons.

Section 35(1) also adopts and confirms the large body of common law which has come to be known as the common-law doctrine of Aboriginal rights (Slattery 1982–3, 1985, 1987). This doctrine holds that the property rights, customary laws, and governmental institutions of Aboriginal peoples survived the Crown's acquisition of North American territories (Slattery 1985).

Others have examined the specific implications for Aboriginal rights that sections 25 and 35 of the Constitution Act may have for Native land rights (see e.g. Sanders 1983; Slattery 1982–3, 1985, 1987; Pentney 1988a, 1988b). It is important to note, however, that the Constitution Act has 'set the consideration of native law in a new context' (Elias 1989, 4) that appears to be more favourable to the aspirations of Aboriginal people in Canada. This new context is evident in the Supreme Court of Canada ruling in *Sparrow v. The Queen et al.* (1990).

A new era in the relationship between Native peoples and the government of Canada may well begin in the 1990s, depending on ongoing constitutional discussions. The Charlottetown proposals, although defeated, recognized Aboriginal peoples' inherent right to self-government, a recognition that will have significant ramifications for protected areas and conservation in Canada.

The Sparrow Case   On 31 May 1990, the Supreme Court of Canada handed down its landmark judgement in the case of *Sparrow v. The Queen et al.* (1990; hereafter cited as *Sparrow* 1990). Ronald Edward Sparrow, a Musqueam from British Columbia, was charged in 1984 under the Fisheries Act with using a drift net longer than that permitted by the terms of his band's food-fishing licence. Sparrow admitted that the Crown's allegations were correct, but he defended his actions on the grounds that he was exercising an existing Aboriginal right to fish, protected under section 35(1) of the Constitution Act.

Provincial Court Judge Goulet held that the Musqueam did not have an Aboriginal right to fish. Sparrow was convicted. His appeal to County Court (*Sparrow v. The Queen* 1986*a*) was dismissed for similar reasons. The case was then appealed to the British Columbia Court of Appeal (*Sparrow v. The Queen* 1986*b*), which held that the lower courts had erred in ruling that the Musqueam had no Aboriginal fishing rights. The appeal court also ruled that the Aboriginal right to fish existed at the time of enactment of the Constitution Act and was therefore a constitutionally protected right that could no longer be extinguished by unilateral action of the Crown. The court also held, however, that the trial judge's findings of facts were insufficient to lead to an acquittal. The ruling was appealed by Sparrow and cross-appealed by the Crown. On 24 November 1987, the case was argued before the Supreme Court of Canada.

In a unanimous ruling, the Supreme Court of Canada held that there was insufficient evidence on which to decide Sparrow's guilt or innocence. More importantly, however, the court affirmed that the Musqueam people have an unextinguished Aboriginal right to fish. It also set forth a framework for defining the existence and scope of Aboriginal rights in Canada. In this regard, the court held that prior to 1982 Aboriginal rights continued to exist unless they had been extinguished by an action of the Crown that was clearly intended to do so (*Sparrow* 1990, 16). Therefore, contrary to arguments made by the government of British Columbia, legislative action which is merely inconsistent with the concept of Aboriginal title cannot be construed as extinguishing such title. Following enactment of the Constitution Act, Aboriginal rights could no longer be extinguished by the Crown. The Supreme Court further defined the nature of constitutional protection of Aboriginal rights:

> the constitutional recognition afforded by the provision [s. 35(1)] therefore gives a measure of control over government conduct and a strong check on legislative power. While it does not promise immunity from government regulation in a society that, in the twentieth century, is increasingly more complex, interdependent and sophisticated, and where exhaustible resources need protection and management, it does hold the Crown to a substantial promise. The government is required to bear the burden of justifying any legislation that has some negative effect on any Aboriginal right protected under s. 35(1). (*Sparrow* 1990, 26)

In the eyes of the court, both 'conservation' and 'resource management' constitute justifiable grounds for legislation that may have a negative effect on Aboriginal rights. However, even when such measures must be implemented, the court held that Aboriginal people must be consulted so as to mitigate any impact upon their rights.

The implications which the Sparrow case may have for park management are not yet fully understood. It appears, however, that the court has given the government a directive to include Aboriginal people in co-operative management of natural resources. Regardless of the true legal implications, it is clear that the ruling will reinforce the perceptions of Aboriginal people, who believe they deserve special recognition in national park management when their traditional territories coincide with park lands.

Comprehensive Land-claim Policy   Following the Calder case, the federal government released a policy statement announcing its willingness to negotiate the settlement of comprehensive land claims, together with policy objectives to guide its involvement in such negotiations (Canada 1981). Following the recommendations of a task force (Task Force to Review Comprehensive Claims Policy 1985), a substantially modified land-claim policy was unveiled by the federal government late in 1986 (Canada 1987). Notwithstanding the recent Sparrow judgement (*Sparrow* 1990) and additional Aboriginal rights cases that are likely soon to be heard before the Supreme Court of Canada, the minister of Indian Affairs and Northern Development has stated that the 'basic principles' of the current comprehensive land claim policy are not likely to change.

The current comprehensive land-claim policy requires Aboriginal peoples to surrender to the Crown their rights, interests, and Aboriginal title in and to the land, water, and natural resources, in exchange for constitutionally protected rights, benefits, and privileges defined in land-claim settlements. The latter may include:

1. Cash ($30,000 to $35,000 per capita, in 1989 dollars, appears to be the present rate);
2. A grant of land from the Crown in fee simple (totalling approximately 15 to 25 per cent of the settlement area);
3. Preferential and in some cases exclusive rights to hunt, fish, and trap;
4. A share of government's royalties from non-renewable resource development on Crown land in the settlement area; and
5. The right to participate with government in managing renewable resources and in mitigating environmental and social effects of non-renewable resource development.

The comprehensive land-claim policy does not deal explicitly with national parks or other forms of protected areas. This is not surprising, for the intent of the policy and of government's strategy in land-claim negotiations is quite specific: to clear the ill-defined Aboriginal title from the land in question. Whether national parks are included in the rights and benefits Aboriginal peoples obtain in return depends upon the policy and strategy of Aboriginal peoples, as well as the intent of government. It is clear, however, that comprehensive land-claim settlements concluded under the existing and the preceding policy (Canada 1981, 1987) stress environmental conservation and protection of wildlife habitat. Moreover, all land-claim agreements-in-principle and final agreements in the territories deal with national parks. This would suggest that many Aboriginal peoples view national parks with some interest and sympathy.

CANADIAN PARKS SERVICE POLICY, REGULATIONS, AND LEGISLATION RELATING TO ABORIGINAL PEOPLES

Many of Canada's national parks were designated at a time when both the federal and provincial governments did not acknowledge the existence of Aboriginal rights and title. During this period, Aboriginal peoples living on their traditional lands or on reserves encompassed by newly designated parks were given little, if any, input into park planning and management. Indeed, Aboriginal people with reserves in proposed park areas were encouraged by the Canadian Parks Service to sell or trade their reserves for lands outside the proposed parks (see e.g. Berg 1990) and were prevented from hunting and trapping within them. There was little appreciation within government that parks could be used to support and maintain Aboriginal peoples and to protect their land-based cultures. Instead the Canadian Parks Service stressed the need for the parks system to 'represent' biophysically defined natural areas (Foresta 1985). Adherence to the natural areas framework probably contributed to the estrangement of parks from Aboriginal peoples. The parks identified through the framework may have been excellent choices to represent natural areas, but they were sometimes irrelevant to protecting key wildlife habitat, the element of parks legislation that interested many Aboriginal groups. To Aboriginal peoples dependent upon hunting, fishing, and trapping, the location of a park was the key to its utility and political acceptability.

The attitude of the Canadian Parks Service began to change in the 1970s as the values and aspirations of Aboriginal peoples began to seep into the Canadian body politic. This process was aided by public hearings into oil and gas megaprojects that brought representatives of Aboriginal peoples and environmental and other groups into the same camp. The Berger inquiry into a proposed gas pipeline from the Mackenzie Delta and northern Alaska, for example, noted the need to plan for parks and conservation areas simultaneously with non-renewable resource development (Berger 1977). In addition, Justice Berger proposed a new type of park, a 'wilderness park', to preserve wildlife, wildlife habitat, and natural landscapes in the northern Yukon, and to underpin the still vibrant traditional economy of the Inuvialuit and Dene. This recommendation was a milestone in the debate that has begun to relate Aboriginal issue to national parks.

The 1979 Parks Canada policy tried to respond to Aboriginal and land-claim issues and to Justice Berger's groundbreaking report. The policy contains a number of sections that define a new relationship between local people and potential national parks. In this regard, section 1.3.5 of the National Parks Policy (Parks Canada 1979, 39) states that the Canadian Parks Service 'will contribute toward the cost of special provisions to reduce the impact of park establishment on occupants or other users of lands acquired for a national park'. While not directed specifically at Aboriginal people, this section indicates a willingness on the part of the Canadian Parks Service to be more sensitive to local concerns, including those of Aboriginal peoples, when establishing national parks. Consistent with the federal government's 1973 policy stating its intent to negotiate land claims in Quebec, British Columbia, and the territories, the 1979 parks policy recognized the potential existence of certain Aboriginal rights in section 1.3.13:

> Where new national parks are established in conjunction with settlement of land claims of native people, an agreement will be negotiated between [the Canadian Parks Service] and representatives of local native communities prior to formal establishment of the national park creating a joint management regime for the planning and management of the national park. (Parks Canada 1979, 40)

These ideas are reiterated and expanded somewhat in section 3.2.11:

> Certain traditional extractive activities will be permitted in the following circumstances:
>
> i) In new national parks, guarantees will be provided so that certain traditional subsistence resource uses by local people will be permitted to continue in parts of national parks for one or more generations when such uses are an essential part of the local way of life and when no alternatives exist outside the park boundaries. These exceptions will be agreed to at the time of formal establishment of a new national park and will be outlined in the park management plan.
> ii) Selected activities which are of cultural value in portraying to visitors traditional relationships between man and the land in the park area as part of the park experience may be permitted.
> iii) In new national parks, the treaty rights of Indian people and those rights recognized in native land claims settlements will be honoured and extractive activities which are the subject of such rights can only be terminated after agreement has been reached with the people concerned.
>
> All such activities will be subject to the requirement to protect the ecosystems and maintain viable populations of fish and wildlife species. (Parks Canada 1979, 42)

Similarly, amendments to the National Parks Act[1] appear to recognize the importance of traditional resource harvesting to Aboriginal peoples. Section 5(7) allows specific indigenous people to carry out such harvesting in certain parks in Ontario and Newfoundland. Section 5(10) extends traditional renewable resource harvesting rights in wilderness areas of national parks to Aboriginal peoples with land-claim settlements at the minister's discretion. Finally, section 7(1) allows for regulation of traditional renewable resource harvesting in national parks by order-in-council.

These policies and regulations indicate a growing awareness on the part of the Canadian Parks Service of the possible role that Aboriginal peoples might play in park planning, designation, and management. They allow for possible joint management of national parks that fall within traditional lands of Aboriginal peoples; additionally, they recognize Aboriginal treaty rights and subsistence needs.

The policy, however, does not assure Aboriginal people a place in park management and planning, nor does it guarantee their subsistence use of park resources. Considerable uncertainty surrounds the meaning and interpretation of 'joint management regimes' promised for national parks established in conjunction with comprehensive land-claim settlements. This term seems to imply equal authority on the part of government and Aboriginal peoples in developing and implementing park management plans. Some park planners and managers, however, feel this clause guarantees to Aboriginal people only a right to 'participate' in decision making and does not give them a veto over decisions. Be that as it may, it should be pointed out that the Parks Canada policy embraced the concept of joint management by government and Aboriginal people fully eight years before this same concept was endorsed and adopted in the land-claims policy.

A cursory examination of the recently amended National Parks Act leads one to believe that Aboriginal peoples' continued access to traditional renewable resource use in national parks is now guaranteed by law. Closer inspection of the legislation, however, reveals a loophole which could technically deny them access to the parks for this purpose. As it now stands, the National Parks Act allows 'persons of designated classes' to carry out traditional resource harvesting in national parks located in 'the district of Thunder Bay' in Ontario and 'the districts of St Barbe and Humber West' in Newfoundland (Bill C-30, sections 5.(7)(a) and (b)). Additionally, these activities may be authorized in national park wilderness zones 'pursuant to subsection (7) or any other Act of Parliament', such as a land claim settlement (Bill C-30, section 5.(10)(d)). Obviously most Aboriginal groups do not fall within these categories and are excluded therefore from the existing legislative guarantees.

---

[1]R.S., c. 189, s. 1, amended by Bill C-30, *An Act to Amend the National Parks Act and to Amend an Act to Amend the National Parks Act.*

Nowhere does the new National Parks Act guarantee joint management for Aboriginal peoples whose traditional lands fall within national parks. Such joint management regimes are only specified in the Parks Canada policy, and only then for Aboriginal groups that have successfully completed land-claim settlements. A number of Aboriginal peoples whose traditional lands are affected by national park initiatives, but who have not concluded land-claim settlements with the government—including the Nuu-chah-nulth and the Haida in British Columbia and the Inuit of northern Labrador—may or may not have an opportunity for joint management. On examining both Canada's national parks policy and legislation, Weeks (1986, 118) concludes that 'while the policy comprehends the creation of new national parks with the settlement of native land claims, the legislation does not act positively to provide support for such a proposal.' Although the National Parks Act has since been amended, Weeks's comments are still valid.

Perhaps the most important concession the National Parks Act makes to Aboriginal peoples lies in the term 'national park reserve', introduced into the protected areas lexicon through amendment to the statute in 1972. This designation applies, for example, to the Kluane, Nahanni, Auyuittuq, and Mingan Archipelago regions, which are to become full national parks upon settlement of comprehensive land claims. The 'reserve' designation allowed the Canadian Parks Service to treat and manage the areas in question as national parkland but did not extinguish any Aboriginal rights or title to the areas. Importantly, this designation does not impair the ability of Aboriginal peoples to select parkland in the course of land-claim negotiations.

Canadian legislators seem to have chosen an *ad hoc* approach to accommodating the needs of Aboriginal peoples in national parks. Wood Buffalo National Park and Auyuittuq National Park Reserve provide examples of this *ad hoc* approach. The area around Wood Buffalo National Park was a favoured hunting ground of Aboriginal peoples for many years prior to its establishment as a park (Lothian 1976). When the park was established, Natives who had previously hunted and trapped in the area continued these activities under permit. In 1949, special district game regulations for Wood Buffalo National Park were instituted that superseded the national parks game regulations and allowed for traditional hunting, trapping, and fishing by Aboriginal people (Lothian 1976). Auyuittuq National Park Reserve, on Baffin Island, was established in 1972. Public park planning meetings in the early 1970s resolved that the Inuit, who had inhabited the region for almost 4,000 years, would retain their traditional hunting and fishing rights within the park (Lawson 1985). In addition, the Inuit participate in management through membership on a local park advisory committee. Their role, however, is only to advise the park superintendent and any real decision making powers are limited (Lawson 1985).

Apparently, the interaction between Aboriginal peoples and national parks in Canada is not as clear as might be suggested by national park policy and legislation. Rather than work within a nationwide comprehensive policy regarding Aboriginal peoples, the Canadian Parks Service has tended to follow a more *ad hoc* approach. Land-claim settlements themselves, rather than national park policy or legislation, determine the role of Aboriginal peoples in planning for and managing national parks. This has given rise to subtly different kinds of parks in northern and southern Canada; Aboriginal people in the north, where parks are tied to land claims, play a more important part in park planning and management than Natives in the South. Land claims in northern Canada are likely to be completed sooner than those in southern Canada. In addition, many Aboriginal peoples in the south must look to old treaties and the National Parks Act and policy, rather than to comprehensive land-claim settlements, to protect their interests. The following case studies exemplify these approaches to involvement of Aboriginal peoples in national park designation, planning, and management in both northern and southern Canada.

THE ROLE OF ABORIGINAL PEOPLES IN NATIONAL PARKS:
NORTHERN CANADA LAND-CLAIMS AGREEMENTS

The Inuvialuit Final Agreement

The Inuvialuit of the Beaufort Sea region began land-claim negotiations with the federal government in the mid-1970s. An agreement-in-principle was concluded in 1978, followed by a final agreement in 1984 (Canada 1984). Legislation to approve the final agreement and to amend the National Parks Act in consequence was passed in summer 1984.

The Inuvialuit Final Agreement (IFA) requires the federal government to establish the western portion of the northern Yukon as a national park (Figure 12.1). In line with Justice Berger's recommendations (Berger 1977), the IFA characterizes the Northern Yukon National Park as 'wilderness oriented', and requires that the planning for the park 'maintain its present undeveloped state to the greatest extent possible' (Canada 1984, 18). Moreover, a central aim of the park is 'to protect and manage the wildlife populations and the wildlife habitat within the area'. This objective reflects the national and international importance of the calving grounds of the Porcupine caribou herd, which are partially inside the park. Not only does the IFA commit government to establish the park, define its boundaries, and specify its purposes and objectives, but it also mandates a Wildlife Management Advisory Council, composed of an equal number of government and Aboriginal members to 'recommend a management plan for the national park' (Canada 1984, 18).

The 1978 agreement-in-principle promised that all of the Yukon north slope from the Alaskan border in the west to the Northwest Territories border in the east would be established as a national park. Due to the objections of the Yukon territorial government and the oil and gas industry, the park

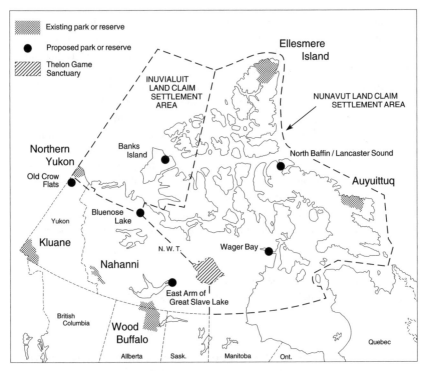

Figure 12.1 Map to show existing and proposed parks and reserves in the north.

boundaries defined in the final agreement were altered to divide the north slope into two zones (Fenge *et al.* 1986). The area to the west of the Babbage River was confirmed as a national park (Figure 12.2), but the eastern portion was excluded from the proposed park to allow for the development of a transportation corridor. Nevertheless, this area was still to be subject to a 'special conservation regime whose dominant purpose is the conservation of wildlife, habitat and traditional native use' (Canada 1984, 18). The Wildlife Management Advisory Council has responsibility for both the eastern and western portions of the north slope. This arrangement grounds the national park in broader wildlife management and environmental conservation needs. Indeed, this grounding applies to much of northern Yukon and adjacent areas in the N.W.T. through the operations of the Porcupine Caribou Management Board.

The IFA makes it very clear that Inuvialuit have the right to harvest wildlife for subsistence purposes throughout the north slope and an exclusive right to do so in the national park. The door is left open, however, for Aboriginal peoples represented by the Council for Yukon Indians (CYI) to acquire hunting rights in the park through their own land-claim settlement. It should be

Figure 12.2
Hikers overlooking Firth River, North Yukon National Park. *Photo: P. Dearden*

pointed out, however, that it was the land-claim settlement rather than the intragovernmental work of the Canadian Park Service that resulted in the establishment of this national park.

The Inuit Land Claim

The Inuit of the eastern and central Arctic signed a land claim agreement-in-principle in April 1990 and expect to sign a final agreement in 1992[2] (Tungavik Federation of Nunavut 1990). This agreement-in-principle deals in some detail with parks, which the Inuit generally see as 'friendly' land-use designations. In 1983, for example, the Nunavut Constitutional Forum (NCF), which represented Inuit in constitutional discussions within the N.W.T., proposed that approximately 25 per cent of the Arctic be set aside for park purposes (Doering 1983). This proposal was not viewed favourably; hence the agreement-in-principle contains less dramatic and less far-reaching provisions on parks.

While the IFA dealt explicitly and definitively with one park, the Nunavut agreement-in-principle does not commit government to set aside any specified

[2]A final land-claim agreement between the Inuit of Nunavut and the federal government was signed in April 1992. This agreement confirms the establishment of Ellesmere Island, North Baffin, and Auyuittuq national parks, and details the role of Inuit in their management. The final agreement was ratified by the Inuit in a referendum held 3–5 November 1992. Legislation to ratify the final agreement on behalf of the Crown is expected to be introduced to Parliament in 1993.

areas as national parks. Instead, it notes: 'The Final Agreement shall provide for the establishment, within a reasonable time period, of at least three National Parks in the Nunavut Settlement Area' (Tungavik Federation of Nunavut 1990, 109). The federal government believes that upgrading Ellesmere Island and Auyuittuq to national parks status from their current designation as reserves and establishing Bylot Island-Borden Peninsula as a national park, will fulfil this obligation. The Inuit, however, note that the agreement-in-principle mentions 'at least three' national parks and hope that the final agreement will commit government to establish more than this minimum number. In line with this view, in the summer of 1990 Inuit land-claim negotiators tabled a position requiring governments to complete the terrestrial and marine park system in Nunavut by the year 2000. While the federal government's chief negotiator notes that this position is supported by Cabinet-approved policy on parks, he reports that government is very hesitant about including such a promise in the land-claim final agreement, for such a promise would be constitutionally protected and legally enforceable.

The number, location, and likely boundaries of national parks in Nunavut are being addressed in land ownership negotiations between the Tungavik Federation of Nunavut (TFN), representing the Inuit, and the federal government. The slated purpose of these negotiations is to define which parcels of land Inuit will own from an agreed-to total of 136,000 square miles. But the Inuit are also trying to persuade the government to establish certain areas as parks to be legally ratified in the final land-claims agreement or soon thereafter. The Inuit strategy is quite clear: parks are to be used to protect key wildlife habitat and so to allow negotiators to concentrate land ownership selection elsewhere. Future negotiations will likely focus on the Thelon Game Sanctuary and the Wager Bay and Bluenose Lake Natural Areas of Canadian Significance as potential parks (see Figure 12.1).

The park management provisions in the Nunavut agreement-in-principle are similar in purpose to those in the IFA. For each park, the Inuit and government are to negotiate an Inuit Impact and Benefits Agreement (IIBA) to channel economic and social benefits from the park to local Inuit. As part of an IIBA, a joint Inuit/government parks planning and management committee can be set up to advise 'on all matters related to park management' (Tungavik Federation of Nunavut 1990, 119). Article 8.4.13 notes that management plans shall be developed by the Canadian Parks Service and 'shall be based on the recommendations of the committee' (ibid.). Such plans have to be approved by the minister responsible for national parks. In conducting negotiations, TFN tried to persuade the federal government to adopt the term 'joint management regime' as used in the Parks Canada Policy and to have this term enshrined in the final agreement. The federal government refused, saying that this concept was vague and open to misinterpretation.

The Nunavut agreement-in-principle also follows the lead of the IFA in characterizing national parks in the Arctic as 'wilderness oriented'. Consequently, article 8.2.13 notes: 'each National Park in the Nunavut Settlement

Area shall contain a predominant proportion of Zones I and II, as such zones are defined in the Parks Canada Policy.'[3] Inuit also hope that national parks will be tools for economic development. Very few outsiders currently visit national parks in the Arctic. Fewer than 1,000 people visit Auyuittuq National Park Reserve every year, and this spectacular area is relatively accessible from southern Canada. Nevertheless, Inuit hope to use money from the land-claim settlement to provide tourist and recreational facilities in communities adjacent to parks, to attract more visitors to these places.

In looking at the environmental and economic opportunities provided by parks in the Arctic, the Inuit are aware of, and would like to emulate, the extraordinary example of the 1980 Alaska National Interest Lands Conservation Act. This statute established a number of national parks, preserves, and heritage sites in Alaska and was itself an outgrowth of the 1971 Alaska Native Claims Settlement Act. Yet while the Inuit believe that parks can be tailored to support their land uses and culture and so are prepared to see them established through their land-claim settlement, government is very hesitant to accede to this suggestion.

THE ROLE OF ABORIGINAL PEOPLES IN NATIONAL PARKS: CASE STUDIES FROM SOUTHERN CANADA

The following case studies are presented to illustrate two ends of a spectrum of Aboriginal peoples' involvement in park designation, planning, and management in southern Canada. Both Pacific Rim and South Moresby/Gwaii Hanaas are designated as national park reserves, pending settlement of Aboriginal land claims encompassing the park areas (Figure 12.3). Both park reserves have yet to be gazetted under the National Park Act. They diverge, however, in the level of Aboriginal involvement in park designation, management, and planning; Aboriginal people have had little involvement at Pacific Rim, while they have had significant influence at South Moresby. Other national parks such as Pukaskwa in Ontario and national park reserves such as Mingan Archipelago in Quebec (see Canada 1989) have levels of Aboriginal involvement falling between the two extremes of Pacific Rim and South Moresby (see Dearden and Berg 1993).

Pacific Rim National Park Reserve

Pacific Rim National Park Reserve was designated in 1970 but has yet to be gazetted under the National Parks Act. It is located on the west coast of Vancouver Island and is divided into three distinct geographic units. The southerly West Coast Trail Unit of the park reserve traverses reserve lands

---

[3]Parks Canada Policy defines Zone I as 'Special Preservation' and Zone II as 'Wilderness'. Access to the former is strictly controlled, while access to the latter is restricted to non-motorized travel for purposes of wilderness recreation (see Chapter 5).

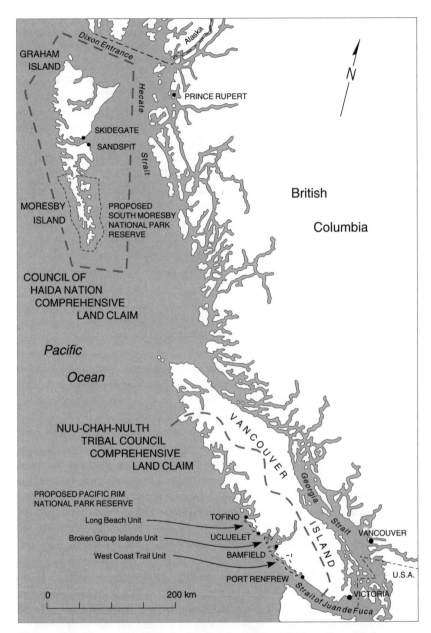

Figure 12.3 The comprehensive land claims of the Haida nation and the
Nuu-Chah-Nulth tribal council and locations of the proposed
Gwaii Haanas/South Moresby and Pacific Rim National Park
Reserves.

of the Nuu-chah-nulth people; these people also have enclave reserves in the Long Beach and Broken Group Islands units of the park (Figure 12.4). In total, there are 28 reserves belonging to seven different Aboriginal bands either next to the park or within its boundaries. There are also 289 recorded archaeological sites 'that relate to the native history within Pacific Rim

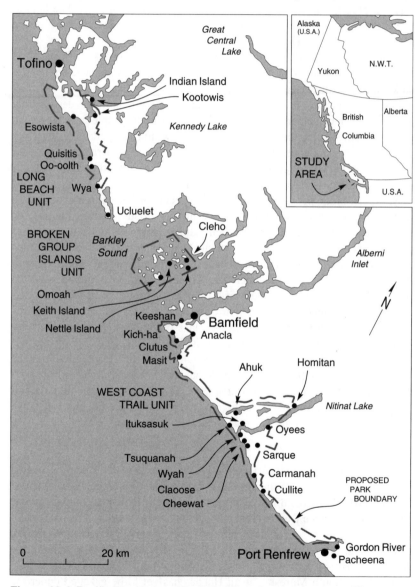

Figure 12.4 Pacific Rim National Park Reserve showing the three different units and principal native reserves.

National Park' (Inglis and Haggarty 1986, 256). The park reserve is part of a larger area occupied by the Nuu-chah-nulth people for approximately 4,000 years (Dewhirst 1978). The Nuu-chah-nulth have never been conquered by Europeans, nor have they formally ceded this territory (with the exception of one small, and illegal, treaty). As a result, their comprehensive land claim was accepted for negotiation by the federal government in 1983. The land in question is much of the west coast of Vancouver Island, including all of the national park reserve (Figure 12.3).

In spite of the fact that the Nuu-chah-nulth people have a significant interest in the park area, a comprehensive land claim that encompasses the entire park, and unextinguished Aboriginal rights to hunt and fish in the park region, Berg (1990) found that they had little input into the designation, planning, or management of the park. Nuu-chah-nulth people have no say in the management of traditional lands that fall within the park, and there are no plans for special consultation with them during the preparation of the park master plan. Park managers plan to treat them like 'any other Canadian citizens' interested in management of the park.

Nuu-chah-nulth people do have some special privileges within the park reserve, as they are allowed to continue hunting, fishing, and gathering for subsistence purposes. However, their taking seafoods and other ocean resources is often curtailed by the federal Department of Fisheries and Oceans (DFO), which maintains jurisdiction over fishery management within the park reserve until it is gazetted under the National Park Act. Additionally, the Nuu-chah-nulth people complain of a number of problems in their relations with park managers. Poor communication is one such problem—an indication, the Nuu-chah-nulth believe, of their lack of input into park management. Before the park reserve was established in 1970, the Canadian Park Service told the Nuu-chah-nulth that the park would bring jobs to the area, but the Nuu-chah-nulth assert that, while park has created local employment, both directly and indirectly through tourism, in most cases their people have not benefited. Instead, the large numbers of park visitors are having a negative impact on their traditional lands and reserves within the park.

South Moresby/Gwaii Hanaas National Park Reserve

South Moresby National Park Reserve (Gwaii Hanaas to the Haida), is located in the southern portion of the Queen Charlotte Islands archipelago (the Haida Gwaii), 170 kilometres offshore from the northern British Columbia coastal community of Prince Rupert (Figure 12.3). On 11 July 1987, a memorandum of understanding to negotiate a national park reserve and national marine park in South Moresby was signed by the prime minister of Canada and the premier of British Columbia (Sewell, Dearden, and Dumbrell 1989). Like Pacific Rim, South Moresby/Gwaii Hanaas has yet to be gazetted under the National Park Act. The park is similar to Pacific Rim National Park Reserve in a number of other respects as well. The proposed park lies within a region inhabited by the Haida people for thousands of years (McMillan 1988) and it is entirely within the territory covered by the comprehensive land claim of the Haida Nation. One Haida group, the Skidegate Indian Band, has reserve lands next to and inside the proposed park boundaries. Finally, numerous Aboriginal heritage sites, including the Haida village of Ninstints— a UNESCO World Heritage Site—are inside the park reserve (Figure 12.5; see also Chapter 15).

The level of Aboriginal involvement in park management at South Moresby/Gwaii Hanaas is much greater than that at Pacific Rim National Park Reserve. The government of Canada and the Haida Nation are currently negotiating the formation of an interim Archipelago Management Board (AMB) comprised of two representatives each from the Haida Nation and the government of Canada (Canada 1990). The interim AMB will examine all initiatives relating to the management of the South Moresby/Gwaii Hanaas archipelago. Once the national park reserve is gazetted under the National Park Act, a permanent AMB will be constituted under an agreement between the Haida and the government of Canada,[4] and it will be responsible for

Figure 12.5
Totem poles at Ninstints, the World Heritage Site on South Moresby/Gwaii Haanas National Park Reserve. *Photo: P. Dearden*

---

[4]The Gwaii Hanaas/South Moresby Agreement was ratified by members of the Haida Nation in May 1990. The Federal environment minister will sign the agreement now that the necessary amendments to the National Park Act have been completed; the Haida will sign once the minister has signed. The following discussion of Haida involvement in park management is based on the Gwaii Hanaas/South Moresby Agreement ratified by members of the Haida Nation in May 1990.

reviewing all aspects of park operation and management, including park management plans and annual work plans. The Haida will also be guaranteed continued access to South Moresby/Gwaii Hanaas for a host of traditional activities, including:

1. Travelling into and within the archipelago
2. Gathering traditional Haida foods
3. Gathering plants used for medicinal or ceremonial purposes
4. Cutting selected trees for ceremonial or artistic purposes
5. Hunting land mammals and trapping fur-bearing animals
6. Fishing for freshwater and anadromous fish
7. Conducting, teaching, or demonstrating ceremonies of traditional, spiritual, or religious significance
8. Seeking cultural and spiritual inspiration
9. Using shelter and facilities essential to the pursuit of the above activities (Canada 1990, section 6.1).

The AMB will be empowered to examine the scope and intent of all Haida subsistence and traditional activities in the proposed park reserve and to ensure that such activities are not contrary to national park purposes (Canada 1990). Finally, the government of Canada will provide training to help Haida people qualify for park employment, and the Haida will participate in the selection of park employees.

DISCUSSION AND CONCLUSION

Before the late 1970s, Canadian national parks were designated with little consideration for Aboriginal peoples. However, following Berger's 1977 ground-breaking northern pipeline enquiry, which recommended the formation of a national park in conjunction with settlement of the Inuvialuit land claim, the Canadian Parks Service became more sensitive to Aboriginal peoples' concerns. In fact, the Parks Canada policy embraced the concept of joint management of parks by government and Aboriginal people fully eight years before this same concept was adopted in Canada's land claims policy.

Land-claim settlements and Aboriginal treaty rights now play as great a part as national park policy or legislation in determining the role of Aboriginal peoples in planning for and managing national parks. Diverse approaches to settlement of land claims, as well as varying treaty rights, result in differing relationships between Aboriginal people and national parks throughout Canada. For example, Aboriginal peoples have a significant park planning and management role in northern Canada, where parks are tied to settlement of land claims. Similar situations are beginning to come about in southern Canada, now that Aboriginal and treaty rights have been given greater recognition by the courts. However, because such rights have only recently gained national prominence, large disparities still exist in the relations that various Aboriginal groups have with the Canadian Parks Service.

The Canadian Parks Service may soon be forced to grapple with these disparities if Aboriginal groups such as the Nuu-chah-nulth, who presently have little input in park management, try to gain equality with other Aboriginal groups like the Haida, who have much greater input. The Canadian Parks Service may have exacerbated this situation through its *ad hoc* approach to relations with Aboriginal peoples. On the one hand, such an approach affords more flexibility, allowing park managers to respond to the exigencies of individual situations. On the other hand, without clearly defined parameters for relations with Aboriginal people, other problems are likely to emerge. For example, as widely differing agreements are reached with various Aboriginal groups, the Canadian Parks Service might unknowingly encourage competition among Aboriginal groups to surpass each other in the quest for greater involvement in park management.

Other complex issues are likely to arise as Aboriginal and treaty rights become more clearly defined. The questions of Aboriginal and treaty rights to hunting and fishing have yet to be dealt with by the Canadian Parks Service. With regard to the former, the courts are giving increasing recognition to Aboriginal rights to hunt and fish. In the *Sparrow* case (1990), the Supreme Court of Canada has given the government a directive to include Aboriginal people in co-operative management of natural resources. The Supreme Court's ruling has a direct impact on management of national parks situated in regions traditionally used by Aboriginal people, or for the future planning of parks proposed for such regions. Given the large number of national parks and unrepresented national park terrestrial natural regions (as defined in the national park system plan) that fall within territory traditionally used by Aboriginal peoples (see Chapter 5), the question of Aboriginal rights should be prominent in the minds of national park planners. It is not yet clear, however, how the Canadian Parks Service intends to respond to this issue.

Similar questions emerge concerning Aboriginal treaty rights to hunt and fish. As part of most treaties in Canada, Aboriginal groups were promised continued rights to hunt and fish on 'unoccupied Crown land'. Can national parks be considered unoccupied Crown land? To our knowledge, this question has yet to be definitively answered. Nonetheless, it will certainly become important as Aboriginal groups begin to test the limits of treaty rights which are being reinvigorated as a result of the new, more sympathetic stance towards such rights in Canadian courts. As in the case of Aboriginal rights, how the Canadian Parks Service will respond to the treaty rights issue is not apparent.

What is clear, however, is that the Canadian Parks Service is having to change its approach to managing existing national parks and to planning for and designating new ones that fall within lands traditionally used by Aboriginal peoples. Aboriginal and treaty rights are gaining new prominence within the Canadian body politic, and Natives will no longer accept paternalistic management from government agencies. A majority of national parks and unrepresented national park terrestrial natural regions fall within territory traditionally used by Aboriginal peoples. Aboriginal and treaty rights are thus likely to have a significant impact on national park management in Canada. The Parks Service is evolving, albeit slowly, to meet the demands of this new situation, but it must give greater attention to the question of how Aboriginal and treaty rights are to be incorporated with park management practices if it is to adequately manage our national parks. In this regard, the Parks Service might concern itself less with who manages protected areas and more with ensuring that protected areas are managed to a uniform high standard.

ACKNOWLEDGEMENT

The authors wish to acknowledge funding for this project through the Social Science and Humanities Research Council of Canada and a University of Victoria Fellowship.

REFERENCES

Court Cases Cited

Calder v. Attorney General of British Columbia
  1969   8 D.L.R. (3rd) 59, 71 W.W.R. 81 (Supreme Court of British Columbia).
Calder v. Attorney General of British Columbia
  1970   13 D.L.R. (3rd) 64, 74 W.W.R. 481 (British Columbia Court of Appeal).
Calder v. Attorney General of British Columbia
  1973   S.C.R. 313, 34 D.L.R. (3rd) 145, [1973] 4 W.W.R. 1 (S.C.C.).
Sparrow v. The Queen
  1986a   County Court, [1986] B.C.W.L.D. 599.
Sparrow v. The Queen
  1986b   9 B.C.L.R. (2nd) 300, 36 D.L.R. (4th) 246, [1987] 2 W.W.R. 577.
Sparrow v. The Queen et al.
  1990   Supreme Court of Canada. Chief Justice Dickson, and Justices McIntyre, La Forest, Lamer, Wilson, L'Heureux-Dubé, and Sopinka, 31 May 1990. *QuickLaw Reports*, file 20311.
References Cited
Abrahamson, D.
  1983   'What Africans Think About African Wildlife', *International Wildlife* 13: 38–41.

Atmosoedarjo, S., L. Daryadi, J. MacKinnon, and P. Hillegers
  1984 'National Parks and Rural Communities', in *National Parks, Conservation, and Development: The Role of Protected Areas in Sustaining Society*, Proceedings of the World Congress on National Parks, Bali, Indonesia, 11–22 October 1982, eds J.A. McNeely and K.R. Miller, Smithsonian Institution Press, Washington D.C., 237–44.

Bayly, J.U.
  1985 'Conservation Through Native Claims', unpublished paper prepared for Parks Canada Centennial, National Assembly Project.

Berg, L.D.
  1990 *Aboriginal People, Aboriginal Rights, and Protected Areas: An Investigation of the Relationship Between the Nuu-chah-nulth People and Pacific Rim National Park Reserve*, unpublished M.A. thesis, Department of Geography, University of Victoria, Victoria, B.C.

Berger, T.R.
  1977 *Northern Frontier, Northern Homeland*, James Lorimer, Toronto. 2 vols.

Berger, T.R.
  1982 'The Nishga Indians and Aboriginal Rights', in *Fragile Freedoms: Human Rights and Dissent in Canada*, ed. T.R. Berger, Irwin, Toronto, 219–54.

Boldt, M.
  1980 'Canadian Native Indian Leadership: Context and Composition', *Canadian Ethnic Studies* 12: 15–33.

Boldt, M.
  1981 'Social Correlates of Nationalism: A Study of Native Indian Leaders in a Canadian Internal Colony', *Comparative Political Studies* 14: 205–31.

British Columbia
  1875 *Papers Connected With the Indian Land Question, 1850–1875*. Richard Wolfenden, Victoria (reprinted 1987).

Brockelman, W., and P. Dearden
  1990 'The Role of Nature Trekking in Conservation: A Case Study in Thailand', *Environmental Conservation* 17: 141–8.

Brody, H.
  1988 *Maps and Dreams: Indians and the British Columbia Frontier*, Douglas and McIntyre, Vancouver.

Calhoun, J.B.
  1972 'Plight of the Ik and Kaidilt Seen as a Chilling Possible End to Man', *Smithsonian* 3: 27–9.

Canada
  1981 *In All Fairness: A Native Claims Policy*, Supply and Services Canada, Ottawa.

Canada
  1984 *Inuvialuit Final Agreement*, Indian Affairs and Northern Development, Ottawa.

Canada
  1987 *Comprehensive Land Claims Policy*, Supply and Services Canada, Ottawa.

Canada
  1989 *Protocole d'Entente entre le Conseil de bande de Mingan et sa Majesté la Reine du Chef du Canada*, copy available from the Office of the Minister of Environment.

Canada
1990   *Gwaii Hanaas/South Moresby Agreement between the Government of Canada and the Council of the Haida Nation*, copy available from the Office of the Minister of Environment.
Cardinal, H.
1969   *The Unjust Society: The Tragedy of Canada's Indians*, Hurtig, Edmonton.
Crush, J.S.
1980   'National Parks in Africa: A Note on the Problem of Indigenization', *African Studies Review* 23: 21–32.
Cumming, P.A., and N.H. Mickenberg, eds
1972   *Native Rights in Canada*, 2nd ed., The Indian Eskimo Association of Canada and General Publishing, Toronto.
Dasmann, R.F.
1976   'National Parks, Nature Conservation and Future Primitive', *Ecologist* 6: 164–7.
Dasmann, R.F.
1984   'The Relationship Between Protected Areas and Indigenous Peoples', in *National Parks, Conservation, and Development: The Role of Protected Areas in Sustaining Society*, Proceedings of the World Congress on National Parks, Bali, Indonesia, 11–22 October 1982, eds J.A. McNeely and K.R. Miller, Smithsonian Institution Press, Washington, 667–71.
Dearden, P., and L. Berg
1993   'Canadian National Parks: A Model of Administrative Penetration', *The Canadian Geographer* (in press).
Dewhirst, J.
1978   'Nootka Sound: A 4,000 Year Perspective', *Sound Heritage* 7: 1–30, on file at Public Archives of British Columbia.
Doering, R.L.
1983   'Nunavut: Options for a Public Lands Regime', working paper No. 3, Nunavut Constitutional Forum, Ottawa.
Duff, W.
1964   *The Indian History of British Columbia. Volume 1. The Impact of the White Man*, Anthropology in British Columbia, memoir No. 5, Provincial Museum of Natural History and Anthropology, Victoria.
Elias, P.D.
1989   'Aboriginal Rights and Litigation: History and Future of Court Decisions in Canada', *Polar Record* 25: 1–8.
Fenge, T., I. Fox, B. Sadler, and S. Washington
1986   'A Proposed Port on the North Slope of Yukon', *Environmental Protection and Resource Development: Convergence for Today*, ed. B. Sadler, Banff School of Management, University of Calgary Press, Calgary, 127–78.
Fenge, T.
1992   'National Parks in the Canadian Arctic: The Case of the Nunavut Land Claim Agreement', *Environments* (in press).
Fisher, R.
1971–   'Joseph Trutch and Indian Land Policy', *B.C. Studies* 12: 3–33.
72

Fisher, R.
1977   Contact and Conflict: Indian-European Relations in British Columbia, 1774–1890, University of British Columbia Press, Vancouver.

Foresta, R.A.
1985   'Natural Regions for National Parks: The Canadian Experience', Applied Geography 5: 179–94.

Frideres, J.S.
1988   Native People in Canada: Contemporary Conflicts, 3rd ed. Prentice-Hall, Scarborough, Ont.

Gardner, J.E.
1979   National Parks and Native People in Northern Canada, Alaska, and Northern Australia, unpublished M.A. thesis, Department of Geography, University of Waterloo, Waterloo, Ont.

Gardner, J.E., and J.G. Nelson
1980   'Comparing National Park and Related Reserve Policy in Hinterland Areas: Alaska, Northern Canada, and Northern Australia', Environmental Conservation 7: 43–50.

Gardner, J.E., and J.G. Nelson
1981   'National Parks and Native Peoples in Northern Canada, Alaska, and Northern Australia', Environmental Conservation 8: 207–15.

Gomm, R.
1974   'The Elephant Men', Ecologist 4: 53–7.

Griffith, R.
1987   'Northern Park Development: The Case of Snowdrift', Alternatives 14: 26–30.

Halffter, G.
1981   'The Mapimi Biosphere Reserve: Local Participation in Conservation and Development', Ambio 10: 93–6.

Harmon, D.
1987   'Cultural Diversity, Human Subsistence, and the National Park Ideal', Environmental Ethics 9: 147–58.

Harrison, J., K. Miller, and J. McNeely
1984   'The World Coverage of Protected Areas: Development Goals and Environmental Needs', in National Parks, Conservation, and Development: The Role of Protected Areas in Sustaining Society, Proceedings of the World Congress on National Parks, Bali, Indonesia, 11–22 October 1982, eds J.A. McNeely and K.R. Miller, Smithsonian Institution Press, Washington, 24–33.

Hough, J.L.
1988   'Obstacles to Effective Management of Conflicts Between National Parks and Surrounding Human Communities in Developing Countries', Environmental Conservation 15: 129–36.

Indigenous Survival International
1986   'Outline of a Proposed Folio on Indigenous Peoples and Conservation', Report of Workshop 13, World Conservation Strategy Conference, Ottawa, 31 May–5 June 1986.

Inglis, R.I., and J.C. Haggarty
1986   Pacific Rim National Park Ethnographic History, unpublished manuscript, on file, Royal British Columbia Museum.

Jenness, D.
  1977   *The Indians of Canada*, 7th ed., University of Toronto Press, Toronto.
Johannes, R.E.
  1982   'Traditional Conservation Methods and Protected Marine Areas in Oceana',
          Ambio 11: 258–61.
Kermani, W.A. and K.M. Khan
  1986   'Protected Areas and Local Populations in Kirthar National Park, Pakistan',
          Parks 11: 2–3.
Klee, G.A.
  1985   'Traditional Marine Resource Management in the Pacific', in *Culture And
          Conservation: The Human Dimension in Environmental Planning*, eds J.A.
          McNeely and D. Pitt, Croom Helm, London, 193–202.
Kovacs, T.J.
  1984   'Northern National Parks and Native People: The Canadian Experience',
          report submitted to First World Conference on Cultural Parks, Mesa Verde
          National Park.
LaViolette, F.E.
  1973   *The Struggle for Survival: Indian Cultures and the Protestant Ethic in Brit-
          ish Columbia*, University of Toronto Press, Toronto.
Lawson, N.
  1985   'Where Whitemen Come to Play: National Parks and Native People in the
          Canadian North', *Cultural Survival Quarterly* 9: 54–6.
Lothian, W.F.
  1976   *A History of Canada's National Parks*, vol. 1, Parks Canada, Ottawa.
Lusigi, W.J.
  1984   'Future Directions for the Afrotropical Realm', in *National Parks, Conser-
          vation, and Development: The Role of Protected Areas in Sustaining Society*,
          Proceedings of the World Congress on National Parks, Bali, Indonesia, 11–
          22 October 1982, eds J.A. McNeely and K.R. Miller, Smithsonian Institution
          Press, Washington, 137–45.
Machlis, G.E., and D.L. Tichnell
  1985   *The State of the World's Parks*, Westview Press, Boulder, Colo.
Madill, D.
  1981   *British Columbia Indian Treaties in Historical Perspective*, Indian and
          Northern Affairs, Research Branch, Corporate Policy, Ottawa.
Marks, S.A.
  1984   *The Imperial Lion: Human Dimensions of Wildlife Management in Central
          Africa*, Westview Press, Boulder, Colo.
McMillan, A.D.
  1988   *Native Peoples and Cultures of Canada: An Anthropological Overview*,
          Douglas and McIntyre, Vancouver and Toronto.
McNeely, J.A., and K.R. Miller, eds
  1984   *National Parks, Conservation, and Development: The Role of Protected
          Areas in Sustaining Society*, Proceedings of the World Congress on National
          Parks, Bali, Indonesia, 11–22 October 1982, Smithsonian Institution Press,
          Washington.
Meeker, J.W.
  1986   'The People Who Read the Day', *Wilderness* 50: 29.

Meganck, R.A., and J.M. Goebel
1979 'Shifting Cultivation: Problems for Parks in Latin America', *Parks* 4: 4–8.
Miller, J.R.
1989 *Skyscrapers Hide the Heavens: A History of Indian-White Relations in Canada*, University of Toronto Press, Toronto.
Miller, K.R.
1984 'The Natural Protected Areas of the World', in *National Parks, Conservation, and Development: The Role of Protected Areas in Sustaining Society*, Proceedings of the World Congress on National Parks, Bali, Indonesia, 11–22 October 1982, eds J.A. McNeely and K.R. Miller, Smithsonian Institution Press, Washington, 20–3.
Mishra, H.R.
1982 'Balancing Human Needs and Conservation in Nepal's Royal Chitwan Park', *Ambio* 11: 246–51.
Mishra, H.R.
1984 'A Delicate Balance: Tigers, Rhinoceros, Tourists and Park Management vs. The Needs of the Local People in Royal Chitwan National Park, Nepal', in *National Parks, Conservation, and Development: The Role of Protected Areas in Sustaining Society*, Proceedings of the World Congress on National Parks, Bali, Indonesia, 11–22 October 1982, eds J.A. McNeely and K.R. Miller, Smithsonian Institution Press, Washington, 197–205.
Morse, B., ed.
1979 *Aboriginal People and the Law*, Carleton University Press, Ottawa.
Myers, N.
1972 'National Parks in Savannah Africa', *Science* 178: 1255–63.
Nash, R.
1970 'The American Invention of National Parks', *American Quarterly* 22: 726–35.
Nelson, J.G., R.C. Scace, B. Sadler, G-H. Lemieux, and S. Washington
1985 'Heritage Issues in Canada: The Second Threshold, 1985-2085', in *Heritage for Tomorrow: Canadian Assembly on National Parks and Protected Areas, Vol. 1*, eds R.C. Scace and J.G. Nelson, Supply and Services Canada, Ottawa, 13–53.
Newby, J.
1984 'The Role of Protected Areas in Saving the Sahel', in *National Parks, Conservation, and Development: The Role of Protected Areas in Sustaining Society*, Proceedings of the World Congress on National Parks, Bali, Indonesia, 11–22 October 1982, eds J.A. McNeely and K.R. Miller, Smithsonian Institution Press, Washington, 130–35.
Nietschmann, B.
1984 'Indigenous Island Peoples, Living Resources and Protected Areas', in *National Parks, Conservation, and Development: The Role of Protected Areas in Sustaining Society*, Proceedings of the World Congress on National Parks, Bali, Indonesia, 11–22 October 1982, eds J.A. McNeely and K.R. Miller, Smithsonian Institution Press, Washington, 333–43.
Nowicki, P.
1985 'Cultural Ecology and "Management" of Natural Resources or Knowing When Not to Meddle', in *Culture And Conservation: The Human Dimension*

in Environmental Planning, eds J.A. McNeely and D. Pitt, Croom Helm, London, 269–82.

Pallemaerts, M.
1986 'Development, Conservation, and Indigenous Rights in Brazil', *Human Rights Quarterly* 8: 374–400.

Parks Canada
1979 *Parks Canada Policy*, Department of Indian and Northern Affairs, Ottawa.

Patterson, E.P.
1972 *The Canadian Indian: A History Since 1500*, Collier-Macmillan Canada, Don Mills, Ont.

Pentney, W.
1988a 'The Rights of the Aboriginal Peoples of Canada in the Constitution Act, 1982. Part I: The Interpretive Prism of Section 25', *University of British Columbia Law Review* 22: 21–59.

Pentney, W.
1988b 'The Rights of the Aboriginal Peoples of Canada in the Constitution Act, 1982. Part II: Section 35: The Substantive Guarantee', *University of British Columbia Law Review* 22: 207–78.

Raunet, D.
1984 *Without Surrender, Without Consent: A History of the Nishga Land Claims*, Douglas and McIntyre, Vancouver.

Reti, I.
1986 'Resolving Conflicts Between Traditional Practices and Park Management', *Parks* 11: 17–9.

Sadler, B.
1989 'National Parks, Wilderness Preservation, and Native Peoples in Northern Canada', *Natural Resources Journal* 29: 185–204.

Sanders, D.
1973 'The Nishga Case', *B.C. Studies* 19: 3-20.

Sanders, D.
1983 'The Rights of the Aboriginal Peoples of Canada', *Canadian Bar Review* 61: 314–38.

Sewell, W.R.D., P. Dearden, and J. Dumbrell
1989 'Wilderness Decisionmaking and the Role of Environmental Interest Groups: A Comparison of the Franklin Dam, Tasmania and South Moresby, British Columbia Cases', *Natural Resources Journal* 29: 147–169.

Slattery, B.
1982-3 'The Constitutional Guarantee of Aboriginal and Treaty Rights', *Queen's Law Review* 8: 232–73.

Slattery, B.
1985 'The Hidden Constitution: Aboriginal Rights in Canada', in *The Quest for Justice: Aboriginal Peoples and Aboriginal Rights*, eds Menno Boldt, J. Anthony Long and Leroy Little Bear, University of Toronto Press, Toronto, 114–38.

Slattery, B.
1987 'Understanding Aboriginal Rights', *Canadian Bar Review* 66: 727–83.

Stix, J.
1982 'National Parks and Inuit Rights in Northern Labrador', *Canadian Geographer* 26: 349–54.
Task Force on Park Establishment
1987 *Our Parks—Visions For The 21st Century*, Heritage Resources Centre, University of Waterloo, Waterloo, Ont.
Task Force to Review Comprehensive Claims Policy
1985 *Living Treaties: Lasting Agreements: Report of the Task Force to Review Comprehensive Claims Policy*, Indian Affairs and Northern Development, Ottawa.
Tennant, P.
1982 'Native Indian Political Organization in British Columbia, 1900–1969: A Response to Internal Colonialism', *B.C. Studies* 55: 3–49.
Theberge, J.
1978 *Northern Transitions*, Canadian Arctic Resources Committee, Ottawa.
Tungavik Federation of Nunavut
1985 'Land Claims, National Parks, Protected Areas and Renewable Resource Economy', in *Arctic Heritage*, Proceedings of a Symposium, 24–8 August 1985, Banff, eds J.G. Nelson, R. Needham, and L. Norton, ACUNS, Ottawa, 285–97.
Tungavik Federation of Nunavut
1990 *Agreement-in-Principle Between the Inuit of the Nunavut Settlement Area and Her Majesty in Right of Canada*, unpublished mimeograph. Ottawa, Tungavik Federation of Nunavut.
Weeks, N.C.
1986 'National Parks and Native Peoples: A Study of the Experiences of Selected Other Jurisdictions with a View to Cooperation in Northern Canada', in *Contributions to Circumpolar Studies, Uppsala Research Report in Cultural Anthropology No. 7*, ed. H. Beach, Department of Cultural Anthropology, University of Uppsala, Uppsala, Sweden, 83–150.
White, A.T.
1986 'Philippine Marine Park Pilot Site: Benefits and Management Conflicts', *Environmental Conservation* 13: 355–59.
World National Parks Congress
1984 'Recommendations of the World National Parks Congress', in *National Parks, Conservation, and Development: The Role of Protected Areas in Sustaining Society*, Proceedings of the World Congress on National Parks, Bali, Indonesia, 11–22 October 1982, eds J.A. McNeely and K.R. Miller, Smithsonian Institution Press, Washington D.C., 756–76.

CHAPTER 13

Marine Parks

The Canadian Experience

DAVID A. DUFFUS AND PHILIP DEARDEN

MARINE ENVIRONMENTAL PROTECTION:
THE GLOBAL ISSUE

The establishment of marine parks and reserves is one aspect of the increased awareness of the need to protect the marine environment. Designating special areas for protection from human influence is a laudable concept, although it is not clear that marine environments can be protected by the same measures as land-based ones, applied through area designation. Oceans do not stay within boundaries imposed for administrative purposes. For this reason environmental protection of marine environments must take on the much larger task of developing systematic protective measures over very large areas, often across political boundaries. We must also see a change in attitude; we have long held that the oceans are virtually infinite in their capacities to provide materials such as food and to absorb our wastes. We are only now altering this perception and accepting the notion that Carson put forth over 30 years ago in the preface of her classic work, *The Sea Around Us*: 'Although man's record as a steward of the natural resources of the earth has been a discouraging one, there has long been a certain comfort in the belief that the sea, at least, was inviolate, beyond man's ability to change and despoil. But this belief, unfortunately, has proved to be naive' (Carson 1961, xi).

We still tend to think of the ocean as a large but manageable resource over which we can assert boundless influence. This is due in part to the existence of a distinct duality. Oceans have their own physical features—cold and warm, salt and fresh, ebb and flow, rock and mud, and all else that create the abiotic component of the marine ecosystem, as well as migratory life ranging from the diatom to the blue whale. The oceans also exist as an idea, a product of human knowledge, behaviour, and perception. Understanding this duality of natural and human constructs is essential to understanding our dealings with the oceans. Marine parks offer a largely unexplored route through which humans can better understand the nature of the marine environment.

The oceans have been a medium of human activity for centuries. Our discovery and settlement of new lands, our commerce, geopolitical drives, sustenance, and pleasure have relied heavily on the world's oceans. We have used oceans as a primary way of waste disposal, relying on their vast ability to dilute and diffuse the most formidable of waste materials. Perhaps the most pervasive problem facing the world's oceans is over-use by humans. There are two routes by which marine environments can be protected. One is through the development of international regulatory agreements that cover a wide range of human interactions with the oceans. Initiatives such as the London Dumping Convention, Marpol, (the convention for the prevention of pollution from ships) the Montreal Guidelines (on nuclear waste disposal), and the environmental sections of the Law of the Sea Convention fall into this category. The second route, and the focus of this chapter, is to protect specific areas by setting them aside as marine parks or reserves.

The First World Congress on Parks in 1962 is probably the origin of the international consensus on the need for preserving marine areas. A recommendation of that conference called on states with seacoasts to examine urgently the possibility of establishing protected marine areas to prevent human interference and to extend some type of formal reservation to nearby ocean areas. Others have since built on that foundation (see e.g. Bjorklund 1974; Salm and Clark 1984; Foster and Lemay 1989a). The Fourth World Wilderness Congress in 1987 in Denver, Colo., proposed a unifying principle for marine park establishment that embraces such concepts as wise use, enjoyment, representativeness and consistency with the World Conservation Strategy, as well as ideals of protection, perpetuity, and management of human activities (Foster and Lemay 1989b).

Few marine parks were established before the 1980s (Silva and Desilvestre 1986). In the past ten years the pace of designation has quickened (Foster and Lemay 1989b), although the various levels of protection and the objectives of different programs still vary widely worldwide.

This chapter will focus on the development of the marine parks policy and programs in Canada. First, we examine policy development from its two roots, the parks aspect and the marine resources aspect. For many years policy developed separately in these areas with little cross-fertilization, until the concept of the marine park entered the policy sphere in the 1960s. Second, the evolution of policy needs special reference to the influence of mixed jurisdiction over resources and conservation in Canada's coastal zone, as well as to the difficulties imposed by the biophysical nature of the marine environment. Because programs other than the national marine parks have also been used for marine protection, we will describe some of these and their utility compared to a national parks program. The chapter closes with an evaluation of the current status and future prospects of the national marine parks, in Canada and other countries.

CANADA'S MARINE PARKS CONTEXT

The development of marine parks is, by its very nature, a product of two loosely related public policy topics: parks and marine resources. For the past two decades Canada has made strides in developing policies for both, but we have not yet woven the two together in a fully functional program of marine area protection.

Parks Policy

Parks and wilderness protection have never had as high a public profile as they now do with the Canadian public. The campaign to protect South Moresby Island off the British Columbia coast did much not only to raise public awareness and political sensitivity to parks and wilderness issues, but also to improve the ability of environmental groups to publicize similar issues (Sewell, Dearden, and Dumbrell 1989).

Since that time other high-profile conflicts over protection of specific areas, not only in the west (e.g. the Carmanah valley) but also in central Canada (e.g. Temagami) have kept parks and wilderness areas high on the political agenda. In response, the minister responsible for national parks has publicly committed the government to completing the terrestrial parks system by the year 2000. Unfortunately, the minister was not quite so generous with regard to marine parks; he viewed eight marine parks within the next decade as being an acceptable goal (House of Commons Debates, 1 February 1990, 7751). This would leave 21 of the 29 marine regions in the current system unrepresented (see Figure 5.3). Even this small commitment was reduced in the federal Government of Canada's Green Plan (Environment Canada 1990), which commits itself only to the establishment of six marine parks by the year 2000. Given current rates of environmental degradation, will there be anything left to protect by the time a satisfactory system of marine parks has been established in Canada?

Marine Resources Policy

Over the last decade, Canada has pursued a fairly aggressive program devised to consolidate control over her territorial waters as well as to participate in decision making for the open oceans (Lee and Fraser 1989). This policy stems from several factors: the need for a comprehensive set of ocean laws; rapidly changing fisheries; access to offshore minerals; increasing militarization of the seas; and greater ocean transportation and trade.

Canada began to extend territorial control in 1964 through the Territorial Sea and Fishing Zones Act. Subsequent additions to that statute in 1969 and 1970 furthered Canada's maritime jurisdiction and exclusive fishing rights. In other policy areas, such as those dealing with marine environmental concerns, Canada participates in the Convention on the Prevention of Marine Pollution by the Dumping of Wastes and Other Matter (the London Dumping Convention), which is implemented through the Canadian Environmental Protection Act. More recently Canada has looked more closely at several ways to control marine environmental issues, such as changes to the Canada Shipping Act and the Montreal Guidelines for the Protection of the Marine

Environment Against Pollution from Land-based Sources (for a complete treatment see Vanderzwaag 1989). The Arctic Waters Pollution Prevention Act of 1972 might also be considered in this light, but its obvious link to the voyage of the *Manhattan*, the U.S. tanker that made its uninvited way through Canadian Arctic waters, make this Act more a geopolitical statement than an environmental protection measure. Interest in oceans was further demonstrated through the establishment of several marine research institutions over the past 20 years (Crowley and Bourgeois 1989).

Canada was also an enthusiastic and significant contributor to the United Nations Law of the Sea Convention between 1974 and 1982. Section 914(5) of this convention obliges states to protect rare or fragile ecosystems and endangered species in the oceans. Most of what has happened in terms of ocean policy in Canada since 1982 has been in the context of this convention. The core policy was published in 1987 and entitled *Ocean Policy for Canada: A Strategy to Meet the Challenges and Opportunities on the Ocean Frontier* (Fisheries and Oceans 1987). This was followed by the establishment of a National Marine Council, the Oceans Technology Promotion Office, and the Arctic Marine Conservation Strategy.

These initiatives have provided the impetus to develop a more specific national strategy to provide environmental protection for marine areas. Two items in particular are significant to a discussion of marine protected areas. First, Canada has laid down a general basis for policy and program development, and arguably a necessity for a marine protection program. Second, all of these policy statements, except those directed to industry and technological development, specifically name protection of marine environments as an objective. It is within this milieu that the marine park policy was published in 1986.

THE EVOLUTION OF CANADA'S MARINE PARKS POLICY

In 1971, in a joint memorandum, the federal ministries regulating fisheries and national parks established a task force to examine the concept of marine parks. This task force recognized five fundamental factors involved in marine park development:

1. There is a fundamental difference between land and marine parks due to the dynamism of the marine environment, which creates a boundary problem;
2. Marine areas need a buffer in the form of a water quality management area, to be achieved by co-ordinated administration of all coastal and marine environments and to be acceptable to both the federal and provincial governments;
3. A park must include the sea bed and the water covering it, areas exposed at low tide, the shore itself, and an area inland from the shoreline;

4. Fisheries, shipping, hunting, military, or other traditional or economically important activities should be allowed to continue or be compensated for, if stopped;

5. Marine parks will be administered by the Canadian Parks Service with amendments to the National Parks Act, except that fishing would be administered by the Department of Fisheries and Oceans and shipping by Transport Canada through the Coast Guard.

The first public draft of a marine parks policy was presented in 1983. Public consultations were carried out until early 1984 through workshops. The completed policy was published in 1986. Its main objective is the same as that for terrestrial parks. The long-term goal is to represent each of Canada's 29 marine natural regions, ten in the Arctic, nine in the Atlantic, five in the Pacific, and five in the Great Lakes area (Figure 5.3). Sites will be selected through a process of consultation with other government agencies and the interested public. Each site will then be subjected to a feasibility assessment, including criteria such as representativeness and size. Parks should include a marine environment and insular and coastal lands whose long-term conservation is feasible; they should offer opportunities for public understanding and enjoyment, benefit the social and economic life of the region, and exclude permanent communities (Environment Canada 1986).

The initial plan was to establish a park in Georgia Strait on the Pacific coast. Mondor (1985) noted that this plan did not succeed for several reasons: it may have been too radical a departure from the traditional land-based park concept; it involved little public participation; and the Canadian Park Service may have seen the potential social, economic, and jurisdictional problems as insurmountable.

Eventually, four marine protected areas contiguous with terrestrial parks were designated: Kouchibouguac in New Brunswick; Pacific Rim in British Columbia; Forillon in Quebec; and Auyuittuq on Baffin Island in Canada's eastern Arctic (Figure 2.1). These can be seen largely as add-ons to existing terrestrial park programs, and their ability to protect the marine environment is limited. For example, attempts to limit smelt fishing in Kouchibouguac met with protests and were defeated; commercial fishing continues in the park (see e.g. Delaney *et al.* 1992).

INFLUENCE OF JURISDICTION AND RESOURCE MANAGEMENT TRADITIONS

A significant problem with establishing marine parks in Canada is the mixed jurisdiction over land, sea, and resources enshrined in the Canadian Constitution. Jurisdiction over the coastal zone of Canada is both federal and provincial. Section 91 of the Constitution Act empowers the federal government to deal with navigation, fisheries, and general law-making in Canada's three-nautical-mile territorial waters. Several federal acts, including the Fisheries Act, the Canada Shipping Act, the Canadian Environmental Protection Act, the Territorial Sea and Fishing Zones Act, the Coastal Fisheries Protection Act, and the Criminal Code may be applicable.

Federal ministries and departments have the responsibility to apply coastal regulations. In Canada's coastal zone the Department of Fisheries and Oceans (DFO) and Transport Canada have the greatest influence through their regulation of fisheries and transportation. In Canada's new marine parks, both departments will be responsible for managing their particular mandates through consultation with the Canadian Parks Service, working under the authority of the National Parks Act. Unfortunately this arrangement lends itself to potential differences in priorities, particularly with regards to fisheries. If, for example, DFO's mandate takes precedence over Park's (which it often does) then the development of a marine park system with preservation as its main priority may run into conflict with commercial fishing.

Coastal provinces also play a significant role in the development and administration of marine parks. Provincial power in the coastal zone is loosely defined under sections 92 and 109 of the Constitution Act. These two sections outline provincial jurisdiction over living and non-living resources, giving the provinces control over such activities as fish processing and marketing and the expanding aquaculture industry. Section 109 of the Constitution Act specifies that '[a]ll Lands, Mines, Minerals and Royalties belonging to the several Provinces of Canada' belong to the provinces. This section is particularly relevant to mining and oil drilling on the sea bed. Despite the federal jurisdiction over coastal waters, the land over which the waters flow is generally assumed to be the property of the province and part of provincial territory.

Current marine parks policy gives the provinces a significant role in determining the site and extent of proposed parks. Negotiations over provincial interests in both living and non-living resources and consideration of the park's impact on the local economy are a necessary part of the process; and as owner of the foreshore and the seabed, the province has considerable leverage in such negotiations. Also, provinces often have a vested interest in how fisheries are managed. This in itself would put political pressure on DFO to allow access to fish stocks. The differing mandates of regulatory authorities can easily compromise the ability of marine parks to 'protect and conserve'.

THE INFLUENCE OF BIOPHYSICAL ASPECTS OF THE MARINE ENVIRONMENT

The fundamental differences between marine and terrestrial environments resulted in the recognition of the need for a separate policy to guide the development of marine protection. Marine parks policy differs from that for terrestrial parks in stressing conservation, not preservation, of resources. This difference stems from two related biophysical aspects of the marine environment: the problems of setting boundaries and the nature of any aquatic medium. These create unique management problems for marine parks that make pure preservation untenable, at least to policy planners.

Boundary problems and the dynamism of marine ecosystems are inter-twined in that protection (conservation in this case) means putting at least some control over human actions that influence natural ecological process. Since ecological processes exist in highly complex systems, they are difficult to separate out in an ecologically meaningful way. Marine ecosystems are considerably different from, and less well known than, terrestrial ones (Pielou 1979; Salm and Clark 1984; Brown 1985; Ray 1985; Rice 1985). In addition, the migratory nature of marine organisms, both in everyday activities and life cycles, pays no attention to man-made maps (Figure 13.1).

If we try to set boundaries using ecological factors instead of administrative expedience, the structure and function, and the very notion of the boundary itself, must be examined. Current thinking has expanded the idea of a bound-ary from a simple fixed barrier to a process. A model for boundary process that explicitly addresses ecological and management concerns has been pro-posed by Schonewald-Cox and Bayless (1986) and discussed in several con-servation and management contexts (see e.g. Kushlan 1979; Newmark 1985; Dearden 1988; Usher 1988). This model visualizes a park boundary as a selectively permeable membrane, so managed to allow cross-boundary access for certain species, activities, and processes and to prevent undesirable spe-cies, activities, and processes from entering the reserved area. Control over

Figure 13.1
Can marine protected areas help fulfil conservation goals for wide-ranging species such as whales? Killer whale (A38) at Robson Bight Ecological Reserve, B.C.   *Photo: D. Duffus*

permeability depends on management practices. In marine parks, however, there are few effective tools for controlling access. For example, a recent spill of 875,000 litres of oil in Washington's coastal waters did considerable damage to Pacific Rim National Park Reserve shore. The spill happened far from the reserve and in a different jurisdiction, but the Pacific Rim National Park authorities could not control the damage.

BEYOND MARINE PARKS

Other measures than national marine parks currently provide some protection for marine areas. Provincial initiatives, such as British Columbia's Provincial Parks and Ecological Reserves program, are discussed in more detail in Dearden (1986, 1987). Orders-in-council can also influence marine areas when they establish local planning and management authorities that manage particular sites and situations, such as the Cowichan Estuary Environmental Management Plan (Vanderzwaag 1989). Federal-provincial agreements, both formal and informal, have created estuary management plans for the Fraser and Squamish rivers in southwestern British Columbia. Other federal programs, such as the establishment of national wildlife areas, may play increased roles in future marine protection planning, although they have yet to be used in this fashion. In addition, international agreements may come into play in marine area protection. The Law of the Sea Treaty, section 914(5), obliges states to protect rare or fragile ecosystems and endangered species in the oceans; as well, UNESCO's Biosphere Reserves program includes conservation of coastal environments (Gregg and McGean 1985; Vanderzwaag 1989).

CURRENT STATUS OF THE CANADIAN
MARINE PARKS PROGRAM

Marine parks planning is underway at several sites. As of late 1992, one park has been established and five sites are under consideration at some stage in the selection and establishment process.

Canada's first national marine park was established on 1 December 1987 through an agreement between Canada and Ontario (McClellan 1992). Fathom Five was a provincial park that was transferred to federal jurisdiction with the establishment of the nearby Bruce Peninsula National Park. This site has long been recognized as important for its shipwrecks and recreational diving. Planning for the management of Fathom Five is now underway.

Saguenay Fiord, at the confluence of the Saguenay and St Lawrence rivers has been assessed as a possible national marine park, and an agreement has been signed between federal and provincial authorities to develop the Saguenay Marine Park. Given its nutrient levels and the current threat to the beluga whale, this site has great natural significance (Figure 13.2).

Figure 13.2
Whale watchers at Saguenay Fiord, Que. The area provides critical habitat for several whale species and supports a sizable regional income from whale-watching. It remains to be seen whether national park designation can be used effectively to prevent habitat deterioration through pollution in the area.   *Photo: P. Dearden*

The West Isles area, in the Bay of Fundy near the Maine-New Brunswick border, has been the subject of intensive study for some time. Although this site has great natural heritage value, social problems, particularly local opposition by fishermen over disruption of their business and way of life, has stalled the project.

Lancaster Sound, off Baffin Island in the Northwest Territories, has been assessed because of its biological importance for marine birds and mammals and its spectacular Arctic land- and seascape. But the sound is a major shipping route, has potential hydrocarbon reserves, and is subject to Inuit land claims. All of these interests will likely become engaged in the park planning process. The problems with establishing a marine park are part of a larger land-use planning issue in this case.

Pacific Rim National Park Reserve has spent years in the park development process. Discussion now focuses on the formal establishment of some areas under the marine park policy. The final designation will probably be an internal Parks Service decision, which will depend on the park's status and the state of the entire marine park initiative when Pacific Rim is established as a national park.

The memorandum of understanding signed between the federal and provincial governments in July 1987 calls for the establishment of a national marine park reserve at South Moresby/Gwaii Hanaas in the Queen Charlotte Islands off the British Columbia coast. The biological and cultural heritage features of this area are unique. Two main obstacles stand in the way of park status. First, agreement must be reached with the Haida over their current land claim and their future role in the management of the park. Second, industrial interests have until 1993 to determine if recoverable offshore hydrocarbon potential exists in the proposed park area, or if exploration rights are extinguished. The area is being administered by the federal government using provincial legislation on an interim basis.

In addition to these five sites, discussions are also underway to establish marine parks in Hudson Bay, along the Labrador coast, and in the Strait of Georgia. Currently all proposals except Fathom Five involve significant jurisdictional and management decisions that may deviate from important tenets of park policy. For example, dealing with land tenure at the Saguenay River site will undoubtedly require authority now in the hands of the provincial government. Subsistence hunting will likely continue at Lancaster Sound. South Moresby may involve co-management with the Haida people. These compromises, of course, do not in themselves doom these parks, but they may well make it more difficult to carry out the national parks' mandate. Will the remaining federal authority be enough to protect the seabird colonies of Lancaster Sound or the critically endangered beluga whales of the Saguenay River mouth? From the viewpoint of resource protection, these questions remain unanswered.

THE FUTURE OF MARINE PARKS

The future of marine parks in Canada will depend on a combination of policy and political will. The two stages of park development—the actual establishment of the park and its subsequent management—will be guided by the policy of the Canadian Parks Service and on negotiations between it and Fisheries and Oceans, Transport Canada, provincial governments, local people, and lobby groups. Given the great diversity of Canada's coastlines and the combinations of social and biological conditions, a national marine park may resemble anything from a terrestrial national park to an anomalous form of reserve with more of an administrative than an ecological existence.

Is this an adequate way of protecting the marine environment? Some observers maintain that flexibility is necessary for park managers to deal effectively with influences originating outside the park boundary (Mondor 1987). Others point out that having a program is a step ahead of having no official recognition at the national level (Lien 1989). Both of these views have their merit. But the lack of a firm policy putting ecological preservation first will create serious problems for negotiators and park managers alike. Every instance of park establishment and planning will have its own set of circumstances and compromises. National marine parks may appear quite rapidly on maps and in brochures, but will they be doing what Canadians believe national parks are meant to do? Will marine parks become mere bureaucratic entities, depending on local political will, fisheries traditions, or other users' interests? The answer to this is quite likely 'yes', although some authors (e.g. Mondor 1992) feel that good co-operation between different government agencies is possible. Will this process protect marine environments and bring the Canadian public closer to the oceans through education and interpretation? The answer is quite likely 'no'.

What solutions have other countries found to the questions involved in establishing marine parks? What priority have they given to preservation, recreation, conservation, and management?

In Japan, marine parks are very much recreation oriented. Marsh (1985) notes that demand for park access is high, due to Japan's population density; marine parks are managed much as city or municipal parks are managed in Canada. Parks are created by both the national government and by local authorities, usually with few conflicts because most parks tend to be small and have little impact on, for example, fisheries. Japan uses a zoning system for its marine parks, creating a buffer zone around a preserved area, primarily as protection from fishing. Fishermen generally respect these zones; little enforcement is needed. This fits well with the overall management approach, which leaves day-to-day management in the hands of local authorities and volunteer organizations.

The Australian approach centres on the park established to protect the Great Barrier Reef. Although recreational use of the area is an important component of park management, the park's emphasis is on protection and conservation. Like Canada's provinces, Australia's state governments exert considerable control over internal resources, but the federal government has a good deal of authority in the coastal zone. A co-operative approach, in which a federal marine park authority is responsible for the entire management of the park, with day-to-day administration carried out by the state government, allows both for general federal control over park management and for considerable input at the state level through administration of regulations and park zoning (Kelleher and Kenchington 1982; Kelleher 1985). The authority itself enjoys a high level of financial and legislative government support.

Augier (1985) outlined problems and potential solutions in marine protection in France. As in many other countries, marine parks have been difficult to establish because France lacks the pertinent legislation. Rarely are existing park or protection acts designed with marine areas in mind. Augier indicates the need for a consultative approach to the development of marine parks and reserves at the local level. European experience also strongly shows the need to raise local awareness through education and the requirement for flexible zoning, for integrating coast-wide plans that incorporate both fisheries and protected areas, and for making allowances for problems emanating in other jurisdictions.

The United States implemented the Marine Protection, Research and Sanctuaries Act (MPRSA) in 1972. Title III of the Act deals specifically with the establishment and management of marine sanctuaries, the core of the American initiative. The program got off to a slow start (Green 1985) and created controversy between developers and the sanctuary program. The multiple-use philosophy in the Act and its relationship to other coastal management acts has reduced support for the concept (Harvey 1983). In fact two states have resisted the program. Hawaii would not support the establishment of a sanctuary to protect important calving areas for humpback whales. Alaska has come out against the entire coastal management strategy as an infringement of state jurisdiction over resources (Archer and Knecht 1987). Title III of MPRSA was reauthorized by Congress in 1988, an event that revived a previously shelved proposal for Monterey Bay in California and resulted in the declaration of the Florida Keys National Marine Sanctuary in 1990.

Changes in the administration's priorities, pressure from the oil industry, and the lack of legislative priority over other coastal management issues has resulted in an inconsistent program in the U.S., although seven sanctuaries have been declared and some complex management planning procedures have been developed (see e.g. Dobbin and Lemay 1985).

Perhaps the two lessons to be learned from other countries' efforts in marine area protection are the need for a strong political and legislative mandate and the requirement for public and regional input into the planning process. In the Australian case, there appears to be a strong commitment through government and resource management across jurisdictions. But the American example clearly indicates that legislative authority on its own does not guarantee an orderly development process.

Other interest groups seem to have a pervasive influence on park establishment and management. Both the Japanese and French cases suggest that park planning should be part of more general coastal management planning. Including local interests early in the planning process would seem to be a good way to deal with their concerns. It should, however, be borne in mind that the whole point of national marine parks is that they are of *national* significance. If primary attention had been given to local economic concerns, there would be very few terrestrial parks today. Changes in local economies are an inevitable result of marine park establishment. To designate and manage parks in complete sympathy with the traditional economies of local communities will leave little of ecological worth for future generations (Figure 13.3). As Marsh (1992) points out, using a regional approach to marine parks planning does allow some objectives to be met, but worldwide, the 'effectiveness in protecting marine environments and rare species is a matter of debate.'

Figure 13.3
Woody Point, Gros Morne National Park, Nfld. Difficulties have been encountered in establishing national parks and implementing conservation measures wherever local communities have a strong fishing tradition.
Photo: P. Dearden

CONCLUSION

Canada is currently at a critical juncture with regard to marine parks. The policy is in place; the program is underway; and we will have national marine parks. There are, however, some significant compromises in the overall policy for marine parks. Nonetheless, our only option is to ensure the best possible planning for and management of marine parks through pressure on the Canadian Parks Service and its parent ministry Environment Canada, to maintain the highest possible standards for environmental protection and educational programs.

Certainly, the rate of marine park establishment leaves much to be desired. The government has already reduced its commitment from eight to six new parks by the end of the decade and has no target date for completing the system. Furthermore the government readily admits (Environment Canada Parks Service 1991) that current opportunities to establish parks in many regions are limited. If this is the case now, the slow rate of park establishment will only lead to increasingly difficult and competitive situations in the future. It would seem to be more logical for the government, if it is genuinely committed to establishing a viable system of marine parks, to move aggressively rather than to adopt the current cautious approach.

The need for ocean protection and management is pressing. Because the oceans are largely out of sight and their ecological processes are still foreign and distant, we have tended to pay less heed to the marine environment. That the function of ocean ecosystems is an absolute necessity for the well-being of the planet is unquestionable. Marine parks themselves play only a minor role in protection; their significance is in public education. Even if marine parks can do little to protect the seas' ecology, their role in education can be brought to its full potential through imaginative and powerful interpretation programs. Graham (1992) believes that we will see a turnaround in both the public and the Parks Service, influenced by a strengthening of cultural and social connections. If so, the influence of a more sympathetic society may then persuade governments to take greater care of the ocean environment.

REFERENCES

Archer, J., and J.H. Knecht
1987   'The U.S. National Coastal Zone Management Program—Problems and Opportunities in the Next Phase', *Coastal Management* 15: 103–20.
Augier, H
1985   *Marine Protected Areas—The Example of France: Appraisal and Prospects*, Nature and Environment Series No. 31, Council of Europe, Strasbourg, France.
Beesley, J.A.
1989   'The Future of International Oceans Management', in *Canadian Ocean Policy: National Strategies and the New Law of the Sea*, eds D. McRae and G. Munro, University of British Columbia Press, Vancouver, 217–37.
Bjorklund, M.
1974   'Achievements in Marine Conservation', *Environmental Conservation* 1: 205–23.
Brown, K.
1985   'The Role of Protected Areas in the Conservation of Coastal and Marine Resources', in *Marine Parks and Conservation: Challenge and Promise*, vol. 1, eds J. Lien, and R. Graham, National and Provincial Parks Association of Canada, Toronto, 51–4.
Carson, R.
1961   *The Sea Around Us*, Oxford University Press, Oxford.
Crowley, R.W., and R.C. Bourgeois
1989   'The Rationale and Future Directions of Canada's Ocean Policy: Domestic Aspects', in *Canadian Ocean Policy: National Strategies and the New Law of the Sea*, eds D. McRae and G. Munro, University of British Columbia Press, Vancouver, 253–65.
Dearden, P.
1986   'Desolation Sound Marine Park, British Columbia', in *Marine Parks and Conservation: Challenge and Promise*, vol. 2, eds J. Lien and R. Graham, National and Provincial Parks Association of Canada, Toronto, 157–67.

Dearden, P.
 1987 'Marine Protective Designations in British Columbia', in *Heritage for Tomorrow: Proceedings of the Canadian Assembly on National Parks and Protected Areas*, vol. 3, eds R.C. Scace and J.G. Nelson, Supply and Services Canada, Ottawa, 123–46.
Dearden, P.
 1988 'Protected Areas and the Boundary Model: Meares Island and Pacific Rim National Park', *Canadian Geographer* 32: 256–65.
Delaney, G., H. Beach, M. Savoie, and F. Leblanc
 1992 'Commercial Fishery Studies in Kouchibouguac National Park, New Brunswick, Canada', in *Science and the Management of Protected Areas*, eds J.H.M. Willson *et al.*, Elsevier, New York, 283–86.
Dobbin, J.A. and M.H. Lemay
 1985 'Preparing Management Plans for U.S. National Marine Sanctuaries: Case Study of the Channel Islands National Marine Sanctuary', in *Marine Parks and Conservation: Challenge and Promise*, vol. 2, eds J. Lien and R. Graham, National and Provincial Parks Association of Canada, Toronto, 55–65.
Environment Canada
 1986 *National Marine Parks Policy*, Environment Canada, Ottawa.
Environment Canada
 1990 *Canada's Green Plan*, Supply and Services Canada, Ottawa.
Environment Canada, Parks Service
 1991 *State of the Parks Report*, Canadian Parks Service, Ottawa.
Fisheries and Oceans
 1987 *Ocean Policy for Canada: A Strategy to Meet the Challenges and Opportunities on the Ocean Frontier*, Fisheries and Oceans, Ottawa.
Foster, N., and M.H. Lemay, eds
 1989a *Managing Marine Protected Areas: An Action Plan*, Department of State Publication 9673, Bureau of Oceans and International, Environmental and Scientific Affairs, Washington.
Foster, N., and M.H. Lemay
 1989b 'Ocean Wilderness: Myth, Challenge, or Opportunity?' in *For the Conservation of the Earth*, ed. V. Martin, Fulcrum Press, Golden, Colo.
Graham, R.
 1992 'The Canadian Marine Parks Program: Opportunities and Options', in *Marine, Lake and Coastal Heritage*, Occasional Paper 15, Heritage Resources Centre, University of Waterloo, Waterloo, Ont., 119–38.
Green, S.
 1985 'The U.S. Marine Sanctuary Program', in *Marine Parks and Conservation: Challenge and Promise*, vol. 2, eds J. Lien and R. Graham, National and Provincial Parks Association of Canada, Toronto, 45–54.
Gregg, W.P., and B.A. McGean
 1985 'Biosphere Reserves: Their History and Their Promise', *Orion* 4: 41–51.
Harvey, S.
 1983 'Title III of the Marine Protection, Research and Sanctuaries Act: Issues in Program Implementation', *Coastal Zone Management Journal* 11: 169–97.

Kelleher, G., and R. Kenchington
1982   'Australia's Great Barrier Reef Marine Park: Making Development Compatible with Conservation', *Ambio* 11: 262–7.
Kelleher, G.
1985   'The Great Barrier Reef Marine Park', in *Marine Parks and Conservation: Challenge and Promise*, vol. 2, eds J. Lien and R. Graham, National and Provincial Parks Association of Canada, Toronto, 17–28.
Kushlan, J.A.
1979   'Design and Management of Continental Wildlife Reserves: Lessons From the Everglades', *Biological Conservation* 15: 282–9.
Lee, E.G., and D.G. Fraser
1989   'The Rationale and Future Directions of Canada's Oceans Policy: International Dimensions', in *Canadian Ocean Policy: National Strategies and the New Law of the Sea*, eds D. McRae and G. Munro, University of British Columbia Press, Vancouver, 238–52.
Lien, J.
1989   'Eau Canada! A New Marine Park System', in *Endangered Spaces: The Future for Canada's Wilderness*, ed. M. Hummel, Key Porter, Toronto, 107–21.
Marsh, J.S.
1985   'Japan's Marine Parks', in *Marine Parks and Conservation: Challenge and Promise*, vol. 2, eds J. Lien and R. Graham, National and Provincial Parks Association of Canada, Toronto, 29–44.
Marsh, J.S.
1992   'Marine Park Initiatives Around the World', in *Marine, Lake and Coastal Heritage*, Occasional Paper 15, Heritage Resources Centre, University of Waterloo, Waterloo, Ont., 21–30.
McClellan, S.
1992   'Fathom Five Provincial Park—A Successful Fifteen Year Old', in *Marine, Lake and Coastal Heritage*, Occasional Paper 15, Heritage Resources Centre, University of Waterloo, Waterloo, Ont., 87–90.
Mondor, C.
1985   'An Historical Overview of the National Marine Parks Concept in Canada', in *Marine Parks and Conservation: Challenge and Promise*, vol. 1, eds J. Lien and R. Graham, National and Provincial Parks Association of Canada, Toronto, 9–44.
Mondor, C.
1987   'Canadian Policy for National Marine Parks', in *Coastal Zone 87: Proceedings of the 5th Symposium on Coastal and Ocean Management*, eds O.T. Magoon *et al.*, 3545–55.
Mondor, C.
1992   'Canada's National Marine Park Policy, Evolution and Implementation', in *Marine, Lake and Coastal Heritage*, Occasional Paper 15, Heritage Resources Centre, University of Waterloo, Waterloo, Ont., 57–70.
Newmark, W.D.
1985   'Legal and Biotic Boundaries of Western North American National Parks: A Problem of Congruence', *Biological Conservation* 33: 197–208.

Pielou, E.C.
　1979　*Biogeography*, Wiley-Interscience, New York.
Ray, C.G.
　1985　'Man and the Sea: The Ecological Challenge', *American Zoologist* 25: 451–68.
Rice, J.
　1985　'New Ecosystems Present New Challenges', in *Marine Parks and Conservation: Challenge and Promise*, vol. 1, eds J. Lien and R. Graham, National and Provincial Parks Association of Canada, Toronto, 45–50.
Salm, R.V., and J.R. Clark
　1984　*Marine and Coastal Protected Areas: A Guide for Planners and Managers*, IUCN, Gland, Switzerland.
Sanger, C.
　1987　*Ordering the Oceans: The Making of the Law of the Sea*, University of Toronto Press, Toronto.
Sewell, W.R.D., P. Dearden, and J. Dumbrell
　1989　'Wilderness Decisionmaking and the Role of Environmental Interest Groups', *Natural Resources Journal* 29: 147–70.
Schonewald-Cox, C.M., and J.W. Bayless
　1986　'The Boundary Model: A Geographical Analysis of Design and Conservation of Nature Reserves', *Biological Conservation* 38: 305–22.
Silva, M., and I. Desilvestre
　1986　'Marine and Coastal Protected Areas in Latin America: A Preliminary Assessment', *Coastal Zone Management Journal* 14: 311–47.
Usher, M.B.
　1988　'Biological Invasions of Nature Reserves: A Search for Generalizations', *Biological Conservation* 44: 119–35.
Vanderzwaag, D.
　1989　'Canada and Marine Environmental Protection: The Changing Tides of Law and Policy', in *Canadian Ocean Policy: National Strategies and the New Law of the Sea*, eds D. McRae and G. Munro, University of British Columbia Press, Vancouver, 95–132.

CHAPTER 14

Canada, Conservation, and Protected Areas

The International Context

—

HAL EIDSVIK

The Canadian contribution to international conservation is elusive, largely because it is unfocused. There is no central accounting system to which one can turn for basic financial data on Canada's international conservation activities. There is no annual report, nor a central or key organization through which trends can be traced. For example, the Canadian International Development Agency (CIDA) makes many of its conservation contributions through its overseas offices, but the dollars spent on conservation are not a significant line item in its $2-billion budget. CIDA does, however, play a critical role in supporting the participation of the developing world in a broad range of conservation activities, but conservation does not appear as an identifiable unit in its annual report.

On examination, Canada's contribution to international conservation raises more questions than answers. When we think about Canada's contribution, do we think only about projects which have physical on-site components? Do we include the intellectual contribution of Canadian scholars or the work of foreign nationals who have studied at Canadian institutions? Are we addressing only species and habitat conservation? Do we include reforestation, watershed stabilization, or soil conservation measures? Are family planning programs a conservation measure? Do we serve conservation objectives by joining the Antarctic Treaty and the Organization of American States?

This chapter will examine some areas of Canadian involvement, identify some issues, and hopefully begin an analysis of this overlooked situation.

NATIONS AND SOVEREIGNTY

Canada, with more than 9,922,000 sq. km of land and inland waters, makes its major contribution to international conservation by being a prudent steward of its own resources. As a supporter of the World Charter for Nature, Canada has a responsibility to the other 155 countries of the United Nations who endorsed this charter in October 1982 (Burhenne and Irwin 1983).

In a real sense, international conservation occurs only through conventions or agreements between international bodies and countries. National sovereignty is closely guarded; it is rare indeed for a nation to forgo its sovereignty and allow the management of some of its resources under a form of international jurisdiction. Article 6 of the World Heritage Convention states:

> While fully respecting the sovereignty of the States on whose territory the cultural and natural heritage is situated and without prejudice to property rights provided by national legislation, the State Parties to this Convention recognize that such heritage constitutes a world heritage for whose protection it is the duty of the international community as a whole to co-operate. (UNESCO 1983)

Co-operation between nations and between international conservation communities is a more accurate description of international conservation than the broad term implies. The high seas and Antarctica are exceptions, where a more truly international form of management and regulation take place. Co-operation on conservation projects takes many forms: multilateral programs through organizations such as the United Nations; bilateral co-operation through treaties or agreements between two nations; co-operation between institutions such as universities, park agencies, or individual parks; co-operation through non-governmental organizations such as the World Wildlife Fund (WWF); or co-operation initiated by individuals. Canadians are involved in many international conservation projects. If one was to ask why, perhaps the most succinct answer comes from the World Wildlife Fund: 'Wildlife knows no political boundaries and some of the most urgent environmental problems occur outside Canada' (WWF 1988, 21).

INTERNATIONAL CONSERVATION ACTIVITIES

International conservation efforts can take many forms, but the protection of species lies at the foundation of these efforts. Ensuring the protection of habitat can involve the full gamut of conservation action, including:

- Fund-raising
- Public education
- Research to identify issues, problems, and resolutions
- Inventory of natural resources
- Social and economic assessment
- Training of management staff
- Public participation programs
- Public or school education programs
- Wildlife, forestry, park, or other forms of ecosystem management
- Protected area identification and establishment
- Protected areas management planning
- Protected area management, administration, and monitoring

In essence, international conservation involves all of the elements involved in park management in Canada plus a deep understanding of the social, economic, and cultural foundations of the country in which a project is being carried out.

The International Conventions

International conventions, treaties or agreements provide a legal mechanism for co-operation between nations. Some of these instruments may be bilateral, such as the Migratory Birds Convention (1916) between the United States and Canada. Others may be of a universal nature, such as the Convention Concerning the Protection of the World Cultural and Natural Heritage, which in 1990 had 112 signatories.

Conventions generally establish obligations of a moral nature; some however may be enforced by national legislation that can impose jurisdiction where none previously existed. Thus, the Convention on International Trade in Endangered Species (CITES 1975) places obligations on provinces as well as the federal government. In contrast the World Heritage Convention as implemented in Canada provides only for moral suasion.

Brief summaries of some of the more important conventions follow:

1. *Convention Concerning the Protection of the World Cultural and Natural Heritage.* This convention was adopted in 1972 by the General Conference of the United Nations Educational, Scientific, and Cultural Organization (UNESCO) and came into force in 1975. The objective of the convention is to ensure support by the international community for world heritage sites, which are recognized as being held in trust by nations for humankind. Natural and cultural sites identified by states and recorded on a World Heritage List by decision of a committee are given special protection, with the possibility of financial and technical assistance through a World Heritage Fund. By January 1990, 112 countries were party to the convention, and the World Heritage List included natural properties in 36 countries. This designation is given only to a few outstanding protected areas. Canada currently has ten sites with this designation (see Figure 14.1 and Table 14.1).

States having designated cultural or natural sites on the World Heritage List must take specific measures for their conservation. Obligations under the convention also include the payment of compulsory dues amounting to 1 per cent of each country's annual dues to UNESCO. The Secretariat of the Convention is provided by UNESCO. Technical advice on the natural sites is provided by the International Union for the Conservation of Nature and Natural Resources (IUCN), usually called the World Conservation Union, and technical advice on cultural sites is provided by the International Council for Monuments and Sites (ICOMOS).

2. *Convention on International Trade in Endangered Species of Wild Fauna and Flora (CITES).* This convention came into force in 1975 and now has

Figure 14.1
The Combined Rocky Mountain National Parks (Banff, Jasper, Yoho, Kootenay) have been designated as a World Heritage Site. Research indicates that this is the only protected area assemblage on the continent big enough to be able to provide protection for wide-ranging mammals in the future. Here in the photograph, visitors on horseback enjoy exploring the Lake Louise area, Banff National Park.   *Photo: P. Dearden*

Table 14.1 Canadian World Heritage Sites

Natural Sites	Cultural Sites
Nahanni National Park	Ninstints National Historic Site
Kluane National Park*	Head-Smashed-In Buffalo Jump
Wood Buffalo National Park	Quebec City (historic centre)
Gros Morne National Park	L'Anse aux Meadows National Historic Site

Rocky Mountain World Heritage Parks, including:
  Banff National Park
  Jasper National Park
  Yoho National Park
  Kootenay National Park
  Mount Assiniboine Provincial Park (B.C.)
  Mount Robson Provincial Park (B.C.)
  Hamber Provincial Park (B.C.)
  Burgess Shales World Heritage Site

Note: *Kluane/Wrangell-St Elias was a joint Canadian-U.S. nomination.

100 contracting parties. The aim of the convention is to establish worldwide controls over trade in endangered wildlife and wildlife products, in recognition of the fact that unrestricted commercial exploitation is one of the major threats to the survival of species. More than 2,000 endangered species of wild animals and plants are listed in three appendices to the convention. Each party to the convention has designated national management and scientific authorities in charge of administering the licensing system, in direct co-operation with their foreign counterparts. CITES provides countries with up-to-date information and with a direct communications network linking national enforcement agencies. Technical assistance is available for the training of personnel, and identification aids and other materials are made available to facilitate implementation of the convention.

3. *Convention on Wetlands of International Importance especially as Waterfowl Habitat.* The objectives of the Wetlands Convention (signed in 1971 and also known as the Ramsar Convention) are to stem the loss of wetlands and ensure their conservation for their importance in ecological processes as well as for their rich fauna and flora. The convention provides for general obligations for contracting parties relating to the conservation of wetlands throughout the territory and for specific obligations pertaining to wetlands included on a List of Wetlands of International Importance.

By 1990, some 432 sites covering in excess of 28 million ha had been designated as wetland sites of international significance for their ecology, botany, zoology, limnology, or hydrology. Of these areas, Canada has dedicated 12.9 million ha (World Resources Institute 1990) under the jurisdiction of the Canadian Wildlife Service. Placing an area on the Ramsar list has considerable impact upon the conservation of the area and upon public recognition of the global importance of these sites.

4. *Convention on the Conservation of Migratory Species of Wild Animals.* This convention was adopted in 1979 and came into force in 1983; by 1990 there were 30 contracting parties (World Resources Institute 1990). The purpose of the convention is to provide a mechanism for international co-operation for the conservation and management of migratory species in need of urgent conservation measures at an international level. The convention offers financial, technical, and training assistance supporting conservation efforts by developing countries. It urges international and national organizations to give priority in their aid programs to the management and conservation of migratory species and their habitats in developing countries, the better to enable such countries to implement the convention.

This convention deals with all migratory species including fish and other marine mammals. Canada is not a party to this convention. The primary reasons for this are the inclusion of fish as migratory species and the perceived duplication with other conventions such as the Migratory Birds Convention between Canada and the United States.

Regional Conventions providing for Protected Areas

1. *Migratory Birds Convention.* The Migratory Birds Convention, signed by Canada and the United States in August 1916, was one of the earliest conservation conventions. It regulates the hunting of migratory birds and led to a number of bird sanctuaries in both Canada and the United States. The first such sanctuary was in fact established on Last Mountain Lake in Saskatchewan in 1887, long before the convention.

The joint involvement of Canada and the United States in restoring whooping crane populations from the low 30s to approximately 150, can be directly attributed to this convention. The North American Waterfowl Management Plan (NAWMP) is also closely linked to the 1916 Migratory Birds Convention. NAWMP is a $1.5-billion 15-year program to protect habitats such as wetlands, initiated in 1986 between Canada's Minister of the Environment and the U.S. Secretary of the Interior.

2. *Western Hemisphere Convention.* The 1940 Convention on Nature Protection and Wildlife Preservation in the Western Hemisphere provided that the contracting parties explore at once the possibility of establishing national parks, national reserves, nature monuments, and strict wilderness areas in their territories. It also provided for contracting governments in the Americas to co-operate in promoting its objectives, to lend assistance to one another, and to enter into agreements to increase the effectiveness of this co-operation. On the basis of the principles of the treaty, most of the states in the region

have taken important conservation measures.

Canada joined the Organization of American States in the fall of 1989 and ratified the Western Hemisphere Convention on 8 January 1990. It is premature to predict the impact of this convention, but it is expected to have a significant impact on Canadian conservation co-operation with Latin America.

3. *Polar Bear Convention (1974)*. The agreement on the conservation of polar bears is an example of a species-specific convention. Parties include Canada, the U.S., the former Soviet Union, Norway, and Denmark. The convention, as implied, regulates the hunting of polar bears in all nations of the circumpolar region.

4. *Antarctic Treaty*. Canada became a party to the Antarctic Treaty in 1988. The Antarctic Treaty is a complex series of agreements that had their origin in 1959 and initially involved 12 signatory countries. The Antarctic Treaty system makes provision for Antarctica to be used exclusively for 'peaceful purposes'; all military activities are banned. It is a declared non-nuclear zone in which the protection and conservation of all living resources are given special consideration. A limited number of special protected areas have been established, but much remains to be done. Currently Greenpeace and the governments of Australia and of France are advocating a world park to incorporate the entire continent. Canada officially supports the strengthening of conservation measures in Antarctica but has not decided on which of several approaches to support.

INTERNATIONAL ORGANIZATIONS AND PROGRAMS

UNESCO's Man and the Biosphere Program (MAB)

Additional mechanisms for focusing conservation priorities are special programs of national or international organizations, such as UNESCO's Man and the Biosphere Program (MAB). A biosphere reserve is 'an internationally designated protected area managed to demonstrate conservation objectives' (Peine 1985, 8). In plain terms, if World Heritage Sites are recognized as unique resources, then Biosphere Reserves are 'representative resources'. They are a recent development in conservation (IUCN/UNESCO 1984). As a relatively new conservation tool, much remains to be done to create a truly effective program.

The Biosphere Reserve Program in Canada is managed through the Canadian Commission for UNESCO, which appoints a national steering committee. The program has considerable potential to build on existing relatively minor financial commitments by both UNESCO and the various levels of government involved. There are currently six biosphere reserves in Canada (Table 14.2), although many others have been suggested, particularly as a way to create buffer zones near national parks (see e.g. Dearden 1988; Slocombe 1992).

Table 14.2 Biosphere Reserves in Canada

Waterton Lakes National Park (Alberta)

Mont St Hilaire Conservation Areas (Québec)

Riding Mountain National Park (Manitoba)

Long Point (Ontario)

Charlevoix (Québec)

Niagara Escarpment (Ontario)

The Role of The World Conservation Union (IUCN) and the CNPPA The International Union for the Conservation of Nature and Natural Resources (IUCN), or World Conservation Union, is the largest and most representative partnership of conservation, environment, and wildlife interest groups in the world. Founded in 1948, the union includes 61 states, 121 ministries or other government agencies, and 394 major national and international non-governmental organizations and citizens' groups—a total of 636 members in 120 countries. This unique mix of policy makers, administrators, and activists helps solve common conservation problems. It also provides an independent forum for conservation debate.

The union works in close partnership with the United Nations Environment Program (UNEP) and UNESCO, advises the WWF on conservation priorities, and prepares programs and manages over 300 conservation field projects in 70 countries.

IUCN, primarily through its Commission on National Parks and Protected Areas (CNPPA) founded in 1960, has been deeply involved with national parks from its very beginnings. IUCN/CNPPA activities include:

• Establishing a system of biogeographic provinces of the world (Udvardy 1975), now widely used for assessing the extent of existing protected areas and suggesting regions for immediate attention.
• Publishing lists and directories of protected areas. The Protected Area Data Unit (PADU) of the World Conservation and Monitoring Center (WCMC) was established in 1981 to computerize the data held by IUCN and to promote greater applications of the data.
• Publishing basic conceptual papers dealing with protected area matters, such as regional system reviews, legislation guidelines, and reports on threats to the world's protected areas.
• Publishing the quarterly journal *Parks*, which provides informative articles on management problems and solutions for protected areas.
• Co-operating closely with United Nations agencies involved in protected area matters (e.g. the Food and Agriculture Organization, UNEP, and

UNESCO) at both planning and field levels. This includes providing technical evaluations of natural sites nominated for the World Heritage List to UNESCO's World Heritage Committee.

- Holding meetings in various parts of the world to promote protected areas. CNPPA holds two working sessions per year, rotating among the biogeographic realms. IUCN has organized major international meetings on protected areas, including the First World Conference on National Parks in Seattle, Wash., 1962; the Second World Conference on National Parks in Grand Teton, Wyo., 1972, the International Conference on Marine Parks and Reserves, Tokyo, 1975; the World Congress on National Parks, Bali, Indonesia, October 1982. The 1992 Congress was held in Caracas in February 1992.

- Supporting field projects aimed at establishing and managing national parks and protected areas especially in developing countries. Funded primarily by the WWF, some 1,600 projects involving an estimated expenditure of over $50 million had been implemented in support of protected areas by 1990.

World Conservation Strategy

Among IUCN's major achievements was leadership in the preparation of the World Conservation Strategy (WCS) (IUCN 1980), simultaneously launched in over 30 countries in 1980. Robert Prescott-Allen, now of Victoria, B.C., was the principal editor of the strategy. It has had a dramatic impact on bringing conservation concepts into focus. The WCS focuses on three main objectives:

- to preserve genetic diversity;
- to maintain essential ecological processes;
- to ensure that the utilization of species and ecosystems is sustainable.

Each country harbours plants and animals which contribute to global diversity. Extinction of these species is a global loss, a depletion of the earth's wealth, a loss for all people not just for one nation. The WCS brought about a major shift in direction for international conservation organizations. This shift involved a movement away from preservation of fauna and flora toward more integrated management of natural resources through the preparation of national and regional conservation strategies. This trend has been further reinforced by the publication of a second global conservation strategy entitled *Caring for the Earth: A Strategy for Sustainable Living*, prepared predominantly by Canadians and funded by the IUCN, UNEP and WWF.

World Charter for Nature

Another significant document prepared by IUCN was recently approved by the General Assembly of the United Nations: the World Charter for Nature. Negotiated over a period of seven years, the charter will, one hopes, become for nature what the Human Rights Charter has become for humans. It needs vigorous promotion through school systems and public organizations. It has five general principles:

1. Nature shall be respected and its essential processes shall not be impaired.
2. The genetic viability on the earth shall not be compromised; the population levels of all life forms, wild and domesticated, must be at least sufficient for their survival, and to this end necessary habitats shall be safeguarded.
3. All areas of the earth, both land and sea, shall be subject to these principles of conservation; special protection shall be given to unique areas, to representative samples of all the different types of ecosystems, and to the habitats of rare or endangered species.
4. Ecosystems and organisms, as well as the land, marine, and atmospheric resources that are utilized by man, shall be managed to achieve and maintain optimum sustainable productivity, but not in such a way as to endanger the integrity of those other ecosystems or species with which they coexist.
5. Nature shall be secured against degradation caused by warfare or other hostile activities. (Burhenne and Irwin 1983)

World Wide Fund for Nature (WWF)

The WWF was established in 1961 to mobilize moral and financial support for safeguarding the living world and is among the closest of IUCN's many partners in conservation. Formerly known as the World Wildlife Fund, it has 27 affiliate organizations around the world, some of which, including that in Canada, retain the original name World Wildlife Fund.

WWF has its headquarters along with the World Conservation Union (IUCN) in the World Conservation Centre in Switzerland. These two organizations work closely together to establish a scientific foundation for conservation and to raise the funds to carry out high-priority projects. These include the World Conservation Strategy, support for the World Protected Areas Congress, rescue plans for endangered species, and technical assistance leading to more effective management of protected areas. In 1989, WWF Canada spent approximately $500,000, or one-third of its annual revenue, on international projects.

MONITORING THE GLOBAL COVERAGE OF PROTECTED AREAS

Two essential tools for monitoring the global coverage of protected areas are a biogeographical classification system and a conservation area classification system.

Biogeographical Classification

IUCN and UNESCO have, since 1975, used a biogeographic system developed by Dr Miklos D.F. Udvardy. The classification is based primarily on vegetation, secondly on fauna, and thirdly on the distribution of flowering plants. These foundations are further influenced by climatic and oceanic systems.

In the classification, the world is divided into eight realms (continent-sized units), 227 provinces or subdivisions of realms (13 in Canada; see Table 14.3), and 14 biomes that reflect major vegetational components such as tundra or deserts, as well as major lake systems.

The Udvardy system allows us to evaluate the coverage of global diversity. It is the basis for the monitoring system used by the World Conservation and Monitoring Centre in Cambridge, England. The Udvardy system is less effective when applied at the national level, particularly where the state is small and the topographic and biological diversity is high, as in (e.g.) Costa Rica. The Udvardy classification did, however, provide a base for the work of the Canadian Parks Service on system planning. Within the Canadian Parks Service, the Udvardy system's 13 provinces in Canada were expanded to 39 natural regions (see Figure 14.2). This has provided the basis for further divisions of natural regions by several provincial governments, including British Columbia.

Classification of Conservation Areas

In order to provide comparative data on the number and size of protected areas in the world, IUCN, through the work of Dasmann and others, developed a methodology for classifying protected areas in accordance with their conservation objectives. Ten different categories were used at the time of the World Parks Congress in Bali (McNeely and Miller 1984). In reality, the World Conservation Monitoring Center has reported on only five of these

Table 14.3 Udvardy Biogeographic Classification Applied to Canada

Code	Biogeographic Province	Biome
1.1.2	Sitkan	Temperate broad-leaf forest
1.2.2	Oregonian	" " " "
1.3.3	Yukon Taiga	Temperate needle-leaf forest
1.4.3	Canadian Taiga	" " " "
1.5.3	Lake Forest	Evergreen xclerophyllous forest
1.13.9	Alaskan Tundra	Tundra communities
1.14.9	Canadian Tundra	" "
1.15.9	Canadian High Arctic	" "
1.15.14	Great Lakes	Lake systems
1.17.9	West Arctic Desert	" " .
1.18.11	Grasslands	Temperate mountains
1.21.12	Rocky Mountains	Mixed mountains
1.22.12	Cascade Sierra	" "

Source: Udvardy 1984.

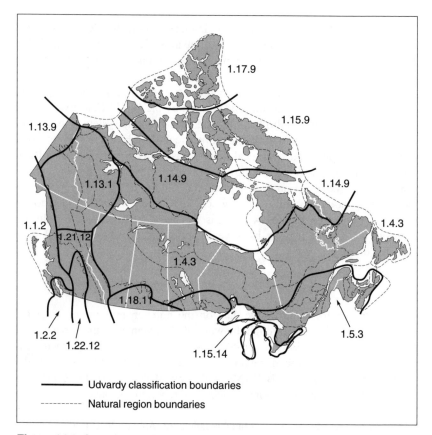

Figure 14.2 Canada showing the Udvardy Biogeographic Classification (see Table 14.3) and the natural regions of the Canadian Parks Service.

categories in the United Nation's Directory of National Parks and Protected Areas.

Data is collected on the basis of IUCN's five key categories for protected areas:

Category I   *Scientific Reserves*: ecological reserves, nature reserves. These areas are generally closed to visitors except by permit; e.g., Robson Bight, Vancouver Island.

Category II   *National Parks and Equivalent Reserves*: These areas have a high degree of resource protection and are often tourism destination areas; e.g. Jasper National Park or Mount Assiniboine Provincial Park.

Category III *Natural Monuments*: Generally, these are relatively small areas, but in the United States they are presidentially designated and may be very extensive. This designation is not widely used in Canada.

Category IV *Habitat and Wildlife Management Areas*: Wildlife sanctuaries. In these areas, habitat may be manipulated to favour one species or another. Hunting may take place, but in general the degree of protection is high; e.g., the Thelon Game Sanctuary in the Arctic.

Category V *Protected Landscapes*. These incorporate semi-natural and cultural landscapes and as such are not likely to include wilderness areas; e.g., the Niagara Escarpment in Ontario.

The IUCN to date has not maintained a separate data set for wilderness areas. In practice, protected areas with management plans often incorporate a wilderness zone. These zones are most likely to occur in large protected areas in categories I–IV.

During the period 1984–90, a IUCN Task Force examined the ten categories used since 1979. Revisions have been proposed to simplify the classification system, to make it more explicit, and to incorporate wilderness areas within the framework. Final decisions on new categories will not be made until the next General Assembly of IUCN in 1994.

Table 14.4 shows the total amount of land in each of the original five categories. When this world data is examined in more detail, Canada emerges as one of the world's leaders in the establishment of protected areas (Table 14.5). North and Central America lead the world in the percentage of area dedicated to conservation (Table 14.6).

When we look at protected areas, we are ultimately concerned with their role in maintaining biological diversity, the variety and variability among

Table 14.4 World Totals of Protected Areas in each Category

Category	Type	Number of Areas	Total area (ha)
1	scientific reserves	526	38,106,074
II	national parks and equivalents	1,050	256,029,904
III	natural monuments	70	6,556,943
IV	habitat and wildlife	1,488	103,504,852
V	protected landscapes	380	19,586,625

Source: IUCN 1985

Table 14.5 Ranking by Country—Categories I–V

Country	Total area (ha)
Greenland	71,050,000
U.S.A.	64,946,135
Australia	35,413,712
Canada	22,949,135

Source: IUCN 1985.

living organisms and the ecological complexes in which they occur' (Mc-Neely *et al.* 1990). But we are faced with a major dilemma, for we do not know what we have. Globally, the number of described species is 1,435,662. 'For convenience many assume that about 10 million species exist, though the final figure is likely to be 30-50 million' (McNeely *et al.* 1990). Compared to some tropical countries, Canada's biological diversity is limited (Table 14.7). This does not, however, reduce the importance of individual species. Only 4 per cent of the world's area is protected; perhaps 96 per cent of biodiversity is not. Therefore, protecting species must extend to our society as a whole. If this job is left only to protected areas, many species will disappear.

A significant factor not included in gross area comparisons is the degree of legal protection provided by higher levels of government, which have much greater ability to counteract undesirable developments in or near protected areas. If all of these considerations were taken into account the ranking of countries in conservation effectiveness would likely be United States, in top place, followed by Canada, New Zealand, South Africa, and Australia. If economic factors—the ability to match the desire to protect with the necessary capital—were not so critical, countries such as Costa Rica, Ecuador, Zimbabwe, Tanzania, and Malawi would rank extremely high in their commitment to conservation.

Table 14.6 Global Protection of Natural Areas 1989

	Number of Areas	Area (ha)	% of Land Area
World	5,289	529,081,551	4.0
Africa	521	101,675,251	3.4
North and Central America	890	193,908,695	9.1
South America	453	80,123,051	4.6
Europe	1,347	31,326,547	6.6

Source: IUCN 1985.

Table 14.7 Canada and Global Comparisons of Biodiversity Among Select Species Groups

	Globe	Canada
Mammals	4,170	210
Birds	9,198	426
Reptiles	6,300	42
Amphibians	4,184	41

Source: World Resources Institute 1990.

Lists of protected areas and management effectiveness are little more than snapshots. In reality, these areas are moving targets; they change with governments and economic and social conditions, and often with the effectiveness of the management team. The raw data from the foregoing tables has only limited usefulness, as does the comparison of total areas by percentage of land protected. More important are questions of effective management and the budget and personnel available to ensure protection.

Other approaches to evaluating the effectiveness of protected areas might deal with the degree of protection, systems planning, management planning, and visitor services, including interpretive programs and scientific or research activities. In all of the foregoing areas, except for scientific research, Canada would rank in the top five park systems in the world. Research during the period 1960-85 was not seen as a priority or a necessity. More recently, as threats to parks become more critical, the need for a sound scientific basis for action has become much more apparent, as Dearden and Rollins point out in Chapter 1.

CONCLUSION

Canada makes a major contribution to international conservation through its federal and provincial park systems. The conservation of habitat for internationally significant species such as the whooping crane, grizzly bear, dall sheep, bison, musk-ox, and polar bear is a major function of the Canadian park system. Canada has also provided leadership through initiatives such as the creation of the International Peace Park at Waterton, Alta, and Glacier National Park, examples which are being followed by many other countries. Participation in international conventions such as CITES and World Heritage is also important. The Migratory Birds Convention between Canada and the U.S. was one of the first international agreements relating to conservation.

Canadians can also take pride in the leadership they provide in the formulation of park policy, in systems and management planning, and in the provision of visitor services. On the other hand, our contribution through training or the provision of technical assistance has, on the whole, been limited.

Nature conservation is a global concern and cannot be neatly compartmentalized by international frontiers. Those engaged in the huge task of establishing, planning, and managing protected areas must take a broad view of what they are doing. Success and failure should be viewed in the framework of a world effort and needs to be measured over generations.

Few countries are even holding their own in the conservation effort. The world becomes a poorer place for wild living resources each year. The funds and staff available are restricted, political will is not always sufficient, and the odds to be faced often appear insurmountable. But there are genuine grounds for hope. There have been some spectacular successes, such as the recovery of the whooping crane. It is encouraging to see the growing list of national organizations, parks authorities, and outstanding individuals who are doing a competent job.

As protected areas become the last remaining natural habitats, they will become even more valuable and an even more important part of sustainable social and economic development. The responsibility of managers of protected areas as custodians of the wild heritage of all the world will certainly grow. To the extent that this responsibility is understood and appreciated by the public and government decision makers, resources for conservation can similarly be expected to grow.

But high levels of international co-operation are also needed to achieve more lasting results. Countries with few resources need to co-operate effectively with their neighbours to ensure that knowledge is shared productively. Technologically advanced countries should share their know-how with those less fortunate. There must be a pooling of resources and mutual support of programs. International conservation programs need to be integrated with regional, national, and provincial programs, and conservation must be closely integrated with other components of each country's development.

Such concerted effort is a huge task requiring a major commitment in people and resources. It is also a complex task that needs the expertise of biologists, geologists, geographers, planners, administrators, sociologists, economists, law enforcement officers, and many others, all brought together to focus on common objectives.

As we look at the problem of conserving nature, the difficulties seem only to increase in depth and complexity. Species are disappearing daily, before we can even name and describe them; but we are just beginning to recognize that genetic loss is deeper and more subtle than we thought, even within unthreatened populations or those on the rebound from near-extinction. Within species cultivated for human use, such as corn or peas or apples, wild or ancestral stocks are vanishing, with a net loss of genetic variation that may have devastating consequences in future. Even when we do manage to save an endangered species from outright extinction, we face an ominous and very long-term loss of genetic diversity within that species—a genetic bottleneck called depauperization. For example, scientists can now graft skin from one cheetah to another without seeing tissue rejection.

> Though there may still be as many as 20,000 cheetahs at large on the plains of Africa, the gene pool of *A. jubatus* appears to be much smaller than it should be for that number—too small, perhaps, to carry the species through any sudden adversities. Insufficient genetic options equals insufficient adaptability. . . . And that's one threat that we humans can't rectify. All we can do is give them time. A depleted population of animals can sometimes recover quickly. A depleted gene pool cannot. . . . Populations fall and rise again at geometric rates but, like some morbidly hurtful memory, genetic impoverishment lingers afterward. (Quammen 1989, 148–9)

These and related problems will require massive co-operation among nations and regions. The environment is international; threats to it are international; and ways of dealing with those threats must also be international. Nature, after all, never set these boundaries.

LIST OF ABBREVIATIONS

CIDA	Canadian International Development Agency
CITES	Convention on International Trade in Endangered Species
CNPPA	Commission on National Parks and Protected Areas
ICOMOS	International Council for Monuments and Sites
IUCN	International Union for the Conservation of Nature and Natural Resources (World Conservation Union)
MAB	Man and the Biosphere
NAWMP	North American Waterfowl Management Plan
PADU	Protected Area Data Unit
UNEP	United Nations Environment Program
UNESCO	United Nations Educational, Scientific, and Cultural Organization
WCMC	World Conservation and Monitoring Centre
WCS	World Conservation Strategy
WWF	World Wide Fund for Nature (formerly World Wildlife Fund)

REFERENCES

Burhenne, E.W., and W.A. Irwin
1983   *The World Charter for Nature: A Background Paper*, Elizabeth Haub Foundation, Washington, D.C.
Dearden, P.
1988   'Protected Areas and the Boundary Model: Meares Island and Pacific Rim National Park', *The Canadian Geographer* 32: 256–65.
International Union for Conservation of Nature and Natural Resources, United Nations Environment Program, and World Wildlife Fund
1980   *World Conservation Strategy: Living Resource Conservation for Sustainable Development*, IUCN/UNEP/WWF, Gland, Switzerland.
Mackinnon, J. *et al.*
1986   *Managing Protected Areas in the Tropics*, IUCN, Gland, Switzerland.
McNeely, J. *et al.*
1990   *Conserving the World's Biological Diversity*, IUCN, Gland, Switzerland, and WRI, CI, WWF, and the World Bank, Washington, D.C.
Peine, J.D. ed.
1985   *Proceedings of the Conference of the Management of Biosphere Reserves*, Great Smoky Mountains National Park, Gatlenburg, Tenn., U.S. Department of the Interior, National Park Service, Washington, D.C.
Quammen, D.
1989   *The Flight of the Iguana: A Sidelong View of Science and Nature*, Anchor, New York.
Sarasin, P.
1913   *International Conference for the Protection of Nature, Minutes*, Berne, Switzerland.
Slocombe, D.S.
1992   'The Kluane/Wrangell-St Elias National Parks, Yukon and Alaska: Seeking Sustainability Through Biosphere Reserves', *Mountain Research and Development* 12: 87–96.
United Nations Educational, Scientific, and Cultural Organization
1972   *World Heritage Convention*, UNESCO, Paris.
World Commission on Environment and Development
1987   *Our Common Future*, Oxford University Press, Oxford and New York.
World Resources Institute
1990   *World Resources 1990–91*, Oxford University Press, Oxford and New York.
World Wildlife Fund Canada
1988   *Annual Report*, World Wildlife Fund Canada, Toronto.

CHAPTER 15

Challenges for the Future

—

RICK ROLLINS AND PHILIP DEARDEN

Over the years, several books have provided striking visual accounts of natural scenery in Canada and of the various park systems in the country. These books have not, however, provided details of the management issues and decision making processes that shape our parks' appearance and function. This kind of commentary can be found in bits and pieces only by thoroughly searching a wide variety of sources. The aim of this book was to assemble under one cover a ready reference for people seeking a better understanding of these issues.

A second objective of this undertaking was to ensure that this book was distinctly Canadian. Most of the literature dealing with the management of parks and protected areas has appeared in foreign publications, mainly American. In the past, the task for people interested in Canadian issues has been to put these works into a Canadian perspective. Some of the more general principles of ecosystem theory or visitor behaviour are more or less universal and easy to apply, but the specifics of environmental characteristics, social traditions, legislated mandates, and policy frameworks are unique to each country. In this book, fundamental principles have been presented in a Canadian context. By extension, these principles can be used as a basis for examining the management of parks and protected areas in other parts of the world.

This book, we hope, provides concepts and understandings needed to assess the effectiveness of Canadian efforts to plan and manage protected areas. In order to critically examine management and planning activities, it is imperative to evaluate the relationship between three dimensions: the role of theory and research; the role of legislation, policies and plans; and the actions taken by resource managers.

In a perfect world, strong links among these three dimensions should be evident in the management of any park or protected area. An example of this might be determining the physical boundaries of a national park. From a theoretical perspective, we could examine the possible location of a park boundary by applying ecological concepts such as island biogeography or minimum viable populations. Using these principles (see Chapter 8), we would examine first the range requirement of a relatively large animal high on the trophic scale found in the park—an indicator species such as the grey wolf. If the size, configuration, and location of park boundaries protect the range of the grey wolf, then the park probably provides adequate protection for simpler, less range-sensitive species. Of course, a more complete ecological examination of a park boundary would need to address the concepts of island biogeography, patch dynamics, fragmentation, stress ecology, and catastrophe theory.

As well considering the ecological basis for a park boundary, we would need to assess the long-term issue of maintaining such a boundary. We would have to examine the strength and clarity of existing legislation, policy, and planning procedures. This book has provided specific examples of policy and legislation in a number of chapters. To set our new park boundary, we would need to examine the National Parks Act, national park policy, national park regulations, and the various planning processes (e.g. the systems plan for national park designation, the management plan for the park, and the natural resource management plan for the park). What we would hope to find in such an analysis is clear direction about where national parks should be located and how large they should be, as well as guidelines for establishing our park boundary. Furthermore, we would hope to find a close correspondence between these guidelines and the various ecological concepts discussed in the book. The clarity of the guidelines and their correspondence to ecological criteria are the bases for evaluating the appropriateness of the related legislation, policy, and planning frameworks.

The third part of analysing our new park boundary would involve a field-based assessment of the actual degree of protection provided by existing park boundaries. Do actual park boundaries reflect those boundaries designated in the park plan? Or, for example, have the boundaries been diminished somewhat by nearby prevailing land-use practices? We have seen that land-use practices such as farming, ranching, hunting, and hydroelectric development outside parks have impacts that carry over into the park itself. Park boundaries may also be compromised by the park services and by facilities such as roads, trails, campgrounds, and park buildings. Evaluating our park boundary would involve an investigation of the extent to which management has been able to effect real protection and whether management actions are consistent with legislation, policies, and plans and with ecological theory and research.

Likewise, the management of visitor use can be addressed by considering the relationship among social science theory and research, legislation, policies, plans, and management in the field. For example, should overnight accommodation be provided in a particular park? Some people have argued that primitive shelters or huts should be provided as an alternative for people not wishing to camp. To answer this question, first we must examine the policy and legislation of the agency responsible for managing the area. To what extent is visitor use defined and encouraged in legislation and policy? Is a classification system described for different kinds of parks or for different zones within parks? Do such systems describe types of visitor use and the kinds of facilities and services that may be provided, including overnight facilities? Is overnight accommodation of this type provided by other agencies in the region (national parks, provincial parks, forest service sites, the private sector)?

Next, we would review recreation literature, looking for models for managing visitor behaviour and considering concepts such as carrying capacity, limits of acceptable change, the Recreation Opportunity Spectrum, Visitor Impact Management, and the Visitor Activity Management Process. We would need specific information about the impacts on park environments of various types of visitor use (including the type of accommodation). Next, we should find out what the public think, both about various types of accommodation and about the impact of these accommodations on the park, perhaps through user surveys, household surveys, focus groups, and public hearings.

Clearly, the decision about the provision of primitive shelters could be facilitated greatly by using social science models and research. Further, decision making would be influenced by the extent to which this kind of information is consistent with the policies and legislative mandates of the agency.

Finally, the resolution of this issue may involve some assessment in the field. For example, one primitive shelter could be provided and evaluated on a trial basis. Its effects on park resources and on the experience of park visitors and its maintenance costs could be monitored. If these are not unacceptable, the agency might consider providing more of this type of shelter. It would also be important to determine if actual impacts were consistent with what may have been predicted from recreation theory and research.

This method of assessing either one particular visitor service or park boundary can be extended to any type of issue in a park or protected area, regardless of the jurisdiction or location. With this in mind, we can now turn our attention to a summary of some of the major issues that remain.

1. *Completing a national system of parks and protected areas.* As Monte Hummel (1989, 267) has outlined:

> Presently the national park systems is only 54 per cent completed, with twenty-one of thirty-nine natural regions represented, leaving us with eighteen regions still to be represented by a minimum of eighteen parks. We have forty-five national wildlife areas, and ninety-nine areas identified as candidates but still unprotected. Of the twenty-nine natural regions identified for national marine parks, only two are currently represented by such protected areas. Eight of the twelve provinces and territories have park system plans, i.e. clearly stated 'finishable wilderness agendas'. New Brunswick, Prince Edward Island, Newfoundland, and Northwest Territories have yet to map their natural regions and set representative targets. Of the eight provincial and territorial jurisdictions that do have such plans, only four are more than halfway down the road to completion. If we set the Brundtland Report recommendation of aiming for 12 per cent of the landscape in legally protected areas, Canada is well short at 6.3 per cent (only 2.6 per cent, if we exclude areas where logging, mining, hunting

are permitted). In terms of area, federal, provincial, and territorial jurisdictions have presently reserved approximately 63 million square kilometres, and protected about 23 million square kilometres, versus a minimum goal of 120 square kilometres.

Canada's Green Plan, released in 1990, commits the federal government to setting aside 12 per cent of the country as protected space. Specific promises included the establishment of five new national parks by 1996 and the negotiation of 13 more by the year 2000. Three new marine parks are promised for 1996 and three more by 2000. Finally, the federal government made a commitment to work with the provinces to develop a system of forest ecological reserves and to promote the protection of wetlands. Given current federal-provincial tensions over the Constitution and the present federal deficit, the federal government will need sustained public support to meet these agendas for setting aside protected areas.

2. *Effective legislation and policies for parks and protected areas.* Many provinces lack clear legislation and policy with regard to parks and protected areas. The consequence of this environmental limbo is a chaotic stream of *ad hoc* decisions and actions. As outlined in Chapter 4, legislation is approved by a legislature and can be enforced in the courts. This is the strongest statement that can be made about the management of parks and protected areas. The National Parks Act of 1930, amended in 1988, provides the legislation for national parks in Canada, but not all provinces have this kind of legislation for their own parks and protected areas. Furthermore, the substance of legislation needs to be examined to determine the real level of legal protection afforded.

Legislation provides the legal basis for management of parks and protected areas, but policies and regulations express day-to-day management guidelines. The adequacy of these policies and regulations needs to be examined for each jurisdiction dealing with parks and protected areas. Even if we agree with the substance of these policies and regulations, we need to be vigilant in determining if they are consistently applied. For example, specific issues such as the proposals to expand the Banff townsite can be argued against on the basis of existing policy and legislation.

3. *Assessing appropriate tourism and recreation.* Human use of parks and protected areas is an important management consideration, because public support for conservation often begins with an appreciation of these resources. The obvious problem is both the types and the levels of use that are appropriate (Figure 15.1). On one hand, there is major concern about the impact of visitors on the natural processes that these areas were established to protect (environmental carrying capacity). On the other hand, we have the challenge of managing parks and protected areas to improve visitors' experiences. This

Figure 15.1
Bearskin rugs offered for sale in Riding Mountain National Park, Man. Is this communicating the right message to park visitors?   *Photo: P. Dearden*

issue is compounded by the very significant tourism demands (and potential tourism revenues) in some places (Figure 15.2). In national parks, the question of visitor impact is partly addressed by the zoning system outlined in the Parks Canada policy (Chapter 5). General strategies for managing visitor experience are discussed in Chapter 10. As these chapters point out, resolution of these issues requires a strong commitment to management objectives.

Figure 15.2
Chateau Lake Louise, with the Lake Louise ski area in the distance. In terms of visitor numbers and aggregate visitor satisfactions, Lake Louise is probably one of the most valuable sites in the national park system. But are these developments consistent with the dominant preservation mandate of the parks? *Photo: P. Dearden*

Furthermore, the development of these objectives requires a good understanding of visitor characteristics (motives, preferences, etc.) as well as an understanding of the impact of tourism on the environment. Often, visitor management strategies are prepared without a good understanding of these relationships.

4. *Regional effects.* We have already mentioned the impact of land-use practices outside of park boundaries on the ecological integrity of protected areas. The reverse of this effect is also true; parks and protected areas have an effect on surrounding land use. This effect may be seen as positive, as in maintaining water quality downstream of a park. Unfortunately, it may also be seen as negative. Wolves preying on livestock outside a park is one such case; another is restricting fishing in a marine park.

Increased tourism is a common consequence of giving protected area status to a region and is usually seen as positive in bringing in revenue and creating employment. On the other hand the attitudes and behaviour of tourists may conflict with local values and customs. Increasingly in the future, park policies and management must be aware of these external linkages. We need more research of both a biophysical and socioeconomic nature to ascertain the nature of these effects.

5. *The role of indigenous peoples.* Many parks and protected areas are located in parts of the country that are important territories for Native peoples. South Moresby Island, Pacific Rim, Head-Smashed-In Buffalo Jump, and Nahanni are examples of this situation. Management of these places requires special sensitivities and strategies. For example, many parks and protected areas in northern Canada allow for some forms of subsistence wildlife harvesting by Native peoples. In most parks and protected areas in the southern part of the country, management regimes have tended to prohibit any form of resource extraction, including hunting. Chapter 3 calls for viewing parks and protected areas as part of a conservation strategy that extends beyond park boundaries to include the notions of sustainable development. Chapter 12 argues that the role of Aboriginal peoples should be expanded to embrace some degree of co-management of protected areas that are also of cultural significance to these people.

6. *Public participation.* Much has been said about the importance of public participation in decision making with regard to national issues such as free trade, Meech Lake, and the imposition of the GST. The federal government held extensive public consultations in developing its Green Plan, addressing environmental issues in Canada, including national parks. National park policy clearly indicates the need for public participation in the designation of new national parks, and some provincial park systems incorporate some public consultation as well. The issue is how public consultation is to be carried out. What kinds of issues will be encouraged? To what extent will public consultation be incorporated in decision making? Certainly, the trend at the national level has been to encourage increasing amounts of public input; unfortunately, the same has not always been the case at the provincial level.

Not only must we provide greater opportunity for public participation, but professional park managers must also learn how to take advantage of the quality of input that is available. Park bureaucrats should not consider themselves the only, nor even the principal, sources of expertise on any given issue. Non-governmental organizations (NGOs) often have considerable expertise and certainly have access to such expertise. The formation of a National Wilderness Caucus is one example in which NGO expertise is helping to create the agenda for national wilderness protection. Nor should this be considered a one-way flow of information. The future success of our parks and protected areas relies largely upon continued public support. That support must continue to be encouraged through appropriate allocation of resources for public education (both inside and outside the parks) on the role of parks in society.

7. *Research.* The challenges described in this volume all point to one thing: park management is going to become increasingly complex. During the first 100 years of parks in Canada, little was invested in research. As the complexity of the management situation increases, so will the need for information and understanding on which to base decisions. A vast increase in

biophysical and socioeconomic scientific research will be required to come to terms with these demands. This will entail not only the establishment of more in-house expertise but also a willingness to enter into co-operative research undertakings with universities and NGOs.

It is important that these issues and challenges be addressed. We have a responsibility to Canadians, to the international community, and to future generations to manage parks and protected areas in Canada as effectively as possible. This is a critical time for the environment in Canada, and particularly for the future of wilderness ecosystems. The decisions we make in this decade will have far-reaching implications for generations to come. Let us hope that we are wise enough to be able to recognize that intergenerational responsibility laid out in the National Park Act and transform it into a guiding principle for all our activities.

REFERENCES

Hummel, M., ed.
    1989   *Endangered Spaces: The Future for Canada's Wilderness*, Key Porter Books, Toronto.

A Statement of Commitment to Complete Canada's Networks of Protected Areas

PREAMBLE

This Statement is intended as a public statement of consolidated political will to complete Canada's networks of protected natural areas by the year 2000. Realization of this commitment will build upon more than a century of conservation efforts in Canada. The Statement's endorsement by three separate federal-provincial councils is a recognition of the need for both inter-jurisdictional and inter-disciplinary cooperation. This Statement is the beneficiary of many international commissions, resolutions and declarations—the World Conservation Strategy, the World Charter for Nature, the World Commission on Environment and Development, Caring for the Earth: A Strategy for Sustainable Living; and most recently, in February 1992, the Caracas Declaration from the Fourth World Congress on Parks and Protected Areas—all of which have signalled the urgency to complete the world's networks of protected areas. The World Commission on Environment and Development has recommended that at least 12% of the planet be set aside in protected areas.

It is understood that nothing in this Statement shall in any way prejudice Aboriginal or treaty rights, the land claims process or self-government negotiations.

PREMISES

On the occasion of Canada's 125th anniversary, the Canadian Council of Ministers of the Environment, the Canadian Parks Ministers' Council, and the Wildlife Ministers' Council of Canada have come together to recognize that:

- Canada's natural heritage—its wildlands, waters and wildlife–unites and defines us all as Canadians
- Canada has a special global responsibility to protect its natural heritage given that:
  - Canada is steward of almost 20% of the planet's wilderness (excluding Antarctica), 20% of its fresh water, and 24% of its remaining wetlands
  - Canada is one of the few nations that still has an opportunity to represent its natural regions and features, and to conserve its critical wildlife habitat
- Protected areas have scientific, educational, inspirational and recreational values for humankind and contribute to sustainable development
- Protected areas are essential to Canada's environmental health, biological diversity, and ecological processes
- The ecological health of protected areas is affected by the quality of the surrounding environment

- The opportunities to protect Canada's natural regions and wildlife habitat are quickly being foreclosed
- Canada's natural heritage should be safeguarded through a variety of protected areas, including national and provincial parks, ecological reserves, wildlife management areas and migratory bird sanctuaries
- Protected areas must be complemented by sound public and private stewardship of all of Canada's lands
- Aboriginal people have a significant and unique role in the protection of Canada's natural heritage
- The protection of Canada's natural heritage cannot be achieved by any one government or agency
- Canadians want to be involved in decisions affecting protected areas

COMMITMENTS

And therefore, in the interest of present and future generations of Canadians, Council members will make every effort to:

- Complete Canada's networks of protected areas representative of Canada's land-based natural regions by the year 2000 and accelerate the protection of areas representative of Canada's marine natural regions
- Accelerate the identification and protection of Canada's critical wildlife habitat
- Adopt frameworks, strategies, and time-frames for the completion of the protected areas networks
- Continue to cooperate in the protection of ecosystems, landscapes and wildlife habitat
- Ensure that protected areas are integral components of all sustainable development strategies

The Honourable Pauline Browes
Minister of State (Environment)
Government of Canada
Canadian Council of Ministers of the Environment

The Honourable Harry J. Enns
Minister of Natural Resources
Government of Manitoba
Canadian Parks Ministers' Council

The Honourable Titus Allooloo
Minister of Renewable Resources and Municipal and Community Affairs
Government of the Northwest Territories
Wildlife Ministers' Council of Canada

Aylmer, Quebec, November 25, 1992

APPENDIX 2

———

Key Words, Concepts, and Study Questions

CHAPTER 1

Key Words/Concepts

- Green Plan
- public attitudes towards environment
- natural ecosystem
- human-controlled ecosystems
- National Parks Act
- national park policy
- climatic change
- CPAWS
- Sierra Club
- special interest groups
- endangered spaces campaign
- World Wildlife Fund
- external influences
- sustainable development

Study Questions

1. Why is society at a critical junction in terms of its relationship with the environment?
2. Discuss the three major political initiatives in park and protected area management since 1988.
3. What has been the role of 'special interest groups' such as the Sierra Club and CPAWS?
4. Discuss the role and scope of external influences on the ecological integrity of protected areas.
5. Discuss the role of science in the management of protected areas.

CHAPTER 2

Key Words/Concepts

- Rocky Mountain Park Act (1887)
- CPR
- national policy
- multiple use
- Dominion Forest Reserves and Parks Act (1916)
- National Parks Act (1930)

- systems plan (1971)
- expropriation
- Aboriginal land claims
- Mackenzie Valley Pipeline Inquiry
- 6 North of 60 Program
- National and Provincial Parks Association (Canadian Parks and Wilderness Society)
- national park policy (1964)
- national park policy (1979)
- national marine parks policy
- Canadian heritage land concept
- endangered species campaign
- Brundtland Commission
- ecological integrity

Study Questions

1. Discuss and compare the early history of Banff with that of Yellowstone.
2. Discuss the significance of the national policy of the Macdonald government (1880s) on the early history of national parks.
3. Discuss the role of James Harkin on the evolution of national parks in Canada.
4. Discuss the significance of the natural regions systems plan.
5. In what way was park establishment in the 1960s different than during Harkin's era?
6. What was the significance of the public response to the creation of a new national park at Kouchibouguac, N.B.?
7. Discuss how the resolution of Aboriginal land claims has influenced completion of the national parks system.
8. Discuss the role of NPPAC (CPAWS) on the development of the national parks system.
9. What impasse provoked the proposal to establish Canadian Heritage Lands (1987)?

CHAPTER 3

Key Words/Concepts

- stewardship
- ASIS
- MAB (Man and Biosphere)
- ESPAS (Environmentally Sensitive Policy Areas)
- private agencies
- non-government organizations (NGOS)
- island effect
- nodes
- corridors
- connectivity
- socioeconomic region

- regional integration
- sustainable development
- buffer zone
- ABC survey method
- Canadian Heritage Lands

Study Questions

1. Explain what is meant by the 'dominant role of government' in protected area management.
2. List 12 functions of national parks and protected areas.
3. Discuss the distinction between special sites and interconnected systems within the contexts of parks and protected areas.
4. Discuss why there is a need for more co-operation and co-ordination in protected area management.
5. Why was the Canadian Heritage Lands Program proposed, and why does it seem destined to die?
6. Identify a 'private group' in your community and discuss the role played by this group in protected area management (e.g. Ducks Unlimited, Naturalist Association, Landowners' Association, etc.)

CHAPTER 4

Key Words/Concepts

- policy
- legislation
- state of the parks
- management plans
- park regulations
- conservation authority
- Niagara Park Commission
- Public Parks Act
- Municipal Act
- Park Assistance Act

Study Questions

1. What is the dual mandate of the National Parks Act?
2. How has the notion of enjoyment evolved over time with respect to interpretations of the National Parks Act?
3. Why is a national parks act needed?
4. Outline the major distinctions between the National Parks Act and the Provincial Parks Act of Ontario.
5. Compare the provincial park legislation and policy for Ontario with that of another province.
6. Compare the degree and form of public access to park-related decision making at each level of park authority described in this chapter.

CHAPTER 5

Key Words/Concepts

- National Parks Act
- national parks policy
- systems plan
- physiographic regions
- forest regions
- natural history themes
- candidate parks
- selection consideration
- zoning system
- VAMP
- accountability
- ecological integrity
- capital property

Study Questions

1. Compare the systems plan discussion with the ecological issues raised by Theberge in Chapter 8.
2. Why does national park policy fail to provide a minimum size for national parks?
3. Discuss the differences and similarities of the zoning system and VAMP.
4. Review a national park management plan. Is the plan consistent with the policy guidelines discussed in this chapter? Are visitor services described with effective market analysis and prescription? Does the natural resources management reflect policy, as well as issues raised by Theberge and by Eagle? How are Aboriginal issues and the interests of local communities addressed?

CHAPTER 6

Key Words/Concepts

- park classification system
- heritage appreciation
- Blue Book
- Hill's site region methodology
- zone
- multiple use
- wilderness experience
- non-native species

Study Questions

1. Outline the four basic reasons (principles) for establishing provincial parks in Ontario.
2. Compare the park classification system in Ontario with the Recreation Opportunity Spectrum (ROS) outlined in Chapter 10.

3. Distinguish between the role of nature reserves and wilderness parks.
4. Distinguish between zoning and park classification.
5. Compare management principles for wilderness parks with those for national parks (Chapter 5).
6. What is unique and special about recreation parks compared to other types of Ontario parks?
7. Distinguish between Hill's site regions (13) and site districts (65).
8. On the basis of the brief description provided of waterway parks, describe management concerns and issues specific to this kind of park.

CHAPTER 7

Key Words/Concepts

- World Conservation Strategy
- 1930 Provincial Parks Act
- park classification scheme
- ecological reserves
- wilderness areas
- provincial parks
- provincial recreation areas
- management plan
- zoning
- Foundations for Action
- privatization
- commercialization

Study Questions

1. Discuss the role of provincial parks with respect to national parks. For example, how does the role of Banff National Park (in Alberta) compare with the role of the adjacent Peter Lougheed Provincial Park, also in Alberta?
2. Discuss the role of Alberta Provincial Parks with respect to the role of other provincial agencies (e.g. Forestry).
3. Although 10.5% of Alberta's area is protected by legislation, a great deal of concern has been raised about the protected area program. Discuss.
4. Compare the zoning and classification system for Alberta Parks with the Ontario park system (Chapter 6).
5. Discuss the appropriateness of managing a park campground by a private contractor rather than by park employees.

CHAPTER 8

Key Words/Concepts

- ecological integrity
- preservation
- protection
- multiple use

- extractive use
- conservation
- wise use
- sustained yield
- environmental impact assessment
- sustainable development
- K-strategists
- summit predators
- species that concentrate
- migratory birds
- long-distance migratory mammals
- Large-Bodied Species
- old-growth forest species
- minimum viable population size
- island biogeography
- patch dynamics
- fragmentation
- stress ecology
- catastrophe theory
- the 1% rule
- demographic-based calculations
- genetics-based calculations
- SLOSS

Study Questions

1. List five 'vital ecological functions' served by parks and other protected areas.
2. What are the most commonly stated criteria for selecting areas?
3. Discuss how the concepts in this chapter address the issues of 'how much, how big, and where?'

CHAPTER 9

Key Words/Concepts

- old-growth forest
- values
- market values
- indicators
- genetic diversity
- benchmark
- production of poducts
- sustainable utilization
- protectors of unique features
- fire suppression
- vegetation plan
- endangered species
- inventory

- special needs
- ecological relationships
- monitoring change
- environmental impacts

Study Questions

1. Discuss the comment that 'natural resource management is value-laden'.
2. Discuss the concept that 'management is . . . value-laden'.
3. Discuss who assigns value with regard to resource management in parks.
4. Contrast fire management from the perspective of timber management with conservation management.
5. Why is the amount and direction of plant community manipulation under constant debate?
6. Discuss the effects of hunting (positive and negative) in a protected area.
7. Why is bear management particularly controversial?

CHAPTER 10

Key Words/Concepts

- recreation diversity
- opportunity classes
- motivations
- activities
- settings
- ROS
- LAC
- recreation carrying capacity
- VIM
- stakeholders

Study Questions

1. How and why is LAC an improvement over carrying capacity?
2. What are the limitations of VAMP, the primary approach by the Canadian Parks Service? How could these limitations be overcome?
3. Why is VIM felt to be the least effective of the four approaches?
4. Examine the visitor services section of a national park management plan, and outline how elements of VIM, LAC, VAMP, ROS, and carrying capacity are expressed.

CHAPTER 11

Key Words/Concepts

- interpretation
- John Muir
- scheduled services

- slide shows
- prop talks
- dramatic presentations
- point duty
- impromptu events
- living interpretation
- visitor centres
- exhibits
- sign
- interpretive trails
- publications
- environmental education
- field trips

Study Questions

1. Outline the three major stages of evolution in interpretive planning.
2. How does interpretation differ from information?
3. What are the seven distinct components of interpretive services?
4. Distinguish between the terms 'interpretation' and 'environmental education'.

CHAPTER 12

Key Words/Concepts

- Catlin's proposal
- First Nations
- Aboriginal title
- reserves
- park reserves
- Crown land
- Aboriginal rights
- marginalized
- the Calder case
- comprehensive land-claim settlements
- the Sparrow case
- fee simple land
- non-renewable resources
- Berger Inquiry
- joint management regime
- national park reserve
- Inuvialuit Final Agreement (IFA)
- Inuit land claim
- unoccupied Crown land
- paternalistic management

Study Questions

1. What types of problems make it imperative to involve Aboriginal peoples in protected area planning and management?
2. Discuss the impact the 1992 Canadian Constitution proposals may have on the role of Aboriginal peoples in national parks.
3. Discuss the implications of the Calder case and the Sparrow case for national parks.
4. Discuss the relationship between comprehensive land claims and national parks.
5. Account for the estrangement of parks from Aboriginal people.
6. Discuss how the role of Aboriginal peoples has led to subtly different kinds of parks in northern and southern Canada.
7. Contrast the involvement of first peoples in the management of Pacific Rim National Park Reserve and in South Moresby/Gwaii Hanaas National Park Reserve.
8. Outline the evolution of Aboriginal involvement in national parks.

CHAPTER 13

Key Words/Concepts

- Green Plan
- Environmental Protection Act
- Ocean Policy for Canada (1987)
- jurisdiction
- resource management traditions
- biophysical aspects
- boundary problems
- conservation
- preservation

Study Questions

1. What are the two routes by which marine environments can be protected?
2. What is meant by the duality of marine environments?
3. What is the fundamental difference between land and marine parks?
4. Discuss the distinction between preservation and conservation with respect to marine parks.

CHAPTER 14

Key Words/Concepts

- CIDA
- World Charter for Nature
- World Heritage Convention
- sovereignty

- Convention Concerning the Protection of the World Cultural and Natural Heritage
- United Nations Education, Scientific and Cultural Organization (UNESCO)
- World Heritage Sites
- Convention on International Trade in Endangered Species of Wild Fauna and Flora (CITES)
- Convention on Wetlands of International Importance Especially as Waterfowl Habitat (Ramsar)
- Convention on the Conservation of Migratory Species of Wild Animals
- Migratory Birds Convention
- Western Hemisphere Convention
- Polar Bear Convention
- Antarctic Treaty
- Man and the Biosphere Program (MAB)
- World Conservation Union (IUCN)
- World Wildlife Fund for Nature (WWF)
- Commission on National Parks and Protected Areas (CNPPA)
- World Conservation Strategy (WCS)
- biogeographical classifications
- IUCN classification of conservation areas

Study Questions

1. Why is it difficult to measure Canada's contribution to international conservation?
2. For each convention described in this chapter, prepare a brief case study of Canada's involvement.
3. This chapter suggests that the highest-ranking countries *vis-à-vis* conservation effectiveness are the U.S., Canada, New Zealand, South Africa, and Australia:
   a) Why are these countries more effective than other countries, particularly tropical countries, where so much of the world's biodiversity is found?
   b) In what ways might these leading conservation countries actually *undermine* or fail to support conservation efforts in other countries?

CHAPTER 15

Key Words/Concepts

- theory and research
- legislation
- policy
- plans
- actions
- Green Plan
- Brundtland Report

Study Questions

1. Using the framework provided in this chapter, prepare case studies of a national or provincial park in your area. Discuss the size and configuration of the park (i.e., the boundaries) with respect to theory, research, policy, plans, and management actions.
2. Prepare another case study with regard to a visitor service issue such as the type of accommodation provided in the park.
3. Prepare an update for your province regarding the level of protection of parks and protected areas today. How close is your province to the 12 per cent target? What obstacles and opportunities exist?

APPENDIX 3

———

Names and Addresses of Government and Non-Government Agencies Related to Parks and Protected Areas

GOVERNMENT AGENCIES

FEDERAL

CANADIAN PARKS SERVICE
Environment Canada
Terrasses de la Chaudière
10, rue Wellington, 28e étage
Hull, PQ, K1A 0H3
Fax: (819) 953-3457
General inquiries: (819) 997-1441
Departmental inquiries:
(819) 997-2800

Regional Offices:

Atlantic Region
Historic Properties, Upper Water St
Halifax, NS, B3J 1S9
(902) 426-3405

Québec Region
3, rue Buade
C.P. 6060, succ. Haute-Ville
Québec, PQ, G1K 4V7
(418) 648-4042

Ontario Region
111 Water Street E., P.O. Box 1359
Cornwall, ON, K6H 6S3
938-5870

Prairie Region
Confederation Bldg., 457 Main St
Winnipeg, MB, R3B 3E8
(204) 983-2120

Western Region
220—4th Ave S.E., 5th Flr
P.O. Box 2989, Stn M
Calgary, AB, T2P 3H8
(403) 292-4444

Yukon
DEPARTMENT OF THE ENVIRONMENT
Environmental Protection Service
204 Range Rd, Ste 101,
Whitehorse, YT, Y1A 3V1
667-3400

Canadian Wildlife Service
204 Range Rd, Ste 202
Whitehorse, YT, Y1A 3V2

Canadian Parks Service
204 Range Rd
Whitehorse, YT, Y1A 3V1

INTERGOVERNMENTAL

CANADIAN HERITAGE RIVERS BOARD
c/o National Parks Branch
Canadian Parks Service
Ottawa, ON, K1A 0H3

CANADIAN PARKS SERVICE
General Inquiries: (819) 994-2691

PROVINCIAL

BRITISH COLUMBIA

MINISTRY OF ENVIRONMENT, LANDS
AND PARKS
Parliament Buildings, Victoria
V8V 1X4
387-1187

PARKS DIVISION
810 Blanshard St, 4th Flr
Victoria, BC, V8V 1X4
387-9997

ALBERTA

DEPARTMENT OF TOURISM, PARKS AND
RECREATION
10155–102nd St
Edmonton, AB, T5L 4L6
Minister's Office
424 Legislative Bldg
Edmonton, AB, T5J 2B6
427-3162

SASKATCHEWAN

SASKATCHEWAN NATURAL RESOURCES
3211 Albert St, Regina, SK, S4S 5W6
General Inquiries: 787-2700

MANITOBA

DEPARTMENT OF NATURAL RESOURCES
314 Legislative Bldg
Winnipeg, MB, R3C 0V8
945-3730

ONTARIO

MINISTRY OF NATURAL RESOURCES
Whitney Blk, 99 Wellesley St W.
Toronto, ON, M7A 1W3
General Inquiries: 314-2000

QUÉBEC

MINISTÈRE DE L'ENVIRONNEMENT
Siège social: 3900, rue Marly
Ste-Foy, PQ, G1X 4E4
Renseignements gén. et accueil:
643-6071

NEW BRUNSWICK

DEPARTMENT OF NATURAL RESOURCES
AND ENERGY
P.O. Box 6000
Fredericton, NB, E3B 5H1
453-2510

NOVA SCOTIA

DEPARTMENT OF NATURAL RESOURCES
Founder's Sq, 2nd Flr
1701 Hollis St, P.O. Box 698
Halifax, NS, B3J 2T9
General inquiries: 424-5935

PRINCE EDWARD ISLAND

DEPARTMENT OF TOURISM, PARKS AND
RECREATION
Shaw Bldg, 3rd Flr
105 Rochford St
Charlottetown, PEI, C1A 7N8
General inquiries: 368-5500

NEWFOUNDLAND

DEPARTMENT OF ENVIRONMENT AND
LANDS
Confederation Bldg, W. Blk,
P.O. Box 8700
St John's, NF, A1B 4J9
729-2574

NORTHWEST TERRITORIES

DEPARTMENT OF ECONOMIC DEVELOP-
MENT AND TOURISM
P.O. Box 1320, Yellowknife, NWT,
X1A 2L9
873-0110

YUKON

DEPARTMENT OF RENEWABLE
RESOURCES
P.O. Box 2703, Whitehorse, YT,
Y1A 2C6
667-5376

INDEPENDENT AGENCIES, BOARDS AND COUNCILS

Northwest Territories
Nunavut Wildlife Management
Advisory Board
P.O. Box 118, Iqaluit, NT, Z0A 0H0
(819) 979-6628

NON-GOVERNMENT AGENCIES

World Wildlife Fund Canada
60 St Clair Avenue East, Suite 201
Toronto, ON, M4T 1N5
(416) 923-8173

Assembly of First Nations
55 Murray St
Ottawa, ON, K1N 5M3
(613) 236-0673

Canadian Nature Federation
453 Sussex Drive
Ottawa, ON
K1N 6Z4
(613) 238-6154

Canadian Parks and Wilderness
Society
160 Bloor Street East, Suite 1150
Toronto, ON, M4W 1B9
(416) 972-0868

Nature Conservancy of Canada
794A Broadview Avenue
Toronto, ON, M4K 2P7
(416) 469-1701

Newfoundland Wilderness Society
P.O. Box 5132
St John's, NF, A1C 5V3

Conservation Council of New
Brunswick
180 St John Street
Fredericton, NB, E3B 4A9
(506) 458-8747

Foundation pour la sauvegarde des
espèces menacées (FOSEM)
8191 Avenue du Zoo
Charlesbourg, PQ, G1G 4G4
(418) 622-0313

Federation of Ontario Naturalists
355 Lesmill Road
Don Mills, ON, M3B 2W8
(416) 444-8419

Temagami Wilderness Society
19 Mercer Street, Suite 307
Toronto, ON, M5V 1H2
(416) 599-0152

Wildlands League
229 College Street, Suite 206
Toronto, ON, M5T 1R4
(416) 595-0443

Manitoba Naturalists Society
302–128 James Avenue
Winnipeg, MB, R3B 0N8

Saskatchewan Natural History Society
1860 Lorne Street
Regina, SK, S4P 2L7
(306) 780-9273

Alberta Wilderness Association
Box 6398, Station D
Calgary, AB, T2P 2E1
(403) 283-2025

Canadian Parks and Wilderness Society (Alberta Office)
11759 Groat Road
Edmonton, AB, T5M 3K6
(403) 458-8658

Outdoor Recreation Council of B.C.
334–1367 West Broadway
Vancouver, BC
V6H 4A9
(604) 737-3000

Sierra Club of Western Canada
314–626 View Street
Victoria, BC, V8W 1J4
(604) 386-5255

Valhalla Wilderness Society
Box 224
New Denver, BC, V0G 1S0
(604) 358-2449

Western Canada Wilderness
Committee
1520 West 6th Avenue
Vancouver, BC, V6J 1R2
(604) 731-6716

Canadian Arctic Resources Committee
111 Sparks Street
Ottawa, ON, K1P 5B5
(613) 236-7379

Yukon Conservation Society
Box 4163
Whitehorse, YK, Y1A 3T3
(403) 668-5678

CPAWS Wildlands League
160 Bloor Street E., #1335
Toronto, ON, M4W 1B9
(b) (416) 324-9760
(f) (416) 972-0760

CPAWS Edmonton
11759 Groat Road
Edmonton, AB, T5M 3K6
(h) (403) 453-8658
(w) (403) 433-9302

CPAWS Calgary/Banff
P.O. Box 608, Sub P.O. Box 91
University of Calgary
Calgary, AB, T1N 1N4
(h) (306) 373-4584
(w) (306) 247-0400

CPAWS Ottawa/Hull
Box 3072, Station D
Ottawa, ON, K1P 6H6
(h) (613) 731-2703
(w) (613) 993-2125
(f) (613) 723-8084

CPAWS Yukon
Site 16, Com 62, R.R. 1
Whitehorse, YK, Y1A 4Z6
(h) (403) 668-6321
(f) (403) 738-7175

CPAWS Saskatchewan
P.O. Box 914
Saskatoon, SK, S7K 3M4
(h) (306) 373-4584
(w) (306) 665-7655

CPAWS British Columbia
Box 33918, Station D
Vancouver, BC, V6J 4L7
(h) (604) 266-3785

CPAWS Nova Scotia
73 Chadwick Street
Dartmouth, NS, B2Y 2M2
(902) 466-7168

CPAWS Manitoba
414 Place Cabana
Winnipeg, MB, R2H 0K4
(204) 237-5947
(204) 949-9052

Index

VAMP, *see* Visitor Activity Management Process

Vancouver Island, 244

vandalism: in parks, 78, 177, 217-18; of species, 140

vegetation, 100-1, 163; management in parks, 163, 170-3; plan, 165; Udvardy classification, 282-4

Vermillion Lakes, 214

Victoria Park (Ontario), 97

Village Lake Louise, 89

VIM, *see* Visitor Impact Management

visitor: activity profile, 196; appreciation, 217; characteristics, 296; issues vs environmental issues, 197; management, 9, 13, 60, 78, 88-91, 94, 130, 159, 163, 180, 192, 292-3; U.S. Forest Service, 200; planning, 186-97; regulation, 175, 185, 194, 217

Visitor Activity Management Process (VAMP), 13, 90, 187, 205; activity profiles, 196; and Canadian Park Service, 187, 194-7, 203-4; and information, 199-200; opportunity assessment, 204; planning process, 195; and public involvement, 203

visitor centres, 221

Visitor Impact Management (VIM), 13, 187, 204-5; and information, 199-200; and National Parks and Conservation Association, 192; process, 193; and public involvement, 203; theory, 199 voyageur routes, 106

Wager Bay Natural Areas of Canadian Significance, 240

Walbran watershed, 94

Wallis, C., 122

Wasaga Beach Provincial Park, 105, 168

waterfowl, 172

Waterloo Region, 47, 48

water management, and parks, 68, 78, 103

water power resources, 26-7

water quality, 6, 39, 50, 52, 125, 157

watersheds, 64, 86, 94

Waterton Lakes Forest Park, 21-3, 25, 112; MAB areas, 54

waterway parks, 62, 98, 106-7

WCED, *see* Brundtland Commission (World Commission on Environment and Development)

Weeks, N.C., 236

West Coast Trail Unit, 146, 241

Western Hemisphere Convention, 278-9

West Isles area, Bay of Fundy, 264

wetlands, 50, 68, 139, 140-1, 171-2, 277, 294

Wetlands Convention, 277

whale watchers, 264

Wheeler, Arthur, 26

White, P.S., 145

white pine, and Pinery Provincial Park, 171

white-tailed deer, 141, 171, 174

Whitney, J.D., 213

whooping crane, 168, 278, 287

Wilcove, D.S., 146

wilderness: areas, 5, 62, 98, 101, 117, 122, 126-7, 138-9; experience, 105, 108; park policy, 6, 35, 79, 101, 233; preservation, 18, 35-7, 211; protection of, 224; and recreational use, 190; zones, 3, 35, 88, 101-2

Wilderness Act (Alta), 117

Wilderness Act (US), 187, 200

Wilderness Areas Act (Alta), 117

Wilderness Areas, Ecological Reserves, and Natural Areas Act (Alta), 114, 120

wildland, 113; ecosystems, 211; and US Wilderness Act, 200; zones, 125

wildlife, 86, 126; areas, 57, 117, 139; Banff National Park, 75; depletion, 52; farm, 141; management, 146-7, 163, 238, 240, 285; and native hunting rights, 71, 297; northern areas, 240; Rocky Mountain Park, 25; sanctuaries, 28, 45; urban, 141; wetlands, 141; Wildlife Act (Alta), 126

Wildlife Management Advisory Council, 237-8

wild river park, 62, 106-7

Wild West Program, 137

The Canadian Parks and Wilderness Society

The Canadian Parks and Wilderness Society envisages a healthy eco-sphere where people experience and respect natural ecosystems. We believe that by ensuring the health of the parts, we ensure the health of the whole, which is our health too. This book is part of a series of conservation titles endorsed by the society. Also in the series are titles such as:

Endangered Spaces, by Monte Hummel
Home Place: Essays on Ecology,
  by J. Stan Rowe
Shadows in the Sun, by Wade Davis
Run of the River, by Mark Hume

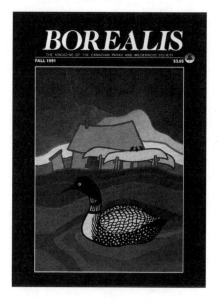

The society has nine chapters across Canada. In addition to conservation programs such as Endangered Spaces, the society also publishes *Borealis* magazine, Canada's national magazine about wilderness, the environment and our place in nature.

The Canadian Parks and Wilderness Society has been involved in local, regional and international programs designed to secure protection for natural ecosystems in Canada.

You can join the Canadian Parks and Wilderness Society and help us protect Endangered Spaces right across Canada. As a member of the society you will also receive a subscription to *Borealis* quarterly magazine. Inside, you will find dramatic, colorful, hard-hitting coverage of wilderness and environmental issues in Canada. And you will discover some of the finest photography of Canadian wilderness that you will find anywhere!

To enrol as a member, enclose payment of $35 (by cheque, VISA or MC) payable to the Canadian Parks and Wilderness Society. Please provide your full name, address and postal code. If you are paying by VISA or Mastercard, please indicate which card you are using, indicate you are paying $35, sign the letter and include your card number and expiry date.

Suite 1135, 160 Bloor Street East
Toronto, Ontario, Canada M4W 1B9
(416) 972-0868